PC Troubleshooting Pocket Reference

Stephen J. Bigelow

McGraw-Hill

New York   San Francisco   Washington, D.C.   Auckland   Bogotá
Caracas   Lisbon   London   Madrid   Mexico City   Milan
Montreal   New Delhi   San Juan   Singapore
Sydney   Tokyo   Toronto

Library of Congress Cataloging-in-Publication Data

Bigelow, Stephen J.
  [PC technician's troubleshooting pocket reference]
  Bigelow's PC technician's troubleshooting pocket reference /
  Stephen J. Bigelow.
          p.   cm.
  Includes index.
  ISBN 0-07-006988-3
  1. Microcomputers—Repairing—Handbooks, manuals, etc.   I. Title.
TK7887.B544   1998
621.39'16'0288—dc21   97-17119
                                                                    CIP

McGraw-Hill

A Division of The *McGraw·Hill* Companies

            6 7 8 9 0   DOC/DOC   9 0 2 1 0 9 8

ISBN 0-07-006988-3

*The sponsoring editor for this book was Scott L. Grillo, the
editing supervisor was Paul R. Sobel, and the production
supervisor was Tina Cameron. It was set in New Century
Schoolbook by Terry Leaden of McGraw-Hill's Professional
Book Group composition unit.*

Printed and bound by R. R. Donnelley & Sons Company.

This book was printed on acid-free paper.

Disclaimer and Cautions

It is IMPORTANT that you read and understand the following information. Please read it carefully!

PERSONAL RISK AND LIMITS OF LIABILITY

The repair of personal computers and their peripherals involves some amount of personal risk. Use **extreme** caution when working with ac and high-voltage power sources. Every reasonable effort has been made to identify and reduce areas of personal risk. You are instructed to read this book carefully *before* attempting the procedures discussed. If you are uncomfortable following the procedures that are outlined in this book, **do not attempt them**—refer your service to qualified service personnel.

NEITHER THE AUTHOR, THE PUBLISHER, NOR ANYONE DIRECTLY OR INDIRECTLY CONNECTED WITH THE PUBLICATION OF THIS BOOK SHALL MAKE ANY WARRANTY EITHER EXPRESSED OR IMPLIED, WITH REGARD TO THIS MATERIAL, INCLUDING, BUT NOT LIMITED TO, THE IMPLIED WARRANTIES OF QUALITY, MERCHANTABILITY, AND FITNESS FOR ANY PARTICULAR PURPOSE. Further, neither the author, publisher, nor anyone directly or indirectly connected with the publication of this book shall be liable for errors or omissions contained herein, or for incidental or consequential damages, injuries, or financial or material losses resulting from the use, or inability to use, the material contained herein. This material is provided AS IS, and the reader bears all responsibilities and risks connected with its use.

Contents

Preparing for Service

Troubleshooting is a lot like taking a test—there is a problem that needs to be solved, and you are "graded" on the speed and success with which you solve that problem. As with any test, a certain amount of preparation is required, and you often have to make some basic assumptions about the problem in order to solve it. Unfortunately, many less-experienced technicians are quick to jump at a solution without performing essential checks and observations. Too often, this results in lost time and wasted materials. This chapter presents you with a set of checklists and guidelines that can help to speed your diagnosis of a problem and keep your troubleshooting on track.

Rules of the Troubleshooting Business

Troubleshooting is a strange pursuit—not an art, not a science, but somewhere in between. Calling yourself a technician is easy, but being a *successful* technician is *not* so easy. The PC industry changes and grows almost daily, profit margins for repair shops are razor-thin, and products become obsolete (and unavailable) seemingly overnight. Because there is so much pressure, PC troubleshooting can be a demanding and unforgiving career. Still, there are rewards for those with the dedication and motivation to persevere. Whether you're already a professional technician trying to get ahead or a computer enthusiast hoping to go professional, the following sections offer some rules to work by:

Rule 1: *Time is money.* PCs are an integral (sometimes vital) part of today's society. Even entry-level jobs require *some* amount of computer literacy. As a consequence, every time a computer fails, someone somewhere is sitting idle. Without computers, people can't do their jobs, they can't make money, they can't even play solitaire until that PC is back in operation. Your job is to return that broken PC to operation as quickly, efficiently, and cost-effectively as possible, while providing the maximum profit for your employer and the minimum cost for your customer. This brings us to Rule 2.

Rule 2: *Focus on subassembly replacement.* Current schematics are virtually impossible to come by. Unless you're a depot technician or an authorized repair center, chances are that you will never actually *see* the circuitry you're repairing. That's a hard fact to face (especially if you're an electronics purist), but it's a fact of life. As a result, you need to focus on subassembly repairs (i.e., if a video board fails, you replace it). The advantage of subassembly replacement is that it can be performed quickly and easily—two factors which lend themselves well to profitability. This leads us to Rule 3.

Rule 3: *Cultivate suppliers.* The phrase "quickly and easily" assumes that you have a readily available source of spare parts (video boards, hard drive controllers, motherboards, and so on). However, resist the urge to become a warehouse; nothing eats up profit faster than inventory, so stock as little as possible. To accomplish this delicate balance, cultivate relationships with as many *quality* suppliers as you can, starting with suppliers in your region. If you have one or two computer stores in your area, establish credit accounts there ASAP, and keep their current catalogs on hand at all times. Finally, remember that there is *nothing* more terrifying than an irate delivery person, so be nice to them *all*.

Rule 4: *Turnaround wins customers.* Customers don't want to wait two weeks or a month before getting their system back—they want it *now*. If your suppliers are any good, you should shoot for a turnaround time of less than a week. Fast turnaround is a competitive advantage, and is a sure way to win customers.

Rule 5: *Stand behind your work.* Fast turnaround doesn't mean much if the PC still doesn't work right. Always be sure to double-check the system's configuration and applications after a repair, and offer a warranty on the service. Warranties not only protect the customer but demonstrate professionalism and confidence in the work (two things a customer will remember later on). Even short warranties (15 or 30 days) serve as a "tweaking period" to ensure that all the applications still work.

Rule 6: *Limit your liability.* Unfortunately, we live in a litigious society where seemingly innocent mistakes or oversights can have enormous consequences (especially for small businesses). Consider having your customers sign a "work order" each time they drop off a system. At a minimum, a work order should cover the following points (a local lawyer can help you with specific verbiage):

1. You're not responsible for any data on the hard drive(s), or any data lost on the hard drive(s). The customer should have complete system backup on hand before delivering a system for service.

2. You will check the system for viruses, but you're not responsible for any computer virus(es) that might be transmitted during the service or viruses that escape detection.

3. You will try to make exact replacements where possible, but you have permission to replace assemblies or components with devices of similar design and capability.

4. The customer must understand that some applications may no longer work properly after a repair because of the installation of different hardware or drivers. It is the customer's responsibility to reconfigure or reinstall any such applications.

Rule 7: *Invest in education.* Another fact of life is that as companies struggle to remain profitable, people often lose their jobs. If you work for someone else, education is the key to your long-term employability. If you get laid off anyway, you'll stand a better chance of being hired somewhere else. Consider pursuing a certificate such as A+, or cross-train in a related discipline such as CNE (Certified Network Engineer).

Troubleshooting Guidelines

Guidelines serve an important purpose in the troubleshooting industry: They provide technicians with a foundation of principles and practices that ensure safety for both the technician and the customer's equipment. This book provides you with guidelines for static control, electricity control, guards and shielding, boot disks, and virus disks.

Static control

Modern PCs depend on extremely complex integrated circuits, and those ICs are very sensitive to ESD (electrostatic discharge). Unfortunately, static electricity is commonplace; it is generated constantly by such innocent means as passing a comb through our hair or putting on a sweater. When ESD is allowed to discharge through an IC, the IC is destroyed. There are no outward signs of ESD damage—no smoke, no fire, and rarely any shock or other physical sensation. Still, the damage is quite real. ESD is controlled by a combination of grounding, protective materials, and environmental management.

- *Use wrist straps.* Grounding wrist straps are the first line of defense against ESD. They attach to your wrist and connect to a grounded surface or outlet through a wire. When properly connected, a wrist strap "bleeds off" any charge on your body and clothing, making it safer to handle delicate electronics.

- *Use antistatic containers.* You have probably noticed that all delicate electronics comes packaged in blue or pink bags. These act as "Faraday cages" which dissipate charges before they can reach the device contained inside. Always keep devices inside antistatic containers until you are ready to actually install them, then place any removed device into an antistatic container immediately.

- *Use an antistatic mat.*   A mat works like a wrist strap by connecting to ground and bleeding off any accumulated charges. You can place boards, ICs, or SIMMs safely on a properly connected antistatic mat without having to place them in containers. Antistatic mats are very popular on PC repair workbenches where sensitive items are regularly installed and removed.

- *Use antistatic chemicals.*   Monitor screens, most synthetic surfaces, and virtually all plastic enclosures are major sources of ESD. When properly and regularly applied, antistatic chemicals can go a long way toward preventing ESD damage from accidental or casual contact with sensitive electronics.

- *Manage temperature and humidity.*   Static builds up easily in cool, dry environments. Work in a warm area with adequate relative humidity (RH). Use a humidifier if necessary to maintain adequate RH.

Electricity control

PCs and their peripherals use raw alternating current as a power source. While the myriad of plugs, outlets, and line cords used today are generally regarded as quite safe for end users, technicians must often work in close proximity to exposed circuitry. In reality, the odds of electrocution are quite slim, but electricity *can* injure or kill when handled carelessly.

- *Keep the PC unplugged when working inside.*   As a rule, unplug the PC (don't just turn it off) during upgrades or repairs.

- *Use only one hand for "hot" measurements.*   If you must make measurements or probe around inside a powered system (especially inside the power supply), keep one hand behind your back. If you should contact a live wire, there is no pathway through your heart.

- *Use properly rated test probes.*   If you attempt to measure high voltages through commercial test probes, you can be electrocuted right through the probe's insulation. Make sure the probe you're using is rated for the expected voltage levels.

Guards and shielding

Modern PCs and peripherals often employ an assortment of metal and plastic shields or guards within the device. Shields and guards serve a variety of purposes, but all should be replaced when service is complete.

- *Replace EMI shields.*   PCs operate at very high frequencies, and the signals they generate can sometimes be transmitted to nearby receivers such as radios and televisions. Ideally, the PC's design should prevent such EMI (electromagnetic interference), but it may also be necessary to add metal shields to attenuate excessive interference. Whenever you remove metal housings or shields from a PC, be sure to replace them before returning the system to service.

- *Replace x-ray shields.* Monitors use extremely high voltages at the CRT, which in turn can liberate x-rays through the CRT glass. The lead contained in CRT glass is usually a sufficient shield, but larger CRTs often employ supplemental x-ray shields around the CRT funnel. When you remove x-ray shields from a monitor, be sure to replace them before running the monitor or returning it to service.

- *Replace all guards and other mechanical assemblies.* Printers typically employ a large assortment of guards and covers (both plastic and metal) to protect delicate mechanical assemblies from dust and accidental contact. You can usually operate a printer for short periods without guards in place, but you should always make it a point to replace any protective assemblies before returning the device to service.

Boot disks

PCs rely heavily on the use of hard drives as the "boot drive" which holds the boot sector and operating system needed to complete the computer's initialization. Unfortunately, hard drives are also one of the most delicate devices used in a computer. When a boot drive fails, the drive (and its vast contents) becomes inaccessible. Still, in order to begin troubleshooting the computer, it must be successfully booted to an operating system. As a result, one of the most valuable tools at your disposal is a boot disk. Generally speaking, a boot disk is little more than a floppy disk that has been formatted as a system disk and loaded with the files and utilities needed to complete the PC's initialization if the boot hard drive cannot. You can follow the procedure below to make a full-featured boot disk:

NOTE: The procedure below assumes that your floppy disk is A:, your main hard drive is C:, and your CD-ROM (if installed) is D:. If your particular system is configured differently, please substitute the correct drive letters.

---

1. *Start at the DOS command line.* You should exit Windows or Windows 95 before proceeding.

2. *Format the floppy disk as a bootable (system) disk.* If your diskette is totally blank, use the FORMAT command, such as:

   ```
   C:\DOS\> format a:    <Enter>
   ```

   Next, make the diskette bootable by transferring system files. Use the SYS command to make the diskette bootable, such as:

   ```
   C:\DOS\> sys a:    <Enter>
   ```

   If you purchase your diskettes preformatted, simply use the SYS command.

3. *Test the diskette.* Reboot your computer and verify that the system will boot successfully to the A: DOS prompt. If so, you have

created a simple boot disk, but there are other steps required to complete a full-featured boot disk.

4. *Copy your startup files.*   Copy the AUTOEXEC.BAT and CON-FIG.SYS files from your hard drive to the boot diskette:

```
C:\> copy config.sys a:      <Enter>
C:\> copy autoexec.bat a:    <Enter>
```

5. *Copy your CONFIG.SYS-related files.*   You should also copy all the files referenced in your startup files. For example, a CON-FIG.SYS file typically has memory managers, low-level plug-and-play drivers, and low-level CD-ROM drivers:

```
REM memory managers first
device = c:\windows\himem.sys
device = c:\windows\emm386.exe ram i = b000-b7ff i = e000-
e7ff i = ee00-efff
dos = umb,high
files = 60
buffers = 40
REM low-level CD-ROM driver
devicehigh = c:\cdd\wcd.sys      /d:wp_cdrom
REM low-level PnP driver
devicehigh = c:\plugplay\drivers\dos\dwcfgmg.syd
```

If this was your CONFIG.SYS file, you would copy the HIMEM.SYS, EMM386.EXE, WCD.SYS, and DWCFGMG.SYS files to your floppy diskette. Your particular system may be a bit different.

6. *Copy your AUTOEXEC.BAT-related files.*   As with CONFIG.SYS, you should copy all the files referenced in AUTOEXEC.BAT. The AUTOEXEC.BAT file usually sets paths, configures the sound card and environment, loads the CD-ROM DOS extension (MSCDEX.EXE), and starts your mouse driver. Suppose you had the AUTOEXEC.BAT file below:

```
PATH = C:\NETMANAG;C:\WINDOWS;C:\WINDOWS\COMMAND
LH C:\CDD\MSCDEX.EXE /D:WP_CDROM /M:20
SET BLASTER = A220 IXX DX T1
SET SNDSCAPE = C:\SNDSCAPE
LH C:\SNDSCAPE\SSINIT /I
LOADHIGH C:\MOUSE.EXE
```

You would need to copy the MSCDEX.EXE, SSINIT.EXE, and MOUSE.EXE files to the floppy disk.

7. *Redirect the CONFIG.SYS and AUTOEXEC.BAT files.*   Use the startup programs from your floppy disk rather than from the hard drive. This helps because it allows the boot disk to start your PC just as if the hard drive were still working, and will allow such necessary functions as sound, CD-ROM access, and mouse operation. Using any text editor like the DOS EDIT utility, you can rewrite the diskette's CONFIG.SYS file, such as:

```
device = a:\himem.sys
device = a:\emm386.exe ram i = b000-b7ff i = e000-e7ff i =
ee00-efff
dos = umb,high
files = 60
buffers = 40
devicehigh = a:\wcd.sys          /d:wp_cdrom
devicehigh = a:\dwcfgmg.syd
```

Save the edited file to your floppy disk (not to your hard drive) as CONFIG.SYS. The original CONFIG.SYS file will be renamed CONFIG.BAK. Next, load AUTOEXEC.BAT into EDIT and alter it, such as:

```
LH A:\MSCDEX.EXE /D:WP_CDROM /M:20
SET BLASTER = A220 IXX DX T1
SET SNDSCAPE = A:\SNDSCAPE
LH A:\SSINIT /I
LH A:\MOUSE.EXE
```

Save the edited file to your floppy disk (not your hard drive) as AUTOEXEC.BAT. The original AUTOEXEC.BAT file will be renamed AUTOEXEC.BAK. Now the PC will start *entirely* from the floppy diskette instead of from the hard drive.

8. *Test the diskette again.*   Reboot the PC and make sure that the boot diskette is capable of starting the entire PC without errors. You should still be able to access things like your CD-ROM drive, play .WAV files through the sound board, and so on. If there are any errors, you probably forgot to change a line in CONFIG.SYS or AUTOEXEC.BAT. Restart EDIT and check both startup files again. Retest your boot disk until the PC can initialize to the A: prompt without errors. At this point, your boot disk is just about complete.

9. *Add some DOS utilities.*   Although you should now be able to boot the system normally from your floppy disk, you will still need tools to deal with hard drive problems. Chances are that you still have plenty of space left on the floppy disk, so go to your DOS directory and copy the following utilities to your boot disk; CHKDSK.*, SCANDISK.*, FDISK.*, FORMAT.*, MEM.*, SYS.*, EDIT.*, MSAV.*, and DEFRAG.*. Of course, if your hard drive is using compression, such as DoubleSpace or Stacker, you'll need to copy those operating files as well.

10. *Store the new boot disk in a safe place.*   Mark the new boot disk clearly, and put it away with your other diskettes.

Problems with boot disks.   Boot disks are handy tools for any troubleshooter, but you should also be aware that they have three major drawbacks:

■ *Boot disks become obsolete fast.*   Every time you make a change to your system (e.g., replace a CD-ROM drive or add a new mouse), your startup files also change, so you will need to update your boot

disk(s) to reflect the changes. Too often, end users and technicians
alike forget to do this, and the boot disk winds up useless when it
is finally needed.

- *Boot disks are very "system-specific."* Exchanging boot disks was
  a simple matter in the early days of PCs, since there were few (if
  any) drivers or TSRs to worry about. As computers have become
  more sophisticated, each CD-ROM, sound board, mouse, and so on
  requires its own drivers. PCs are now quite individual, and a full-
  featured boot disk created for one system will not necessarily work
  on any other system.

- *Boot disks are ideal virus carriers.*   If you *do* make a habit of trying your boot disk in multiple systems, use extra caution to prevent the spread of computer viruses. First, write-protect your boot
  disk to help prevent contracting a virus from other systems. Also
  check your disk regularly to see that it remains virus-free.

Virus disks

Computer viruses are a serious concern for any PC troubleshooter.
You will almost always employ some type of diagnostic software during the course of your troubleshooting. Often, the same diagnostic
disk is reused on system after system, and even taken along when
making service calls in the field. Unfortunately, if a PC with a computer virus manages to infect your diagnostic disk, you will wind up
spreading the virus to any subsequent system. As you might imag-
ine, the consequences for your customer's data can be immeasurable.
Before you employ a boot disk or any form of diagnostic to troubleshoot the system, you should "sterilize" your shop by checking the
system for viruses *first*. The following procedure explains how to create a batch of virus work disks.

NOTE: The procedure below assumes that your floppy disk is
A:, your main hard drive is C:, and your CD-ROM (if installed) is
D:. If your particular system is configured differently, please
substitute the correct drive letters.

---

1. *Start at the DOS command line.*   You should exit Windows or
   Windows 95 before proceeding.

2. *Ensure that your system is virus-free.*   Run a current virus checker which checks for the most important types of viruses, including
   memory-resident viruses. Once the system is clean, you can proceed.

3. *Format ten (10) floppy disks as bootable (system) disks.*   If your
   diskettes are totally blank, use the FORMAT command, such as:

   ```
   C:\DOS\> format a:    <Enter>
   ```

   Next, make the diskettes bootable by transferring system files.
   Use the SYS command to make the diskettes bootable, such as:

   ```
   C:\DOS\> sys a:    <Enter>
   ```

If you purchase your diskettes preformatted, simply use the SYS command.

3. *Test a diskette.* Reboot your computer and verify that the system will boot successfully to the A: DOS prompt. If it will, you have created simple boot disks (you need test only one disk), but there are other steps required to complete a virus-checking disk.

4. *Copy the virus checker to your first bootable floppy disk.* Virus checkers are typically self-contained, single-file tools such as Norton's NAV.EXE, Microsoft's MSAV.EXE, or the shareware tool FPROT.EXE. Copy the necessary executable file to your diskette.

5. *Create an AUTOEXEC.BAT file that will start the virus checker.* Ideally, you want the virus checker to start automatically, so create a simple AUTOEXEC.BAT file which will start the virus checker. For example, MSAV.EXE could use a command line such as:

```
a:\msav.exe
```

You might also add command-line arguments to streamline the virus checker even further. Save the AUTOEXEC.BAT file to your floppy disk.

6. *Test the diskette again.* Reboot the system with your antivirus floppy disk. The system should boot "clean"—with no drivers or TSRs loaded that might confuse the virus checker—and the antivirus program should load. Depending on exactly which virus checker and command-line options you choose, the checker may run through a complete scan automatically, or you may have to manually start testing from the program's menu.

7. *Duplicate the original disk to the other work disks.* Use the DOS DISKCOPY command to duplicate your original virus-checking diskette to the other nine diskettes you have prepared. You may have to swap back and forth between the source (original) and target (new) diskettes several times. When the new diskette is done, DISKCOPY will ask if you want to repeat the procedure.

8. *Mark the diskettes carefully.* You have just created a batch of antivirus work disks. They should be immediately write-protected, and kept together as a set.

NOTE: Step 7 above asks you to create 10 copies of the virus checking software. Even though the disks are exclusively for your use, and you will use only one disk at a time, this kind of "multiple duplication" may violate the license agreement for your antivirus software. Be sure your license allows multiple copies of the software before proceeding.

Using the virus work disks. Whenever a PC comes in for service, use one of your antivirus work disks to boot and check the system before trying a boot disk or diagnostic disk. Professionals always create antivirus diskettes in batches because the diskettes are *disposable*. That is, if a virus is detected and cleaned, the diskette that detected the infection should be *destroyed,* and you should boot the system with a new work disk to locate any other instances of the same virus, or any different viruses. This may seem radical, but it is cheap insurance against cross-contamination of the diskette. Once a system is booted with a work disk and checks clean, you can put that work disk away, and boot the system again with a diagnostic or boot disk as required. It is also advisable to check the PC for viruses again once the repair is complete.

Problems with antivirus tools.   The protocol outlined above should help to protect you (and your customer) from virus attacks. Still, there are two situations where trouble can occur:

- *Virus checkers get obsolete fast.*   Viruses are proliferating with the aid of powerful new programming languages and vast avenues of distribution such as the Internet. You will need to update your virus work disks regularly with the very latest antivirus software. Too often, technicians buy an antivirus package and continue to use it for years. The software certainly remains adept at detecting the viruses it was designed for, but it does not take into account the many new strains that crop up regularly. As a result, older virus checkers may allow newer viruses to pass undetected.

- *Technicians get cheap with their floppy disks.*   If a work disk detects and eliminates a virus, it should be considered contaminated, and you should *throw it away.* Start again with a fresh work diskette. Continue checking and eradicating viruses until the system checks clean. The 40 cents or so that the diskette costs is not worth the risk of contracting the virus.

Evaluating Startup Problems

There are many problems that can plague the PC, but perhaps the most troubling problems occur during startup—when the computer fails to start at all or does not start completely. Startup problems make it almost impossible to use diagnostics or other utilities that we depend on to help isolate problems. With the advent of Windows 95, there are even more difficulties that can develop. This part of the chapter offers you a series of possible explanations for full and partial system failures.

When a system doesn't start at all

1. *If there is **no** power light, and you **cannot** hear any cooling fan:*

   - *Check the ac voltage.*   Use a voltmeter and confirm that there is adequate ac voltage at the wall outlet.
   - *Check the ac cord.*   The ac cord may be loose or disconnected.
   - *Check the power supply fuse(s).*   The main fuse may have opened. Replace any failed fuse.

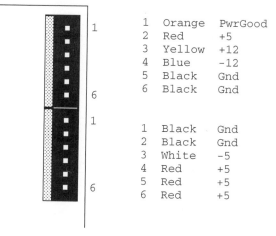

1	Orange	PwrGood
2	Red	+5
3	Yellow	+12
4	Blue	-12
5	Black	Gnd
6	Black	Gnd
1	Black	Gnd
2	Black	Gnd
3	White	-5
4	Red	+5
5	Red	+5
6	Red	+5

Figure 1.1 Motherboard power connection.

NOTE: If you replace a main fuse and the fuse continues to fail, you may have a serious fault in the power supply. Try replacing the power supply.

2. *If there is **no** power light, but you **do** hear the cooling fan running:*

 ■ *Check the ac voltage.* Use a voltmeter and confirm that there is adequate ac voltage at the wall outlet. Unusually low ac voltages (such as during "brownout" conditions) can cause the power supply to malfunction.

 ■ *Check the power supply cables.* Verify that the power supply cables are attached properly and securely to the motherboard. A typical connection scheme is shown in Figure 1.1.

 ■ *Check the power supply voltages.* Use a voltmeter to verify that each output from the power supply is correct. Table 1.1 illustrates the proper voltage for each wire color. If any output is very low or absent (especially the + 5-volt output), replace the power supply.

 ■ *Check the "Power Good" signal.* Use a voltmeter and verify that the "Power Good" signal is + 5 volts. If this signal is below 1.0 volt, it may inhibit the CPU from running by forcing a continuous Reset condition. Since the "Power Good" signal is generated by the power supply, replace the power supply.

3. *If the power light is **on**, but there is **no** apparent system activity:*

 ■ *Check the power supply voltages.* Use a voltmeter to verify that each output from the power supply is correct. Table 1.1

TABLE 1.1   Motherboard Power Connections

Pin	P8 assign-ment	Color	P9 assign-ment	Pin	Color
1	Power Good	Orange	1	GND	Black
2	+5 V (or NC)	Red	2	GND	Black
3	+12 V	Yellow	3	−5 V	White
4	−12 V	Blue	4	+5 V	Red
5	GND	Black	5	+5 V	Red
6	GND	Black	6	+5 V	Red

illustrates the proper voltage for each wire color. If any output is very low or absent (especially the +5-volt output), replace the power supply.

- *Check the "Power Good" signal.*   Use a voltmeter and verify that the "Power Good" signal is +5 volts. If this signal is below 1.0 volt, it may inhibit the CPU from running by forcing a continuous Reset condition. Since the "Power Good" signal is generated by the power supply, replace the power supply.
- *Check the CPU.*   Check to see that the CPU is cool, that the heat-sink/fan assembly is fitted on correctly, and that the CPU itself is inserted properly and completely into its socket.
- *Check the CPU socket.*   If the CPU is seated in a ZIF (zero insertion force) socket, make sure that the socket's tension lever is closed and locked into place.
- *Check the MCP.*   If there is a separate math coprocessor on the motherboard (i286 and i386 systems), make sure that the MCP is inserted properly and completely into its socket.
- *Check the expansion boards.*   Make sure that all expansion boards are seated properly. Any boards that are not secured properly, or that are inserted unevenly, can short bus signals and prevent the PC from starting.
- *Check the motherboard for shorts.*   Inspect the motherboard at every metal standoff and make sure that no metal traces are being shorted against a standoff or screw. You may want to free the motherboard and see if the system starts. If it does, use nonconductive spacers (such as a small piece of manila folder) to insulate the motherboard from each metal standoff. If the system still fails to start (and all voltages from the power supply are correct), replace the motherboard.

When a system starts but won't initialize

1. *The power light is **on**, but you hear two or more **beeps** (there is **no** video):*

- *Check the video board.* Video problems can easily halt the initialization process. Turn off and unplug the PC, then make sure that your video board is inserted completely into its expansion slot.

- *Determine the beep code.* A catastrophic fault has been detected in the power-on self-test (POST) before the video system could be initialized. BIOS makers use different numbers and patterns of beeps to indicate failures. You can determine the exact failure by finding the BIOS maker (usually marked on the motherboard BIOS IC), then finding the error message in Section 5. In the vast majority of cases, the fault will be traced to the CPU, RAM, motherboard circuitry, video controller, or drive controller.

2. *The power light is* **on**, *but the system* **hangs** *during initialization (video will probably be active)*:

- *Determine the POST code.* The power-on self-test (POST) has detected a fault, and is unable to continue with the initialization process. BIOS makers mark the completion of each POST step by writing hexadecimal completion codes to port 80h. Turn off and unplug the PC, then insert a POST board to read the completion codes. Reboot the computer and find the last code to be written before the initialization stops—that is the likely point of failure. You can determine the meaning of that POST code by finding the BIOS maker (usually displayed in the initial moments of power-up), then locating the corresponding error message in Section 5. Note that without a POST board available, it will be *extremely* difficult to identify the problem.

3. *You see a message indicating a* **Setup** *problem:*

- *Start the CMOS Setup.* The system parameters entered into CMOS RAM do not match the hardware configuration found during the POST. Enter your Setup routine. Most systems use one of the key combinations listed in Table 1.2. If you are working on an older system (early i386 and i286 systems), you will probably need to boot the PC from a Setup disk. If there is no Setup disk available, you may be able to find a suitable routine at `oak.oakland.edu:/SimTel/msdos/at` or `ftp.uu.net:/systems/msdos/simtel/at`.

TABLE 1.2   Setup Key Combinations for Typical BIOS Makers

AMI BIOS	\<Del\> key during the POST
Aware BIOS	\<Ctrl\> + \<Alt\> + \<Esc\>
DTK BIOS	\<Esc\> key during the POST
IBM PS/2 BIOS	\<Ctrl\> + \<Alt\> + \<Ins\> after \<Ctrl\> + \<Alt\> + \<Del\>
Phoenix BIOS	\<Ctrl\> + \<Alt\> + \<Esc\> or \<Ctrl\> + \<Alt\> + \<S\>

- *Check the CMOS Setup.*   Review each entry in the CMOS Setup—especially things like drive parameters and installed memory—and make sure that the CMOS entries accurately reflect the actual hardware installed on your system. If they do not, correct the error(s), save your changes, and reboot the system.
- *Test the CMOS battery.*   See if CMOS RAM will hold its contents by turning off the PC, waiting several minutes, then rebooting the PC. If Setup problems persist and you find that the values you entered have been lost, change the CMOS backup battery.

4. *The boot drive **cannot** be located. You see **no** drive light activity:*

- *Check the drive's power cable.*   The most frequent cause of drive problems is power connections. Inspect the 4-pin power cable and see that it is attached properly and completely to the drive.
- *Check the power supply voltages.*   Use a voltmeter and verify that the +5 and +12 voltage levels (especially +12 volts) are correct at the 4-pin connector. Table 1.3 shows the value of each pin. If either voltage is low or absent, replace the power supply.
- *Check the drive's signal cable.*   Locate the wide ribbon cable that connects to the drive and make sure it is attached correctly and completely at the drive *and* controller ends. Look for any scrapes or nicks along the cable that might cause problems.
- *Start the CMOS Setup.*   Most systems use one of the key combinations listed in Table 1.2. If you are working on an older system (early i386 and i286 systems), you will probably need to boot the PC from a Setup disk. If there is no Setup disk available, you may be able to find a suitable routine at oak.oakland.edu:/SimTel/msdos/at or ftp.uu.net:/systems/msdos/simtel/at.
- *Check the CMOS Setup.*   Review the drive parameters entered in the CMOS Setup, and make sure that the CMOS entries accurately reflect the actual boot drive installed on your system. If they do not, correct the error(s), save your changes, and reboot the system.

TABLE 1.3   **Pin Assignments of a 4-pin Power Connector**

Pin	Level
1	+12 volts
2	+12 GND*
3	+5 GND*
4	+5 volts

*In actual practice, the +12 and +5 GND lines are combined at the power supply.

- *Check the drive's controller.*   Make sure that the drive controller board is installed properly and completely in its expansion slot, and see that any jumpers are set correctly.
- *Try the boot diskette.*   Try booting the system from your boot floppy. If the system successfully boots to the A: prompt, your problem is limited to the hard drive system. Try switching to the C: drive. If the drive responds (and you can access its information), there may be a problem with the boot sector. Try a package like PC Tools or Norton Utilities to try to "fix" the boot sector. If you can't access the hard drive, try a diagnostic to check the drive controller and drive.
- *Check for boot-sector viruses.*   A boot-sector virus can render the hard drive unbootable. If you haven't checked for viruses yet, use your antivirus work disk now, and focus on boot-sector problems.
- *Replace the drive.*   If you cannot determine the problem at this point, try replacing the drive with a known-good working drive. Remember that you will have to change the CMOS Setup parameters to accommodate the new drive.
- *Replace the drive controller.*   If all else fails, try a new drive controller board.

5. *The boot drive **cannot** be located. The drive light remains **on** continuously:*

- *Check the drive's signal cable.*   This typically happens if the signal cable is inserted backwards at one end. In most cases, this type of problem happens after a drive is replaced or a controller upgraded. Make sure the cable is inserted in the correct orientation at both ends.
- *Replace the drive.*   If you cannot determine the problem at this point, try replacing the drive with a known-good working drive. Remember that you will have to change the CMOS Setup parameters to accommodate the new drive.
- *Replace the drive controller.*   If all else fails, try a new drive controller board.

6. *You see **normal** system activity, but there is **no** video:*

- *Check monitor power.*   Make sure the monitor is plugged in and turned on. This type of oversight is really more common than you might think.
- *Check the monitor itself.*   Check to make sure that the monitor works (you may want to try the monitor on a known-good system). If the monitor fails on a known-good system, replace the monitor.
- *Check the monitor cable.*   Trace the monitor cable to its connection at the video board, and verify that the connector is inserted securely.
- *Check the video board.*   It is possible that the video board has failed. Try a known-good monitor. If the problem persists, replace the video board.

When a system starts but crashes/reboots intermittently

1. *The system randomly **crashes** or **reboots** for no apparent reason:*

   ■ *Check for viruses.*   Some viruses (especially memory-resident viruses) can cause the PC to crash or reboot unexpectedly. If you haven't run your virus checker yet, do so now.

   ■ *Check the power supply cables.*   Verify that the power supply cables are attached properly and securely to the motherboard. A typical connection scheme is shown in Figure 1.1.

   ■ *Check the power supply voltages.*   Use a voltmeter to verify that each output from the power supply is correct. Table 1.1 illustrates the proper voltage for each wire color. If any output is low (especially the +5-volt output), replace the power supply.

   ■ *Check the CPU.*   With all power off, check to see that the CPU is cool, that the heat-sink/fan assembly is fitted on correctly, and that the CPU itself is inserted properly and completely into its socket. If the CPU overheats, it will stall, taking the entire system with it.

   ■ *Check the CPU socket.*   If the CPU is seated in a ZIF (zero insertion force) socket, make sure that the socket's tension lever is closed and locked into place.

   ■ *Check all SIMMs.*   With all power off, make sure that all SIMMs are seated properly in their holders and locked into place. You may try removing each SIMM, cleaning the contacts, and reinstalling the SIMMs.

   ■ *Check the expansion boards.*   Make sure that all expansion boards are seated properly. Any boards that are not secured properly, or that are inserted unevenly, can short bus signals and cause spurious reboots. If you have recently installed new expansion hardware, make sure that there are no hardware conflicts between interrupts, DMA channels, or I/O addresses. You can find an index of these resources in Section 5.

   ■ *Check the motherboard for shorts.*   Inspect the motherboard at every metal standoff and make sure that no metal traces are being shorted against a standoff or screw. You may want to free the motherboard and see if the crashes or reboots go away. If so, use nonconductive spacers (such as a small piece of manila folder) to insulate the motherboard from each metal standoff. If the system continues to crash or reboot (and all voltages from the power supply are correct), replace the motherboard.

Conflict troubleshooting

The PC provides only a limited number of interrupts (IRQs), DMA channels, and I/O addresses for devices to use. No two devices can use the same resources—if the same resource is assigned to two devices, they will compete for control. Conflicts can result in problems ranging from erratic device behavior to system lockups and crashes. The procedure below offers a reliable method for locating and eliminating device conflicts:

- Power the computer down and remove the new expansion device.

- Start the machine to the DOS mode and run the MSD.EXE program that is in your \WINDOWS directory (you can also try any number of shareware or commercial diagnostics that detect resource assignments).

- The MSD program will let you look at which interrupts, DMA channels, and I/O addresses are currently in use on your system. Record those on a sheet of paper (or print the report to a printer) and exit the program.

- Examine the new device and check its resource assignments against the resources already in use. Chances are that the new device will be using an IRQ, DMA, or I/O assignment already shown in your MSD report.

- Change the conflicting resource. For example, if you find an IRQ conflict, change the IRQ on your new device to an IRQ that is not in use. If the device's resources are set through software, simply proceed to the next step.

- Turn the system off again and place the device back in your computer.

- Run any setup software for the new device. It should be recognized properly.

- If you cannot find any available resources, you will have to disable at least one other device in order to free up the resources for your new device.

- If the new device works under Windows, be sure to run any Windows installation software. If the device is running under Windows 95, run the Add New Hardware wizard.

Boot symptoms and Windows 95

Symptom 1: *The Windows 95 boot drive is no longer bootable after restoring data with the DOS Backup utility.*   This happens frequently when a replacement drive is installed, and you attempt to restore the Windows 95 backup data. Unfortunately, the DOS version of Backup is not configured to restore system files. Start Backup and restore your root directory with "System Files," "Hidden Files," and "Read Only Files" checked. Next, boot the system from an MS-DOS 6.x upgrade setup disk #1 or a Windows 95 startup disk, then use the SYS command to make the hard drive bootable, such as:

```
A:\> sys c:  <Enter>
```

You should then be able to restore the remainder of your files. To back up a Windows 95 system, your best approach is to use the Windows 95 Backup program. Once the new drive is installed, partitioned, and formatted, install a new copy of Windows 95, start Windows 95 backup, *then* restore the remaining files to the drive.

Symptom 2: *Windows 95 will not boot, and ScanDisk reports bad clusters that it cannot repair.*   This is a problem encountered with Western Digital hard drives. If your WD drive fails in this way, you can recover the drive, but you will lose all information on it. Back up as much information from the drive as possible before proceeding:

■ Download the Western Digital service files WDATIDE.EXE and WD_CLEAR.EXE from WD at http://www.wdc.com/. You can also get these files from AOL by typing keyword WDC.

■ Copy these files to a "clean" boot floppy diskette.

■ Boot to DOS from a "clean" diskette (no CONFIG.SYS or AUTOEX-EC.BAT files) and run WD_CLEAR.EXE. This utility clears all data on the media (and destroys all data).

■ Next, run the WDATIDE.EXE utility to perform a comprehensive surface scan.

■ Repartition and reformat the drive, then restore your data.

Symptom 3: *You see a "Bad or missing <filename>" error message on startup.*   A file used by Windows 95 during startup has probably become corrupt. Locate the file mentioned in the error message. If you can find the file, erase it and try reinstalling it from original Windows 95 disks or CD.

Symptom 4: *Windows 95 reports damaged or missing core files, or a "VxD error" message.*   During startup, Windows 95 depends on several key files being available. If a key file is damaged or missing, Windows 95 will not function properly (if it loads at all). Run Windows 95 Setup again and select the Verify option in Safe Recovery to replace the missing or damaged file(s).

Symptom 5: *After installing Windows 95, you can no longer boot from a different hard drive.*   The Windows 95 Setup program checks all hard disks to find just one that contains the 80h designator in the DriveNumber field of a boot sector. Windows 95 will typically force the first drive to be bootable, and prevent other drives from booting. However, there are two ways to correct the problem after Windows 95 is installed:

■ Use the version of FDISK included with Windows 95 to set the primary active partition.

■ Use a disk editor utility to change a disk's DriveNumber field so that you can boot from that hard disk.

Symptom 6: *Windows 95 Registry files are missing.*   There are two Registry files: USER.DAT and SYSTEM.DAT. They are also backed up as USER.DA0 and SYSTEM.DA0. If a .DAT file is missing, Windows 95 will automatically load the corresponding .DA0 file. If both the .DAT and .DA0 Registry files are missing or corrupt, Windows 95 will start in the Safe Mode, offering to restore the Registry. However, this cannot be accomplished without a backup.

Either restore the Registry files from a tape or diskette backup, or run
Windows 95 Setup to create a new Registry. Unfortunately, restoring
an old registry or creating a new registry from scratch will reload programs and readd hardware to restore the system to its original
state—a long and difficult procedure. In the future, use the following
DOS procedure to back up the Registry files to a floppy disk:

```
attrib -r -s -h system.da?
attrib -r -s -h user.da?
copy system.da? A:\
copy user.da? A:\
attrib +r +s +h system.da?
attrib r +s +h user.da?
```

Symptom 7: *During the Windows 95 boot process, I get an "Invalid
System Disk" error message.* This often happens during the first
reboot during Windows 95 Setup, or when you boot from the startup
disk. When you see a message such as:

```
Invalid system disk
Replace the disk, and then press any key
```

there may be several possible problems:

- *Check for viruses.* Your disk may be infected with a boot-sector
  virus. Run your antivirus work disk and check closely for boot-sector viruses.

- *Remove memory-resident antivirus software.* Windows 95 setup
  may fail if there is antivirus software running as a TSR, or if your
  BIOS has enabled boot-sector protection. Make sure that any boot-
  sector protection is turned off before installing Windows 95.

- *Check for disk management software.* Windows 95 may not detect
  disk management software such as Disk Manager, EZ-Drive, or
  DrivePro, and may overwrite the master boot record (MBR). See
  the documentation that accompanies your particular management
  software for recovering the MBR.

To reinstall the Windows 95 system files, follow the steps below:

1. Boot the system using the Windows 95 Emergency Boot Disk.
2. At the MS-DOS command prompt, type the following lines:

```
c:
cd\windows\command
attrib c:\msdos.sys -h -s -r
ren c:\msdos.sys c:\msdos.xxx
a:
sys c:
del c:\msdos.sys
ren c:\msdos.xxx c:\msdos.sys
attrib c:\msdos.sys +r +s +h
```

3. Remove the Emergency Boot Disk and reboot the system.

Symptom 8: *Windows 95 will not install on a compressed drive.*
You are probably using an old version of the compression software
which Windows 95 does not recognize. While Windows 95 should be
compatible with all versions of SuperStor, it does require version 2.0
or later of Stacker. Make sure your compression software is recent,
and see that there is enough free space on the host drive to support
Windows 95 installation.

Symptom 9: *The hard drive indicates that it is in the "MS-DOS
compatibility mode."* For some reason, Windows 95 is using a real-
mode (DOS) driver instead of a protected-mode (32-bit) driver.

■ *Check your drivers.*   Make sure that any software related to the
  hard drive (especially hard disk drivers) is using the protected-
  mode version. Windows 95 should install equivalent protected-
  mode software, but you may need to contact the drive manufacturer and obtain the latest Windows 95 drivers.

■ *Check your drive managers.*   If you are using Disk Manager,
  make sure that you're using version 6.0 or later. You can get the
  latest patch (DMPATCH.EXE) from the Ontrack web site at
  `http://www.ontrack.com/`.

■ *Check your motherboard BIOS.*   Windows 95 may use DOS compatibility mode on large EIDE hard disks (hard disks with more
  than 1024 cylinders) in some computers. This may occur because
  of an invalid drive geometry translation in the system ROM BIOS
  that prevents the protected-mode IDE device driver from being
  loaded. Contact your system manufacturer for information about
  obtaining an updated BIOS.

Symptom 10: *Disabling the protected-mode disk driver(s) hides the
partition table when FDISK is used.*   As with Symptom 9, there are
problems preventing 32-bit operation of your hard drive(s). Do *not*
use the "Disable all 32-bit protected-mode disk drivers" option.
Instead, upgrade your motherboard BIOS to a later version.

Symptom 11: *You cannot achieve 32-bit disk access under Windows
95.*   If the Windows 95 system refuses to allow 32-bit disk access,
there may be a conflict between the motherboard CMOS Setup
entries and the BIOS on your EIDE controller. For example, if both
BIOS have settings for logical block addressing (LBA), make sure
only one entry is in use.

Symptom 12: *Windows 95 does not recognize a new device.*   In
some cases, Windows 95 is unable to recognize a new device. When
this happens, check to see if there is a hardware conflict between the
device and other devices in the system (you can see conflicts represented in the Device Manager with small yellow exclamation
marks). Also make sure that any necessary drivers have been
installed properly. If problems continue, remove the new device

through your Device Manager, and reinstall it through the Add New Hardware wizard.

Symptom 13:   *Windows 95 does not function properly when installed over Ontrack's Disk Manager.*   While Disk Manager should typically be compatible with Windows 95, there are some points to keep in mind:

■ *Check your Disk Manager version.*   If you are using Disk Manager, make sure that you're using version 6.0 or later. You can get the latest patch (DMPATCH.EXE) from the Ontrack web site at http://www.ontrack.com/.

■ *Check the slave drive with Disk Manager.*   While the Windows 95 file system is *supposed* to work properly with a slave drive using only Disk Manager, there are some circumstances where problems can occur:

1. When a Windows 3.1x virtual driver replaces the Windows 95 protected-mode driver (such as WDCDRV.386).
2. When the cylinder count in CMOS for the slave drive is greater than 1024 cylinders.
3. When the motherboard CMOS settings for the slave drive are set to auto-detect.

Symptom 14:   *You have problems using a manufacturer-specific hard disk driver (such as Western Digital's FastTrack driver WDC-DRV.386) for 32-bit access under Windows 95.*   Generally speaking, Windows 95 has 32-bit protected-mode drivers for a wide variety of EIDE devices—in actual practice, you should not need a manufacturer-specific driver. If Windows 95 has not removed all references to the driver from SYSTEM.INI, you should edit the file and remove those references manually, then reboot the system. Be sure to make a backup copy of SYSTEM.INI before editing it.

2

Drive Troubleshooting

Computers serve little purpose without some means of long-term storage, and over the years, a large number of drives have been developed to provide access to vast amounts of information. This chapter explains the construction and troubleshooting procedures for floppy disks, hard drives, CD-ROM drives, tape drives, and a series of other popular drive alternatives.

Floppy Drives

Floppy disk drives remain the standard removable-media mass-storage device. Although they are remarkably slow and offer puny storage capacities when compared to hard drives and other mass-storage devices, their high reliability, inexpensive media, and universal compatibility will keep floppy drives around for years to come. Table 2.1 compares the specifications of the most popular floppy drive types.

Floppy drive interface

Floppy drives use a 34-pin signal interface and a 4-pin "mate-n-lock" power connector. Both connections are illustrated in Figure 2.1.

Floppy disk troubleshooting

Symptom 1: *The floppy drive is completely dead (the disk does not even initialize when inserted).* If the drive light doesn't illuminate during power-up, or you see an error message indicating that the drive is not ready, follow the steps below:

■ *Check the power connector.* Make sure the 4-pin power connector is inserted properly and completely. If the drive is being powered by a Y-connector, make sure any interim connections are secure. Use a voltmeter and measure the +5-volt (pin 4) and +12-volt (pin 1) levels as shown in Table 1.3. If either voltage (especially the +12-volt supply) is unusually low or absent, replace the power supply.

TABLE 2.1 Comparison of Floppy Drive Specifications

Specification	5.25 in (360 kbytes)	5.25 in (1.2 Mbytes)	3.5 in (720 kbytes)	3.5 in (1.44 Mbytes)	3.5 in (2.88 Mbytes)
Bytes per sector	512	512	512	512	512
Sectors per track	9	15	9	18	36
Tracks per side	40	80	80	80	80
Sectors per cluster	2	1	2	1	2
FAT length (sectors)	2	7	3	9	9
Number of FATs	2	2	2	2	2
Root directory length	7 sectors	14 sectors	7 sectors	14 sectors	15 sectors
Maximum root entries	112	224	112	224	240
Total sectors on disk	708	2371	1426	2847	5726
Media base	Ferrite	Ferrite	Cobalt	Cobalt	Cobalt
Coercivity (oersteds)	300	300	600	600	720
Media descriptor byte	FDh	F9h	F9h	F0h	F0h
Encoding format	MFM or FM	MFM or FM	MFM	MFM	MFM
Data rate (kbytes/s)	250 or 125	500 or 250	500	500	500

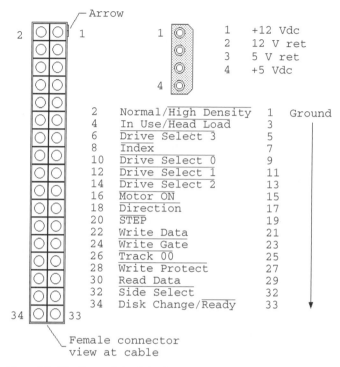

Figure 2.1   The floppy drive interface.

- *Check the signal connector.*   Make sure the 34-pin IDC header is connected securely at both the drive and the controller. If the cable is visibly worn or damaged, try a new one.
- *Check the CMOS Setup.*   Enter the CMOS Setup routine and make sure that the drive is listed and selected properly. For example, if the drive is listed in CMOS as an A: drive but is physically cabled as a B: drive, the controller won't recognize it. Pay particular attention to the drive type (1.44 Mbytes, 1.2 Mbytes, and so on).
- *Replace the floppy drive.*   Try a known-good floppy drive.
- *Replace the drive controller.*   If problems persist with a known-good floppy drive, replace the floppy controller.

Symptom 2:   *The floppy drive rotates a disk, but will not seek to the desired track.*   DOS may report this type of problem as a "Seek Error." This is almost always a drive fault and is generally the result of a jammed or defective stepping motor assembly.

- *Clean the floppy drive.*   Make sure that the R/W heads are clean and free of debris.

- *Check the drive assembly for damage.*   Make sure the R/W head positioning assembly is free of obstructions. Try inserting a diskette and check for any mechanical problems that might prevent the heads from stepping.

- *Check the signal connector.*   Examine the 34-pin signal cable for visible wear or damage—the STEP line may be broken. Try a new signal cable.

- *Replace the floppy drive.*   Try a known-good floppy drive.

- *Replace the drive controller.*   It is unusual for such a problem to reside in the controller, but if problems persist with a known-good drive and cable, try a new floppy controller.

Symptom 3:   *The floppy drive heads seek properly, but the spindle does not turn.*   This symptom suggests that the spindle motor is inhibited or defective, but all other functions are working properly. In most cases, the floppy drive is defective.

- *Check the drive assembly for damage.*   Make sure the spindle motor assembly is free of obstructions. Try inserting a diskette and check for any mechanical problems that might prevent the spindle motor from turning.

- *Check the signal connector.*   Examine the 34-pin signal cable for visible wear or damage—the MOTOR ON line may be broken. Try a new signal cable.

- *Replace the floppy drive.*   Try a known-good floppy drive.

- *Replace the drive controller.*   It is unusual for such a problem to reside in the controller, but if problems persist with a known-good drive and cable, try a new floppy controller.

Symptom 4:   *The floppy drive will not read from / write to the diskette. All other operations appear normal.*   DOS will typically report this kind of problem as a "Disk Read" or "Disk Write" error. Often, this problem can be corrected with cleaning.

- *Clean the floppy drive.*   Make sure that the R/W heads are clean and free of debris.

- *Try a known-good diskette.*   A faulty diskette can generate some very perplexing read/write problems.

- *Check the drive assembly for damage.*   Make sure that the diskette is clamped properly when it is inserted into the drive, and that there are no obstructions in the drive mechanism.

- *Check the signal connector.*   Examine the 34-pin signal cable for visible wear or damage—the READ DATA, WRITE GATE, or WRITE DATA line may be broken. Try a new signal cable.

- *Replace the floppy drive.*   Try a known-good floppy drive.

■ *Replace the drive controller.* It is unusual for such a problem to reside in the controller, but if problems persist with a known-good drive and cable, try a new floppy controller.

Symptom 5: *The drive is able to write to a write-protected disk.* Before concluding that there is a drive problem, remove and examine the disk itself to ensure that it is actually write-protected. If the disk is not write-protected, write-protect it appropriately and try the disk again. If the disk is already protected:

■ *Clean out the drive.* Use compressed air to blow out any dust or debris that may be obstructing the write-protect sensor.

■ *Replace the floppy drive.* In virtually all cases, there is a fault in the drive's write-protect detection circuit. Try a known-good floppy drive.

■ *Check the signal connector.* Examine the 34-pin signal cable for visible wear or damage—the WRITE PROTECT signal line may be broken. Make sure that the cable is installed properly at the drive and controller ends. Try a new signal cable.

■ *Replace the drive controller.* It is unusual for such a problem to reside in the controller, but if problems persist with a known-good drive and cable, try a new floppy controller.

Symptom 6: *The drive can recognize either high or double-density media, but not both.* DOS typically reports an error such as "Bad Media Type." This is almost always the result of a fault in the floppy drive.

■ *Clean out the drive.* Use compressed air to blow out any dust or debris that may be obstructing the media type sensor.

■ *Replace the floppy drive.* In virtually all cases, there is a fault in the drive's media type detection circuit. Try a known-good floppy drive.

■ *Check the signal connector.* Examine the 34-pin signal cable for visible wear or damage—the MEDIA TYPE signal line may be broken. Make sure that the cable is installed properly at the drive and controller ends. Try a new signal cable.

■ *Replace the drive controller.* It is unusual for such a problem to reside in the controller, but if problems persist with a known-good drive and cable, try a new floppy controller.

Symptom 7: *Double-density (720-kbyte) 3.5-in disks are not working properly when formatted as high-density (1.44-Mbyte) disks.* The solution is very simple:

■ *Do not manually punch media holes in the diskette*—double-density disks use different media from high-density disks, and "fooling" a disk that way will result in unreliable operation.

Symptom 8: *DOS reports an error such as "Can Not Read From Drive A:" even though a diskette is fully inserted in the drive and the drive LED indicates that access is being attempted.* There are several likely causes of such a problem:

■ *Clean the floppy drive.* Make sure that the R/W heads are clean and free of debris.

■ *Try a known-good diskette.* A faulty diskette can generate some very perplexing read/write problems.

■ *Check the drive assembly for damage.* Make sure that the diskette is clamped properly when it is inserted into the drive, and that there are no obstructions in the drive mechanism.

■ *Check the signal connector.* Examine the 34-pin signal cable for visible wear or damage—the DISK CHANGE line may be broken. Try a new signal cable.

■ *Replace the floppy drive.* Try a known-good floppy drive.

■ *Replace the drive controller.* It is unusual for such a problem to reside in the controller, but if problems persist with a known-good drive and cable, try a new floppy controller.

Symptom 9: *When a new diskette is inserted in the drive, a directory from a previous diskette appears.* You may have to reset the system in order to get the new diskette to be recognized. This is the classic "phantom directory" problem. It is usually due to a drive fault.

■ *Check the signal connector.* Examine the 34-pin signal cable for visible wear or damage—the DISK CHANGE line may be broken. Try a new signal cable.

■ *Check the drive jumpers.* Some floppy drives allow the DISK CHANGE signal to be enabled or disabled. If your drive has such a jumper, make sure the signal is enabled.

■ *Replace the floppy drive.* Try a known-good floppy drive.

■ *Replace the drive controller.* It is unusual for such a problem to reside in the controller, but if problems persist with a known-good drive and cable, try a new floppy controller.

NOTE: If you suspect a phantom directory, *do not* initiate any writing to the diskette—its FAT table and directories could be overwritten, rendering its contents inaccessible without careful data recovery procedures.

Symptom 10: *Your 3.5-in high-density floppy disk cannot format high-density diskettes (but can read and write to them just fine).* This is a problem that plagues older computers (i286 and i386 systems) to which aftermarket high-density drives were added. The problem is a lack of BIOS support for high-density formatting—the system is just too old. In such a case, you have a choice:

- *Upgrade your motherboard BIOS.*   Use a BIOS version that fully supports 3.5-in high-density diskettes.

or

- *Use the DRIVER.SYS utility.*   The DOS DRIVER.SYS utility adapts the system by allowing an existing 3.5-in high-density drive to format properly. A typical CONFIG.SYS command line would be

```
device = c:\dos\driver.sys /D:1
```

See Section 8 for an index of DOS commands and syntax.

Symptom 11:   *You cannot upgrade an XT-class PC with a 3.5-in floppy disk.*   XT systems support up to four double-density 5.25-in floppy disk drives. They will not support 3.5-in floppy disks at all. To install 3.5-in floppy disks:

- *Check your DOS version.*   You will need to have DOS 3.3 or higher installed on the system.

- *Install an 8-bit floppy controller.*   Disable any existing floppy controller and add an 8-bit ISA floppy drive controller board which uses an on-board BIOS to supplement floppy disk operations.

- *Check your DIP switches.*   Since XT-class PCs do not use CMOS, make sure that the system DIP switches are set properly.

Symptom 12:   *You are unable to "swap" floppy drives so that A: becomes B: and B: becomes A:.*   This often happens on older systems when users want to make their 3.5-in aftermarket B: drive into their A: drive and relegate their aging 5.25-in drive to B: instead. In most cases, one or more of the following steps have been omitted:

- *Check the signal cable.*   For floppy cables with a wire twist, the endmost connector is A:, and the connector prior to the twist is B:. Reverse the connectors at each floppy drive to reverse their identities. If the cable has *no* twist (this is rare), reset the jumper ID on each drive so that your desired A: drive is set to DS0 (Drive Select 0) and your desired B: drive is jumpered to DS1. If you accomplish this exchange but one drive is not recognized, try a new floppy signal cable.

- *Check the CMOS Setup.*   Make sure that you enter CMOS and reverse the A: and B: drive specifications. Save your changes and restart the PC.

Symptom 13:   *When using a combination floppy drive (called a "combo drive"), one of the drives does not work, while the other works fine.*   This problem is often caused by a drive fault.

- *Check the power connector.*   Make sure that both +5 volts and +12 volts are adequately provided to the drive through the 4-pin "mate-n-lock" connector.

■ *Replace the floppy drive.* Part of the combo drive's circuitry has failed. Try a known-good combo drive.

Symptom 14: *There are no jumpers available on the floppy disk, so it is impossible to change settings.* This is not a problem as much as it is an inconvenience. Typically, you can expect "unjumpered" floppy disks to be set to the following specifications: Drive Select 1, Disk Change (pin 34) enabled, and Frame Ground enabled. This configuration supports dual drive systems with twisted floppy cables.

Symptom 15: *The floppy drive activity LED stays on after the computer is powered up.* This is a classic signaling problem which occurs after changing or upgrading a drive system.

■ *Check the signal cable.* One end of the cable is almost certainly reversed. Make sure that both ends of the cable are installed properly and completely.

■ *Replace the drive controller.* It is rare for a fault in the drive controller to cause this type of problem, but if trouble persists, try a known-good floppy controller board.

Hard Drives

Hard drives have quickly become one of the most powerful and progressive parts of the PC. Tremendous storage capacities and outstanding speed allow unmatched performance—including use as virtual memory. However, PCs also depend on the hard drive. Drive problems can prevent a system from booting, and data loss can render weeks (or months) of work inaccessible.

Hard drive interfaces

There are four major interfaces used with hard drives: ST506/412, ESDI, IDE/EIDE, and SCSI. The ST506/412 interface is illustrated in Figure 2.2, and the ESDI (Enhanced Small Device Interface) pinout is shown in Figure 2.3. These are older interfaces, and you will almost never encounter them unless working on an early-model i386 or older system. The IDE/EIDE interface is shown in Figure 2.4. IDE/EIDE drives are extremely popular, and most end-user systems made since 1989 carry an IDE (Integrated Drive Electronics) drive. EIDE (Enhanced IDE) drives and interfaces appeared in 1994 and have now largely replaced IDE in new systems, though the 40-pin interface is exactly the same. SCSI (Small Computer System Interface) drives are outstanding in server or multitasking systems. Figure 2.5 shows a standard 50-pin SCSI connection, and Figure 2.6 shows a 68-pin SCSI connection.

Hard drive troubleshooting

NOTE: Drive troubleshooting has the potential to destroy any data on the drive(s). Before attempting to troubleshoot hard disk

CONTROL Cable			
Pin	Name	Pin	Name
1	Ground	2	−Head select 8
3	Ground	4	−Head select 4
5	Ground	6	−Write gate
7	Ground	8	−Seek complete
9	Ground	10	−Track 0
11	Ground	12	−Write fault
13	Ground	14	−Head select 1
15	Ground	16	Not connected
17	Ground	18	−Head select 2
19	Ground	20	−Index
21	Ground	22	−Ready
23	Ground	24	−Step
25	Ground	26	−Drive select 1
27	Ground	28	−Drive select 2
29	Ground	30	−Drive select 3
31	Ground	32	−Drive select 4
33	Ground	34	−Direction In

DATA Cable			
Pin	Name	Pin	Name
1	Drive selected	2	Ground
3	Reserved	4	Ground
5	Reserved	6	Ground
7	To control cable pin 15	8	Ground
9	Reserved	10	Reserved
11	Ground	12	Ground
13	+Write data	14	−Write data
15	Ground	16	Ground
17	+Read data	18	−Read data
19	Ground	20	Ground

Figure 2.2 The ST506/412 drive interface.

drive problems, be sure to back up as much of the drive as possible. If there is no backup available, do not repartition or reformat the drive unless it is *absolutely* necessary and all other possible alternatives have been exhausted.

Symptom 1: *The hard drive is completely dead.* If the drive does not spin up, the drive light doesn't illuminate during power-up, or you see an error message indicating that the drive is not found or not ready, follow the steps below:

CONTROL Cable			
Pin	Name	Pin	Name
1	Ground	2	−Head select 3
3	Ground	4	−Head select 2
5	Ground	6	−Write gate
7	Ground	8	−Config/status data
9	Ground	10	−Transfer acknowledge
11	Ground	12	−Attention
13	Ground	14	−Head select 0
15	Ground	16	−Sector/address mark found
17	Ground	18	−Head select 1
19	Ground	20	−Index
21	Ground	22	−Ready
23	Ground	24	−Transfer request
25	Ground	26	−Drive select 0
27	Ground	28	−Drive select 1
29	Ground	30	−Drive select 2
31	Ground	32	−Read gate
33	Ground	34	−Command data
DATA Cable			
Pin	Name	Pin	Name
1	−Drive selected	2	−Sector/address mark found
3	−Command complete	4	−Address mark enable
5	Reserved for step mode	6	Ground
7	+Write clock	8	−Write clock
9	Cartridge changed	10	+Read/reference clock
11	−Read/reference clock	12	Ground
13	+Write data	14	−Write data
15	Ground	16	Ground
17	+Read data	18	−Read data
19	Ground	20	−Index

Figure 2.3 The ESDI drive interface.

- *Check the power connector.* Make sure the 4-pin power connector is inserted properly and completely. If the drive is being powered by a Y-connector, make sure any interim connections are secure. Use a voltmeter and measure the +5-volt (pin 4) and +12-volt (pin 1) levels as shown in Table 1.3. If either voltage (especially the +12-volt supply) is unusually low or absent, replace the power supply.

Pin	Name	Pin	Name
1	Reset	2	Ground
3	DD7	4	DD8
5	DD6	6	DD9
7	DD5	8	DD10
9	DD4	10	DD11
11	DD3	12	DD12
13	DD2	14	DD13
15	DD1	16	DD14
17	DD0	18	DD15
19	Ground	20	Key (slot only)
21	DMARQ	22	Ground
23	−I/O write data (−DIOW)	24	Ground
25	−I/O read data (−DIOR)	26	Ground
27	−I/O channel ready (−IORDY)	28	unused
29	−DMA acknowledge (−DMACK)	30	Ground
31	Interrupt request (INTRQ)	32	−Host 16-bit I/O (−IOCS16)
33	DA1	34	−Passed diagnostics (−PDIAG)
35	DA0	36	DA2
37	−Host chip sel 0 (−CS1FX)	38	−Host chip sel 1 (−CS3FX)
39	−Drive active (−DASP)	40	Ground

Figure 2.4 The IDE/EIDE drive interface.

■ *Check the signal connector.* Make sure the drive's signal interface cable is connected securely at both the drive and the controller. If the cable is visibly worn or damaged, try a new one.

■ *Check the CMOS Setup.* Enter the CMOS Setup routine and make sure that all the parameters entered for the drive are correct. Heads, cylinders, sectors per track, landing zone, and write pre-compensation must all be correct—otherwise, POST will not recognize the drive.

■ *Replace the hard drive.* Try a known-good hard drive. If a known-good drive works as expected, your original drive is probably defective.

■ *Replace the drive controller.* If problems persist with a known-good hard drive, replace the drive controller.

Signal	Pin	Pin	Signal	
Ground	1	2	Data 0	
Ground	3	4	Data 1	
Ground	5	6	Data 2	
Ground	7	8	Data 3	
Ground	9	10	Data 4	
Ground	11	12	Data 5	
Ground	13	14	Data 6	
Ground	15	16	Data 7	
Ground	17	18	Data parity	
Ground	19	20	Ground	
Ground	21	22	Ground	
Reserved	23	24	Reserved	
Open	25	26	TERMPWR	
Reserved	27	28	Reserved	
Ground	29	30	Ground	
Ground	31	32	−ATN	(−Attention)
Ground	33	34	Ground	
Ground	35	36	−BSY	(−Busy)
Ground	37	38	−ACK	(−Acknowledge)
Ground	39	40	−RST	(−Reset)
Ground	41	42	−MSG	(−Message)
Ground	43	44	−SEL	(−Select)
Ground	45	46	−C/D	(−Control/Data)
Ground	47	48	−REQ	(−Request)
Ground	49	50	−I/O	(−Input/Output)

Figure 2.5 The 50-pin SCSI interface.

Symptom 2: *You see drive activity, but the computer will not boot from the hard drive.* In most cases, there is a drive failure, a boot-sector failure, or DOS/Windows file corruption.

■ *Check the signal connector.* Make sure the drive's signal interface cable is connected securely at both the drive and the controller. If the cable is visibly worn or damaged, try a new one.

■ *Check the CMOS Setup.* Enter the CMOS Setup routine and make sure that all the parameters entered for the drive are correct. Heads, cylinders, sectors per track, landing zone, and write prec-ompensation must all be correct—otherwise, POST will not recognize the drive.

■ *Check the software.* Boot from a floppy disk and try accessing the hard drive. If the hard drive is accessible, chances are that the boot files are missing or corrupt. Try a utility such as DrivePro's Drive Boot Fixer or DISKFIX with PC Tools.

■ *Check the hardware.* If you cannot access the hard drive, run a diagnostic such as TouchStone Software's CheckIt. Test the drive

Signal	Pin	Pin	Signal	
Ground	1	35	Data 12	
Ground	2	36	Data 13	
Ground	3	37	Data 14	
Ground	4	38	Data 15	
Ground	5	39	Data parity 1	
Ground	6	40	Data 0	
Ground	7	41	Data 1	
Ground	8	42	Data 2	
Ground	9	43	Data 3	
Ground	10	44	Data 4	
Ground	11	45	Data 5	
Ground	12	46	Data 6	
Ground	13	47	Data 7	
Ground	14	48	Data parity 0	
Ground	15	49	Ground	
Ground	16	50	Ground	
TERMPWR	17	51	TERMPWR	
TERMPWR	18	52	TERMPWR	
Reserved	19	53	Reserved	
Ground	20	54	Ground	
Ground	21	55	−ATN	(−Attention)
Ground	22	56	Ground	
Ground	23	57	−BSY	(−Busy)
Ground	24	58	−ACK	(−Acknowledge)
Ground	25	59	−RST	(−Reset)
Ground	26	60	−MSG	(−Message)
Ground	27	61	−SEL	(−Select)
Ground	28	62	−C/D	(−Control/data)
Ground	29	63	−REQ	(−Request)
Ground	30	64	−I/O	(−Input/output)
Ground	31	65	Data 8	
Ground	32	66	Data 9	
Ground	33	67	Data 10	
Ground	34	68	Data 11	

Figure 2.6 The 68-pin SCSI interface.

and drive controller. If the controller responds but the drive does not, try repartitioning and reformatting the hard drive. If the drive still doesn't respond, replace the hard drive outright. If the controller doesn't respond, replace the hard drive controller.

Symptom 3: *One or more subdirectories appear lost or damaged.* Both the root directory of a drive and its FAT contain references to subdirectories. If data in either the root directory or the file alloca-

tion table is corrupt, one or more subdirectories may be inaccessible
by the drive.

■ *Repair the directory structure.*   Use DISKFIX (with PC Tools) or
  ScanDisk (with DOS 6.2 or later) to check the disk's directory
  structure for problems.

Symptom 4:   *There are errors during drive reads or writes.*
Magnetic information does not last forever, and sector ID information can gradually degrade to a point where you encounter file errors.

■ *Repair the file structure.*   Use a utility such as DISKFIX or
  ScanDisk to examine the drive and search for bad sectors. If a
  failed sector contains part of an .EXE or .COM file, that file is now
  corrupt and should be restored from a backup.

■ *Perform a low-level format (if possible).*   This is an ideal solution
  because LL formatting rewrites sector ID information, but the
  sophistication of today's drives makes LL formatting almost impossible. If the drive manufacturer provides a "drive preparation" utility, you should back up the drive, run the utility, FDISK, FORMAT,
  and restore the drive.

Symptom 5:   *The hard drive was formatted accidentally.*   A high-
level format does not actually destroy data; rather, it clears the file
names and locations kept in the root directory and FAT. This prevents DOS from finding those files.

■ *Recover the files.*   Use a utility such as UNFORMAT (with PC
  Tools) which can reconstruct root directory and FAT data contained
  in a MIRROR file. This is not always a perfect process, and you
  may not be able to recover all files.

NOTE: In order for MIRROR data to be useful, do *not* save new
files before running UNFORMAT.

Symptom 6:   *A file has been deleted accidentally.*   Mistyping or for-
getting to add a drive specification can accidentally erase files that
you did not intend to erase.

■ *Recover the files.*   Use a utility such as UNDELETE (with PC
  Tools and DOS) to restore the deleted file. This is not always a perfect process, and you may not be able to recover every file.

NOTE: In order for UNDELETE to be useful, do *not* save new
files before running UNDELETE.

Symptom 7:   *The hard drive's root directory is damaged.*   A faulty
root directory can cripple the entire disk, rendering all subdirectories
inaccessible.

■ *Recover the files.* Use a utility like DISKFIX (with PC Tools) to reconstruct the damaged FATs and directories. If you have been running MIRROR, DISKFIX should be able to perform a very reliable recovery. You may also try other recovery utilities, such as DrivePro or ScanDisk.

■ *Reformat the drive (if necessary).* If you cannot recover your root directory, you will have little choice but to reformat the drive and restore its contents from a backup.

Symptom 8: *Hard drive performance appears to be slowing down over time.* In virtually all cases, diminishing drive performance is caused by file fragmentation. Far less commonly, you may be faced with a computer virus.

■ *Boot the system "clean."* Start the PC with a "clean" boot disk and make sure there are no TSRs or drivers being loaded.

■ *Check for computer viruses.* If you haven't done so already, run your antivirus checker and make sure that there are no memory-resident or file-based viruses.

■ *Check for fragmentation.* Start your defragmentation utility (such as COMPRESS with PC Tools or DEFRAG with DOS) and check to see the percentage of file fragmentation. If there is more than 10 percent fragmentation, you should consider running the defragmentation utility after preparing Windows.

■ *Shut down the Windows swap file.* Before defragmenting a drive, reboot the system normally, start Windows, access the Virtual Memory controls for your version of Windows, and shut down virtual memory. Then leave Windows and boot the system "clean" again.

■ *Run the defragmentation utility.* Restart your defragmentation utility and proceed to defragment the disk. This process may take several minutes depending on the size of your drive.

■ *Recreate the Windows swap file.* Once defragmentation is complete, reboot the system normally, start Windows, access the Virtual Memory controls for your version of Windows, and recreate a permanent swap file to support virtual memory. You should now notice a performance improvement.

Symptom 9: *You can access the hard drive correctly, but the drive light stays on continuously.* A continuous LED indication is not *necessarily* a problem as long as the drive seems to be operating properly.

■ *Check the drive for drive light jumpers.* Examine the drive itself for any jumper that might select "latched" mode vs. "activity" mode. Set the jumper to activity mode to see the drive light during access only.

■ *Check for drive light errors.* Some drive types (especially SCSI drives) use the drive activity light to signal drive and controller errors. Check the drive and controller documents and see if there is any error indicated by the light.

■ *Check the controller for drive light jumpers.*   If there is no drive
light jumper on the drive, examine the drive controller for any
jumpers that might select latched mode vs. activity mode. If the
drive controller is integrated onto the motherboard, check the
motherboard documentation. Set the jumper to activity mode.

Symptom 10:   *You cannot access the hard drive, and the drive light
stays on continuously.*   This usually indicates a reversed signal
cable, and is most common when upgrading or replacing a drive system.

■ *Check the signal cable.*   One end of the signal cable is almost certainly reversed. Make sure that both ends of the cable are installed
properly and completely.

■ *Replace the drive controller.*   It is rare for a fault in the drive controller to cause this type of problem, but if trouble persists, try a
known-good drive controller board.

Symptom 11:   *You see a "No Fixed Disk Present" error message displayed on the monitor.*   This kind of problem can occur during installation or at any point in the PC's working life.

■ *Check the power connector.*   Make sure the 4-pin power connector
is inserted properly and completely. If the drive is being powered
by a Y-connector, make sure any interim connections are secure.
Use a voltmeter and measure the +5-volt (pin 4) and +12-volt (pin
1) levels as shown in Table 1.3. If either voltage (especially the
+12-volt supply) is unusually low or absent, replace the power
supply.

■ *Check the signal connector.*   Make sure the drive's signal interface
cable is connected securely at both the drive and the controller. If
the cable is visibly worn or damaged, try a new one.

■ *Check the CMOS Setup.*   Enter the CMOS Setup routine and
make sure that all the parameters entered for the drive are correct. Heads, cylinders, sectors per track, landing zone, and write
precompensation must all be correct—otherwise, POST will not
recognize the drive.

■ *Check for hardware conflicts.*   Make sure that there are no other
expansion devices in the system using the same IRQs or I/O
addresses used by your drive controller. If there are, change the
resources used by the conflicting device.

■ *Check for termination.*   If your drive system uses a SCSI interface, make sure that the SCSI cable is terminated properly.

■ *Replace the hard drive.*   Try a known-good hard drive. If a known-
good drive works as expected, your original drive is probably defective.

■ *Replace the drive controller.*   If problems persist with a known-
good hard drive, replace the drive controller.

Symptom 12: *Your drive spins up, but the system fails to recognize the drive.* Your computer may flag this as a "Hard-disk error" or "Hard-disk controller failure" during system initialization.

■ *Check the signal connector.* Make sure that the interface signal cable is inserted properly and completely at the drive and controller. Try a new signal cable.

■ *Check any drive jumpers.* Make sure that a primary (master) drive is configured as primary, and a secondary (slave) drive is configured as secondary. For SCSI drives, make sure that each drive has a unique ID setting, and that the SCSI bus is terminated properly.

■ *Check the CMOS Setup.* Enter the CMOS Setup routine and make sure that all of the parameters entered for the drive are correct. Heads, cylinders, sectors per track, landing zone, and write precompensation must all be correct—otherwise, POST will not recognize the drive.

■ *Check the partition.* Boot from a floppy disk and run FDISK to check the partitions on your hard drive. Make sure that there is at least one DOS partition. If the drive is to be your boot drive, the primary partition must be active and bootable. Repartition and reformat the drive if necessary.

■ *Replace the hard drive.* Try a known-good hard drive. If a known-good drive works as expected, your original drive is probably defective.

■ *Replace the drive controller.* If problems persist with a known-good hard drive, replace the drive controller.

Symptom 13: *Your IDE drive spins up when power is applied, then rapidly spins down again.* The drive is defective, or it is not communicating properly with its host system.

■ *Check the power connector.* Make sure the 4-pin power connector is inserted properly and completely into the drive.

■ *Check the signal connector.* Make sure that the interface signal cable is inserted properly and completely at the drive and controller. Try a new signal cable.

■ *Check any drive jumpers.* Make sure that a primary (master) drive is configured as primary, and a secondary (slave) drive is configured as secondary. For SCSI drives, make sure that each drive has a unique ID setting, and that the SCSI bus is terminated properly.

■ *Replace the hard drive.* Try a known-good hard drive. If a known-good drive works as expected, your original drive is probably defective.

Symptom 14: *You see a "Sector not found" error message displayed on the monitor.* This problem usually occurs after the drive has been in operation for quite some time, and is typically the result of a media failure. Fortunately, a bad sector will affect only one file.

- *Recover the file.*   Try a utility such as SpinRite (from Gibson Research) or another data recovery utility and attempt to recover the damaged file. Note that you may be unsuccessful, and have to restore the file from a backup later.

- *Check the media.*   Use a disk utility such as ScanDisk to evaluate the drive, then locate and map out any bad sectors that are located on the drive.

- *Perform a low-level format (if possible).*   Lost sectors often occur as drives age and sector ID information degrades. LL formatting restores the sector IDs, but LL formatting is performed at the factory for IDE/EIDE and SCSI drives. If there is a LL formatting utility for your particular drive (available right from the drive manufacturer) and ScanDisk reveals a large number of bad sectors, consider backing up the drive completely, running the LL utility, repartitioning, reformatting, then restoring the drive.

- *Restore any necessary files.*   If ScanDisk maps out bad sectors, you may need to restore those files from a backup.

Symptom 15: *You see a "1780 or 1781 ERROR" displayed on the monitor.*   The classical 1780 error code indicates a "Hard Disk 0 Failure," while the 1781 error code marks a "Hard Disk 1 Failure."

- *Boot the system "clean."*   Start the PC with a "clean" boot disk and make sure there are no TSRs or drivers being loaded.

- *Check for computer viruses.*   If you haven't done so already, run your antivirus checker and make sure that there are no memory-resident or file-based viruses.

- *Check the software.*   If you can access the hard drive once your system is booted, chances are that the boot files are missing or corrupt. Try a utility such as DrivePro's Drive Boot Fixer or DISKFIX with PC Tools. Otherwise, you will need to repartition and reformat the disk, then restore disk files from a backup.

- *Check the hardware.*   If you cannot access the hard drive, run a diagnostic such as TouchStone Software's CheckIt. Test the drive and drive controller. If the controller responds but the drive does not, try repartitioning and reformatting the hard drive. If the drive still doesn't respond, replace the hard drive outright. If the controller doesn't respond, replace the hard drive controller.

Symptom 16: *You see a "1790 or 1791 ERROR" displayed on the monitor.*   The classical 1790 error code indicates a "Hard Disk 0 Error," while the 1791 error code marks a "Hard Disk 1 Error."

- *Check the signal connector.*   Make sure that the interface signal cable is inserted properly and completely at the drive and the controller. Try a new signal cable.

- *Check the partition.*   Boot from a floppy disk and run FDISK to check the partitions on your hard drive. Make sure that there is at least one DOS partition. If the drive is to be your boot drive, the primary partition must be active and bootable. Repartition and reformat the drive if necessary.

■ *Replace the hard drive.* Try a known-good hard drive. If a known-good drive works as expected, your original drive is probably defective.

■ *Replace the drive controller.* If problems persist with a known-good hard drive, replace the drive controller.

Symptom 17: *You see a "1701 ERROR" displayed on the monitor.* The 1701 error code indicates a hard drive POST error—the drive did not pass its POST test.

■ *Check the power connector.* Make sure the 4-pin power connector is inserted properly and completely. If the drive is being powered by a Y-connector, make sure any interim connections are secure. Use a voltmeter and measure the +5-volt (pin 4) and +12-volt (pin 1) levels as shown in Table 1.3. If either voltage (especially the +12-volt supply) is unusually low or absent, replace the power supply.

■ *Check the CMOS Setup.* Enter the CMOS Setup routine and make sure that all of the parameters entered for the drive are correct. Heads, cylinders, sectors per track, landing zone, and write precompensation must all be correct—otherwise, POST will not recognize the drive.

■ *Perform a low-level format (if possible).* ST506/412 and ESDI drives may require low-level (LL) formatting, but LL formatting is performed at the factory for IDE/EIDE and SCSI drives. If there is a LL formatting utility for your particular drive (available right from the drive manufacturer), consider backing up the drive completely, running the LL utility, repartitioning, reformatting, then restoring the drive.

Symptom 18: *The system reports random data, seek, or format errors.* Random errors rarely indicate a permanent problem, but identifying the problem source can be a time-consuming task.

■ *Check the power connector.* Make sure the 4-pin power connector is inserted properly and completely. If the drive is being powered by a Y-connector, make sure any interim connections are secure. Use a voltmeter and measure the +5-volt (pin 4) and +12-volt (pin 1) levels as shown in Table 1.3. If either voltage (especially the +12-volt supply) is unusually low, replace the power supply.

■ *Check the signal connector.* Make sure that the interface signal cable is inserted properly and completely at the drive and the controller. Try a new signal cable. Try rerouting the signal cable away from the power supply or "noisy" expansion devices.

■ *Check the drive orientation.* If problems occur after remounting the drive in a different orientation, you may need to repartition and reformat the drive or return it to its original orientation.

- *Check the drive controller.* Try relocating the drive controller away from cables and "noisy" expansion devices.

- *Check the turbo mode.* Your ISA drive controller may have trouble operating while the system is in turbo mode. Take the system out of turbo mode. If the problem disappears, try a new drive controller.

- *Check the media.* Use a utility such as ScanDisk to check for and map out any bad sectors. Once bad sectors are mapped out, you may need to restore some files from your backup.

- *Check the hardware.* Try the drive and controller in another system. If the drive and controller work in another system, there is probably excessive noise or grounding problems in the original system. Reinstall the drive and controller in the original system and remove all extra expansion boards. If the problem goes away, replace one board at a time and retest the system until the problem returns. The last board you inserted when the problem returned is probably the culprit. If the problem persists, there may be a ground problem on the motherboard. Try replacing the motherboard as an absolute last effort.

Symptom 19: *You see a "Bad or Missing Command Interpreter" error message.* This is a typical error that appears when a drive is formatted in one DOS version but loaded with another. Compatibility problems occur when you mix DOS versions.

- *Boot the system "clean."* Start the PC with a "clean" boot disk and make sure there are no TSRs or drivers being loaded.

- *Check for computer viruses.* If you haven't done so already, run your antivirus checker and make sure that there are no memory-resident or file-based viruses.

- *Check the format.* Make sure that the drive is partitioned and formatted with the version of DOS you intend to use. Also be sure to use FORMAT with the /S switch or SYS C: in order to transfer system files to the drive.

Symptom 20: *You see an "Error reading drive C:" error message.* Read errors in a hard drive typically indicate problems with the disk media, but may also indicate viruses or signaling problems.

- *Check the signal connector.* Make sure that the interface signal cable is inserted properly and completely at the drive and the controller. Try a new signal cable.

- *Boot the system "clean."* Start the PC with a "clean" boot disk and make sure there are no TSRs or drivers being loaded.

- *Check for computer viruses.* If you haven't done so already, run your antivirus checker and make sure that there are no memory-resident or file-based viruses.

- *Check the drive orientation.* If problems occur after the drive is remounted in a different orientation, you may need to repartition and reformat the drive or return it to its original orientation.

- *Check the media.*   Use a utility such as ScanDisk to check for and map out any bad sectors. Once bad sectors are mapped out, you may need to restore some files from your backup.

- *Replace the hard drive.*   Try a known-good hard drive. If a known-good drive works as expected, your original drive is probably defective.

Symptom 21: *You see a "Track 0 not found" error message.*   A fault on track 00 can disable the entire drive, since track 00 contains the drive's file allocation table (FAT). This can be a serious error which may require you to replace the drive.

- *Check the signal connector.*   Make sure that the interface signal cable is inserted properly and completely at the drive and controller. Try a new signal cable.

- *Check the partition.*   Boot from a floppy disk and run FDISK to check the partitions on your hard drive. Make sure that there is at least one DOS partition. If the drive is to be your boot drive, the primary partition must be active and bootable. Repartition and reformat the drive if necessary.

- *Replace the hard drive.*   Try a known-good hard drive. If a known-good drive works as expected, your original drive is probably defective.

Symptom 22: *Software diagnostics indicate an average access time that is longer than that specified for the drive.*   The average access time is the average amount of time needed for a drive to reach the track and sector where a needed file begins.

- *Check the drive specifications.*   Verify the timing specifications for your particular drive.

- *Check for fragmentation.*   Start your defragmentation utility (such as COMPRESS with PC Tools or DEFRAG with DOS) and check to see the percentage of file fragmentation. If there is more than 10 percent fragmentation, you should consider running the defragmentation utility after preparing Windows (see Symptom 8).

- *Check the diagnostics.*   Keep in mind that different software packages measure access time differently. Make sure that the diagnostic subtracts system overhead processing from the access time calculation. Try one or two other diagnostics to confirm the measurement.

- *Check several similar drives.*   Before you panic and replace a drive, try testing several similar drives for comparison.

- *Replace the hard drive.*   If only the suspect drive measures incorrectly, you may not *need* to replace it, but you should at least maintain frequent backups in case the drive is near failure.

Symptom 23: *Software diagnostics indicate a slower data transfer rate than specified.* This is often due to "less-than-ideal" data transfer rates rather than an actual hardware failure.

- *Check the CMOS Setup.* Enter the Setup routine and verify that any enhanced data transfer modes are enabled (such as PIO Mode 3). This can increase the data transfer rate substantially.

- *Check the drive specifications.* Verify the timing specifications for your particular drive.

- *Check for fragmentation.* Start your defragmentation utility (such as COMPRESS with PC Tools or DEFRAG with DOS) and check to see the percentage of file fragmentation. If there is more than 10 percent fragmentation, you should consider running the defragmentation utility after preparing Windows (see Symptom 8).

- *Check the diagnostics.* Keep in mind that different software packages measure access time differently. Make sure that the diagnostic subtracts system overhead processing from the access time calculation. Try one or two other diagnostics to confirm the measurement.

- *Check for low-level formatting.* If the drive is an IDE/EIDE type, make sure that the original user did not perform a low-level format—this may remove head and cylinder skewing optimization and result in a degradation of data transfer. This error cannot be corrected by end-user software.

- *Check SCSI termination.* If the drive is a SCSI type, make sure the SCSI bus is terminated properly. Poor termination can cause data errors and result in retransmissions that degrade overall data transfer rates.

Symptom 24: *Your low-level format operation is taking too long, or it hangs up the system.* NOTE: This procedure does *not* apply to IDE/EIDE or SCSI drives. You probably see a large number of format errors such as code 20 or 80. You may also see "Unsuccessful Format" error messages.

- *Check the low-level format DEBUG string.* Make sure that your DEBUG command is correct for the ST506/412 or ESDI drive being used. A list of typical DEBUG strings is given in Table 2.2.

- *Check the CMOS Setup.* Make sure that the drive parameters entered for the drive in CMOS are correct. When working on an XT (without CMOS), check that the drive controller board is set correctly for the drive.

- *Check the signal connector.* Make sure that the interface signal cables are inserted properly and completely at the drive and controller. Try some new signal cables.

- *Check the turbo mode.* Your ISA drive controller may have trouble operating while the system is in turbo mode. Take the system out of turbo mode. If the problem disappears, try a new drive controller.

TABLE 2.2 A Listing of Typical Low-Level Format Commands Using DEBUG

G = C800:5
G = CC00:5
G = C800:CCC
G = C800:6
G = D800:5
G = DC00:5

Symptom 25: *You are unable to access the low-level format utility from the DEBUG address.* NOTE: This procedure does *not* apply to IDE/EIDE or SCSI drives.

- *Check the low-level format DEBUG string.* Make sure that your DEBUG command is correct for the ST506/412 or ESDI drive being used. A list of typical DEBUG strings is given in Table 2.2.

- *Check the CMOS Setup.* Some systems will not low-level format a drive while its parameters are entered in the CMOS Setup, so enter your CMOS Setup menu and remove the drive type entries. If that fails to clear the problem, return to the CMOS Setup again and restore the drive parameters.

- *Check the controller's BIOS ROM.* Make sure the controller's on-board BIOS is fully enabled. Otherwise, the DEBUG command may not be interpreted properly. Also make sure that the controller's base address matches with the DEBUG command.

Symptom 26: *The low-level format process regularly hangs up on a specific head/cylinder/sector.* NOTE: This procedure does *not* apply to IDE/EIDE or SCSI drives.

- *Check the hard error list.* Not all portions of an ST506/412 or ESDI drive are usable. These are called "hard errors," and the low-level format procedure must recognize and avoid these hard errors. Some low-level format procedures require you to enter these hard errors manually. If you forget to enter a hard error (or enter the wrong location), the format process will stop when the hard error is encountered. Try low-level formatting the drive again, but make sure to enter the proper hard error locations.

- *Check the CMOS Setup.* Make sure that the drive parameters entered for the drive in CMOS are correct. When working on an XT (without CMOS), check that the drive controller board is set correctly for the drive.

Symptom 27: *The FDISK procedure hangs up or fails to create or save partition record for the drive(s).* You may also see an error message such as "Runtime error." This type of problem often indicates a problem with track 00 on the drive.

■ *Check the signal connector.* Make sure that the interface signal cables are inserted properly and completely at the drive and controller. Try some new signal cables.

■ *Check the CMOS Setup.* Enter the CMOS Setup routine and make sure that all the parameters entered for the drive are correct. Heads, cylinders, sectors per track, landing zone, and write precompensation must all be appropriate. Check with the drive maker and see if there is an alternative "translation geometry" that you can enter instead.

■ *Check your version of FDISK.* Make sure that the version of FDISK you are using is the same as the DOS version on your boot diskette—older versions may not work.

■ *Check preexisting partitions.* Run FDISK and see if there are any partitions already on the drive. If there are, you may need to erase the existing partitions, then create your new partition from scratch. Remember that erasing a partition will destroy any data already on the drive.

■ *Check the media.* Use a utility such as DrivePro (from MicroHouse) or ScanDisk to check for physical defects, especially at track 00. If there is physical damage in the boot sector, you should replace the drive.

■ *Check for emergency utilities.* Some drive makers provide low-level preparation utilities which can rewrite track 00. For example, Western Digital provides the WD_CLEAR.EXE utility. If problems still persist, replace the hard drive.

Symptom 28: *You see a "Hard Disk Controller Failure" or a large number of defects in the last logical partition.* This is typically a CMOS Setup or drive controller problem.

■ *Check the CMOS Setup.* Enter the CMOS Setup routine and make sure that all the parameters entered for the drive are correct. If the geometry specifies a larger drive, the system will attempt to format areas of the drive that don't exist, resulting in a large number of errors.

■ *Replace the drive controller.* Try a new hard drive controller.

■ *Replace the hard drive.* If a new controller does not correct the problem, the drive should be replaced.

Symptom 29: *The high-level (DOS) format process takes too long.* In almost all cases, long formats are the result of older DOS versions.

■ *Check your DOS version.* MS-DOS version 4.x tries to recover hard errors, which can consume quite a bit of extra time. You will probably see a number of "Attempting to recover allocation units" messages. Your best course is to upgrade to MS-DOS version 6.22

(or MS-DOS 7.0 with Windows 95). Later versions of DOS abandon hard error retries.

Symptom 30: *The IDE drive (<528 Mbytes) does not partition or format to full capacity.*   When relatively small hard drives do not realize their full capacity, the CMOS Setup is usually at fault.

■ *Check the CMOS Setup.*   The drive parameters entered into CMOS must specify the *full* capacity of the drive. If you use parameters that specify a smaller drive, any extra capacity will be ignored. If there are more than 1024 cylinders, you must use an alternative "translation geometry" to realize the full drive potential. The drive maker can provide you with the right translation geometry.

■ *Check the DOS version.*   Older versions of DOS use a partition limit of 32 Mbytes. Upgrade your older version of DOS to 6.22 (or MS-DOS 7.0 with Windows 95).

Symptom 31: *The EIDE drive (>528 Mbytes) does not partition or format to full capacity.*   This type of problem may also be due to a CMOS Setup error, but it is almost always due to poor system configuration.

■ *Check the CMOS Setup for drive geometry.*   The drive parameters entered into CMOS must specify the *full* capacity of the drive. If you use parameters that specify a smaller drive, any extra capacity will be ignored. If there are more than 1024 cylinders, you must use an alternative "translation geometry" to realize the full drive potential. The drive maker can provide you with the right translation geometry.

■ *Check the CMOS Setup for LBA.*   EIDE drives need logical block addressing to access more than 528 Mbytes. Make sure that there is an entry such as "LBA Mode" in CMOS. Otherwise, you may need to upgrade your motherboard BIOS to have full drive capacity.

■ *Check the drive controller.*   If you cannot upgrade an older motherboard BIOS, install an EIDE drive controller with its own controller BIOS. This will supplement the motherboard BIOS.

■ *Check the drive management software.*   If neither the motherboard nor the controller BIOS will support LBA mode, you will need to install drive management software such as EZ-Drive or Drive Manager from Ontrack.

Symptom 32: *You see "Disk Boot Failure," "nonsystem disk," or "No ROM Basic—SYSTEM HALTED" error messages.*   There are several possible reasons for these errors.

■ *Check the signal connector.*   Make sure that the interface signal cables are inserted properly and completely at the drive and controller. Try some new signal cables.

- *Boot the system "clean."*   Start the PC with a "clean" boot disk and make sure there are no TSRs or drivers being loaded.

- *Check for computer viruses.*   If you haven't done so already, run your antivirus checker and make sure that there are no memory-resident or file-based viruses.

- *Check the CMOS Setup.*   Enter the CMOS Setup routine and make sure that all the parameters entered for the drive are correct. Heads, cylinders, sectors per track, landing zone, and write precompensation must all be entered.

- *Check the partition.*   Boot from a floppy disk and run FDISK to check the partitions on your hard drive. Make sure that there is at least one DOS partition. If the drive is to be your boot drive, the primary partition must be active and bootable.

- *Replace the hard drive.*   Try a known-good hard drive. If a known-good drive works as expected, your original drive is probably defective.

- *Replace the drive controller.*   If problems persist with a known-good hard drive, replace the drive controller.

Symptom 33:   *The hard drive in a PC is suffering frequent breakdowns (i.e., every 6 to 12 months).*   When drives tend to fail within a few months, there are some factors to consider.

- *Check the PC power.*   If the ac power supplying your PC is "dirty" (i.e., there are lots of spikes and surges), power anomalies can often make it through the power supply and damage other components. Remove any high-load devices such as air conditioners, motors, or coffeemakers from the same ac circuit used by the PC, or try the PC on a known-good ac circuit.

- *Check drive utilization.*   If the drive is being worked hard by applications, consider upgrading RAM or adding cache to reduce dependency on the drive.

- *Check file fragmentation.*   Periodically run a utility like DEFRAG to reorganize the files. This reduces the amount of "drive thrashing" that occurs when loading and saving files.

- *Check the environment.*   Constant, low-level vibrations, such as those in an industrial environment, can kill a hard drive. Smoke (even cigarette smoke), high humidity, very low humidity, and caustic vapors can ruin drives. Make sure the system is used in a stable office-type environment.

Symptom 34:   *A hard drive controller is replaced, but during initialization, the system displays error messages such as "Hard Disk Failure" or "Not a recognized drive type." The PC may also lock up.*

- *Replace the drive controller.*   Some drive controllers may be incompatible in some systems. Check with the controller manufacturer and see if there have been any reports of incompatibilities with your PC. If so, try a different drive controller board.

Symptom 35: *A new hard drive is installed, but it will not boot, or a message appears such as "HDD controller failure."* The new drive has probably not been installed or prepared properly.

- *Check the power connector.*   Make sure the 4-pin power connector is inserted properly and completely. If the drive is being powered by a Y-connector, make sure any interim connections are secure. Use a voltmeter and measure the +5-volt (pin 4) and +12-volt (pin 1) levels as shown in Table 1.3. If either voltage (especially the +12-volt supply) is unusually low or absent, replace the power supply.

- *Check the signal connector.*   Make sure the drive's signal interface cable is connected securely at both the drive and controller. If the cable is visibly worn or damaged, try a new one.

- *Check the CMOS Setup.*   Enter the CMOS Setup routine and make sure that all the parameters entered for the drive are correct. Heads, cylinders, sectors per track, landing zone, and write precompensation must all be correct—otherwise, POST will not recognize the drive.

- *Check the drive preparation.*   Run FDISK from a bootable diskette to partition the drive, then run FORMAT to initialize the drive. Then run SYS C: to make the drive bootable.

Symptom 36: *You install Disk Manager to a hard drive, then install DOS, but DOS formats the drive back to 528 Mbytes.* After Disk Manager is installed, you must create a "rescue disk" to use in conjunction with your DOS installation. There are two means of accomplishing this. First:

- Create a "clean" DOS bootable disk.

- Copy two files from the original Disk Manager disk to your bootable disk: XBIOS.OVL and DMDRVR.BIN.

- Create a CONFIG.SYS file on this bootable disk with these three lines:

```
DEVICE = DMDRVR.BIN
FILES = 35
BUFFERS = 35
```

- Remove the bootable diskette and reboot the system.

- When you see "Press space bar to boot from diskette," do so—the system will halt.

- Insert the rescue disk in drive A:, and press any key to resume the boot process.

- At the A: prompt, remove your rescue disk, insert the DOS installation disk, then type SETUP.

- You will now install DOS files without overwriting the Disk Manager files.

or

- Create a "clean" DOS bootable disk.

- Insert the original Disk Manager diskette in the A: drive and type:

  ```
  DMCFIG/D = A:
  ```

- You will be prompted to insert a bootable floppy in drive A:.

- You will need to remove and insert the bootable disk a few times as Drive Manager files are copied.

- Remove the floppy and reboot the system.

- When you see "Press space bar to boot from diskette," do so—the system will halt.

- Insert the rescue disk in drive A:, and press any key to resume the boot process.

- At the A: prompt, remove your rescue disk, insert the DOS installation disk, then type SETUP.

- You will now install DOS files without overwriting the Disk Manager files.

Symptom 37: *ScanDisk reports some bad sectors, but cannot map them out during a surface analysis.* You may need a surface analysis utility for your particular drive, which is provided by the drive maker. For example, Western Digital provides the WDATIDE.EXE utility for its Caviar series of drives. It will mark all known defects and compensate for lost capacity by utilizing spare tracks.

NOTE: These types of surface analysis utilities are typically destructive. Make sure to have a complete backup of the drive before proceeding. Also, depending on your drive's capacity, the utility may take a very long time to run.

Symptom 38: *The drive will work as a primary drive, but not as a secondary (or vice versa).* In most cases, the drive is simply jumpered incorrectly, but there may also be timing problems.

- *Check the drive jumpers.* Make sure that the drive is jumpered properly as a primary (single drive), primary (dual drive), or secondary drive.

- *Check the drive timing.* Some IDE/EIDE drives do not work as primary or secondary drives with certain other drives in the system. Reverse the primary/secondary relationship. If the problem persists, try the drives separately. If the drives work individually, there is probably a timing problem, so try a different drive as the primary or secondary.

Symptom 39: *You cannot get 32-bit access to work under Windows 3.1x.* You are probably not using the correct hard drive driver.

- *Check your EIDE BIOS.* If your motherboard (or drive controller) BIOS supports LBA, obtaining a driver should be easy. Either the drive maker provides a 32-bit driver on a diskette accompanying the drive, or a driver can be downloaded from the drive maker's BBS or Internet Web site.

■ *Check the drive software.* If the motherboard (or drive controller) does not support LBA, you can install Ontrack's Disk Manager (6.03 or later) and run DMCFIG to install the 32-bit driver software.

Symptom 40: *Drive diagnostics reveal a great deal of wasted space on the drive.* You probably have a large drive partitioned as a single large logical volume.

■ *Check the cluster size.* Table 2.3 shows a comparison of partition size vs. cluster size. If you deal with large numbers of small files, it may be more efficient to create multiple smaller partitions utilizing smaller clusters.

Symptom 41: *You install a Y-adapter which fails to work.* Some Y-adapters are incorrectly wired and can cause severe damage to any device attached to them.

■ *Examine the power connector.* Make certain that both of the female connectors are lined up with the two chamfered (rounded) corners facing up and both of the squared corners facing down. The four wires attached to the female connectors should now be in the following order from left to right:
Yellow (12 V), Black (ground), Black (ground), Red (5 V)
If this order is reversed on one of the connectors, then your Y power adapter is faulty and should not be used.

Symptom 42: *During the POST, you hear a drive begin to spin up and produce a sharp noise.* This problem has been encountered with some combinations of drives, motherboards, and motherboard BIOS. This type of problem can easily result in data loss (and media damage).

TABLE 2.3 Partition Size vs. Cluster Size

Partition size	Sectors/clusters	Cluster size
0–15 Mbytes	8	4 kbytes
16–127 Mbytes	4	2 kbytes
128–255 Mbytes	8	4 kbytes
256–511 Mbytes	16	8 kbytes
512–1023 Mbytes	32	16 kbytes
1024–2145 Mbytes	64	32 kbytes

- *Check the motherboard BIOS.* Contact the PC system manufacturer and see if a BIOS upgrade is necessary. Try a BIOS upgrade.

- *Replace the drive controller.* Often a new drive controller may
  resolve the problem if the motherboard BIOS cannot be replaced.

Hard Drives and Disk Manager

It is often too expensive or too inconvenient to upgrade a motherboard BIOS or drive controller in order to accommodate a large
(EIDE) hard drive. Ontrack's Disk Manager software provides a software driver that partitions and formats the drive, then supports full
access even when there is no direct hardware support in the PC. Late
versions of Disk Manager are also compatible with Windows 3.1x and
Windows 95. As with most driver software, however, there are some
circumstances where trouble can occur.

Disk Manager troubleshooting

Symptom 1: *You are having difficulty installing Ontrack's Disk
Manager software from the B: drive.* Ontrack software must be
installed from the A: drive. If your A: drive is the wrong size for your
Ontrack distribution diskette, copy the diskette to a floppy disk sized
properly for drive A:, then try reinstalling Disk Manager.

Symptom 2: *Windows 95 does not appear to function properly with
Disk Manager.* This is usually due to an older version of Disk
Manager.

- *Check your Disk Manager version.* Only Disk Manager 6.0 or
  higher will function properly with Windows 95. You can download
  the DMPATCH.EXE utility from Ontrack or Western Digital to
  update your DDO (dynamic drive overlay) to version 6.03d.

Symptom 3: *Windows 95 reports that it is in the DOS compatibility
mode, even though Disk Manager 6.0x (or later) is in use.* A real-
mode driver is running and preventing 32-bit access.

- *Check the CMOS Setup.* The CMOS setting for your hard drive
  should use a number equal to or less than 1024 for cylinders. The
  drive's documentation may offer an alternative "translation geometry" that can be entered in CMOS.

- *Disable the 32-bit disk driver.* Your 32-bit disk driver must be disabled before installing Windows 95. Open SYSTEM.INI and disable the following line in the [386Enh] area:

  ```
  ;32BitDiskAccess = On
  ```

     or

  ```
  32BitDiskAccess = Off
  ```

- *Check your Disk Manager version.* Only Disk Manager 6.0 or
  higher will function properly with Windows 95. You can download

the DMPATCH.EXE utility from Ontrack or Western Digital to update your DDO (dynamic drive overlay) to version 6.03d.

Symptom 4:   *There is trouble using the drive manufacturer's disk driver for 32-bit access under Windows 95.*   Windows 95 has built-in support for EIDE devices and does not need the 32-bit drivers that you may have used with Windows 3.1x.

■ *Check your SYSTEM.INI file.*   Open your SYSTEM.INI file and remove any references to 32-bit disk access or manufacturer-specific disk drivers.

Symptom 5:   *Disk Manager refuses to work properly with Windows 95 and disk compression.*   You probably have an older version of Disk Manager.

■ *Check your Disk Manager version.*   Only Disk Manager 6.0 or higher will function properly with Windows 95. You can download the DMPATCH.EXE utility from Ontrack or Western Digital to update your DDO (dynamic drive overlay) to version 6.03d.

■ *Check your compression software.*   If you are using a compression utility other than DriveSpace, check with the compression utility manufacturer to see if there are any compatibility issues with Disk Manager and Windows 95.

Symptom 6:   *When loading, Disk Manager does not identify the hard disk correctly.*   This usually occurs because drive ID queries are intercepted incorrectly.

■ *Disable the drive controller BIOS.*   When using Disk Manager, try disabling the BIOS on your hard drive controller.

■ *Replace the drive controller.*   Try formatting the drive using a different drive controller.

Symptom 7:   *You are having trouble removing Disk Manager.*   This calls for a complete repartitioning of the drive. Be sure to have a complete drive backup before proceeding.

■ *Boot from a "clean" floppy disk.*   Make sure the disk has FDISK and FORMAT.

■ *Repartition the drive.*   Run FDISK to repartition the drive (this overwrites the boot information), then reformat the drive with FORMAT.

■ *Restore your data.*   Restore the contents of your backup to the drive.

Symptom 8:   *Disk Manager appears to be conflicting with other programs.*   Disk Manager first loads into conventional memory, where it consumes 6 kbytes. It then moves to take 4 kbytes of upper memory, leaving behind a 62-byte "footprint" at the top of conventional memory. This can sometimes conflict with other programs or drivers. You can change the way Disk Manager loads into memory:

■ *Try staying in conventional memory.*   When you see the boot message which tells you to press the space bar to boot from a floppy, press the "S" key instead, and then answer "Y" to the next question. This will cause Disk Manager to stay in conventional memory rather than moving to high memory, and may resolve the conflicts you are experiencing. If this resolves the problem, there is a special version of Disk Manager (LOADLOW.ZIP) which will load into conventional memory automatically. You can download the file from Ontrack.

Symptom 9:   *When installing DOS on a drive with Disk Manager, the drive wound up with only 504 Mbytes of accessible space.*   You must load Disk Manager *before* booting from a floppy.

■ *Start the boot process from your hard drive.*   When you see a message such as "Press space bar to boot from diskette," press the space bar, insert your DOS boot disk, then press any key. The DDO will have loaded *before* booting your DOS setup disk.

Symptom 10:   *You see a message such as "DDO Integrity Error" and the hard drive cannot be accessed.*   The sector containing the DDO has probably been corrupted.

■ *Boot the system "clean."*   Start the PC with a "clean" boot disk and make sure there are no TSRs or drivers being loaded.

■ *Check for computer viruses.*   If you haven't done so already, run your antivirus checker and make sure that there are no memory-resident or file-based viruses.

■ *Check the power supply.*   Use a voltmeter to check the +12-volt and +5-volt signals powering the drive. If either voltage appears unusually low (or high), the supply may be defective. You may install a diagnostic board such as PC Power Check (from Data Depot) to check for spikes or surges that may be passing through the supply.

■ *Try reinstalling Disk Manager.*   This effectively repartitions your drive, so be ready to restore your files from a backup.

■ *Replace the hard drive.*   If you cannot reinstall Disk Manager (or the error message returns shortly thereafter), try a new hard drive.

Symptom 11:   *You get only 16-bit file access under Windows for Workgroups using a secondary drive with Disk Manager.*   When Disk Manager is installed on the primary drive, the DDO is loaded during the boot process, from the "nondata area" of the drive. As a result, there is no device = dmdrvr.bin line in the CONFIG.SYS file. However, if Disk Manager is used only on the secondary drive (and the primary drive was prepared with conventional DOS only), the `device` = line *will* be entered in CONFIG.SYS, and the DDO is loaded differently. When Disk Manager is loaded to a secondary drive in this fashion, only 16-bit file access is available.

■ *Install Disk Manager to the primary drive.*   Back up all the data on your primary drive, and install Disk Manager. This will cause the DDO to be loaded during the boot process and allow 32-bit file access on both the primary *and* secondary drives.

Symptom 12: *When booting from a Disk Manager "rescue disk," the hard drive letters are assigned differently.*   This is because DOS assigns drive letters before the DDO is invoked. Start booting from the hard drive to install the DDO, *then* boot from the floppy.

■ *Start the boot process from your hard drive.*   When you see a message such as "Press space bar to boot from diskette," press the space bar, insert your DOS boot disk, then press any key. The DDO will have loaded *before* booting your DOS setup disk.

Symptom 13: *Data on the Disk Manager drive is corrupted after another drive-related utility is installed.*   Chances are that if software uses DOS and Interrupt 13 calls to access the hard drive, the software should interact correctly with Disk Manager, and corruption should not occur. When the utility bypasses DOS and Interrupt 13, however, data corruption *can* result. Check with the utility maker and see if there have been any reports of compatibility problems with Disk Manager.

Symptom 14: *Disk Manager cannot auto-identify a hard drive.* Instead, a list of drives will appear. This is often because of caching drive controllers interfering with Disk Manager. There are two options for dealing with this problem:

■ Select the proper drive from the list and continue as usual.
   or
■ Temporarily disable the controller's cache.

Hard Drives and EZ-Drive

EZ-Drive is a software enhancement product very similar to Disk Manager—it provides "large drive" support for older BIOS. This eliminates the need to update your motherboard BIOS or drive controller. It also works around problems with BIOS versions that hang up when working with drives larger than 2.1 Gbytes. EZ-Drive can be found on the diskette bundled with many new hard drives.

EZ-Drive troubleshooting
Symptom 1: *EZ-Drive is interfering with local-bus IDE controllers.* Some local-bus IDE chipsets and drivers do not work properly with EZ-Drive. The following list outlines the major known issues:

- *Appian ADI2.*   This is fully compatible with EZ-Drive. The companion HVLIDE.SYS driver is also fully compatible with EZ-Drive.

- *ADI2C143.SYS.*   This driver is fully compatible with EZ-Drive. Install EZ-Drive to your hard disk first, then install one of the drivers into your CONFIG.SYS file.

- *CMD640x.*   This is fully compatible with EZ-Drive. The companion CMD640X.SYS driver is also fully compatible with EZ-Drive. Install EZ-Drive to your hard disk first, then install the driver into your CONFIG.SYS file.

- *PC Tech RZ1000.*   This system is *not* supported, and ZEOS/Phoenix BIOS does *not* need EZ-Drive, as it natively supports large (EIDE) drives. If EZ-Drive sets up a large drive, it will take over from the BIOS, and the drive will be *slower* than it would be with BIOS support alone.

- *Opti 611A & 621A.*   These are *not* supported by any product or hardware. The OPTIVIC.SYS (dated 5-11-94) driver is incompatible with large drives both with and without EZ-Drive.

Symptom 2:   *The keyboard or mouse does not function normally after exiting Windows on a drive using EZ-Drive.*   This is almost always due to a mouse driver being attached to a keyboard.

- *Change your keyboard driver.*   A mouse driver installation may change a line in SYSTEM.INI to something like

```
Keyboard = C:\MOUSE\mousevkd.386
```

    To correct the problem, change that line in the SYSTEM.INI file back to

```
Keyboard = *vkd
```

    You will need to restart Windows for your changes to take effect.

Symptom 3:   *QEMM 7.5 will not load in stealth mode in a system with EZ-Drive.*   You will need to add a switch to the QEMM command line.

- *Update the command line.*   Add the following switch to the QEMM command line in CONFIG.SYS:

```
XSTI = 76
```

Symptom 4:   *Windows crashes with EZ-Drive installed on the drive.* There is a known issue with Award BIOS version 4.50G.

- *Update your version of EZ-Drive.*   Download EZPCH502.EXE from MicroHouse BBS at (303) 443-9957. This file is a self-extracting file that will update the EZ-Drive MBR.

Symptom 5:   *You are having trouble removing EZ-Drive.*   In order to remove EZ-Drive, the master boot record (MBR) will have to be rewritten. You should have a complete system backup before proceeding.

■ *Check the CMOS Setup.*   Disable any MBR virus protection features in the BIOS. Save your changes (if any) and reboot the system.

■ *Boot the system "clean."*   Start the PC with a "clean" boot disk and make sure there are no TSRs or drivers being loaded. Make sure your boot diskette contains the correct version of FDISK.

■ *Rewrite the MBR.*   Run the command FDISK /MBR to rewrite the drive's master boot record and eliminate EZ-Drive.

NOTE: If the hard drive was set up as a Custom Drive Type, access to the data on the drive will be lost. Restore the drive's contents from your backup.

Symptom 6: *You see a "No IDE Drive Installed" message from EZ-Drive.*   Normally, EZ-Drive should be able to identify a drive even when there are no geometry figures in CMOS. Occasionally, it will fail to identify the drive, and an error message will be generated.

■ *Check your CMOS Setup.*   Enter the proper geometry figures (heads, sectors, cylinders, and so on) for your hard disk. As an alternative, set the CMOS drive type to "auto-detect."

Symptom 7: *You have trouble removing EZ-Drive from a system with an LBA option in BIOS.*   In most cases, you have upgraded the drive controller or motherboard BIOS, and no longer need EZ-Drive support. Be sure to have a complete backup of the drive before proceeding. If you are using EZ-Drive 5.00 or later, you can try the following procedure:

■ Insert the EZ-Drive distribution diskette and run EZ.
■ Choose the "Change Installed Features" option.
■ Enable the Windows NT Compatibility Mode for EZ-Drive 5.00.

For EZ-Drive 5.02, you can use the procedure below:

■ Disable floppy boot protection for EZ 5.02 or later.
■ Choose the "Save Changes" option and exit EZ-Drive.
■ Reboot the system and enter your CMOS Setup.
■ Set your CMOS drive geometry to "auto-detect."
■ Enable the LBA mode.
■ Save your changes and exit the CMOS Setup.
■ Reboot the system from a bootable floppy diskette (bypassing EZ-Drive).

■ If all drives/directories are still accessible, run the command FDISK/MBR to remove EZ-Drive MBR.

■ If not all drives/directories are accessible, the BIOS LBA translation is different from the translation EZ-Drive used. In that case, boot directly from a floppy, run FDISK /MBR, repartition and format the drive using FDISK and FORMAT, then restore your data.

Symptom 8: *You are continuously receiving the message "Hold down the CTRL key...."* In virtually all reported cases of this symptom, the problem is caused by an infection with the "Ripper" virus. You could try using an antivirus checker, but chances are that even clearing the virus will damage the master boot sector. If you have EZ-Drive 5.00 or later, try the following procedure:

■ Boot directly from a bootable floppy diskette, then insert the EZ-Drive distribution diskette.

■ Type EZ/MBR and press <Enter>.

■ Run EZ.

■ Choose the "Change Installed Features" option.

■ Enable Windows NT Compatibility Mode for 5.00.

For EZ-Drive 5.02, you can use the procedure below:

■ Disable floppy boot protection for EZ 5.02 and later.

■ Choose the "Save Changes" option.

■ Run your virus scan software.

NOTE: Any time a virus is suspected or found, any diskettes used in the system recently should also be suspected of infection. Discard all boot and antivirus disks used to detect and eliminate any virus.

Symptom 9: *A system hangs after booting from a nonsystem disk.* The user boots a system with a nonbootable diskette in the floppy drive. Once the message "Non system disk or disk error" is displayed, the user removes the floppy and reboots the system. Now the system hangs up and will not boot. All cases of this error have been linked to the "Antiexe" virus. If you have EZ-Drive 5.00 or later, try the following procedure:

■ Boot directly from a bootable floppy diskette, then insert the EZ-Drive distribution diskette.

■ Type EZ/MBR and press <Enter>.

■ Run EZ.

■ Choose the "Change Installed Features" option.

■ Enable Windows NT Compatibility Mode for 5.00.

For EZ-Drive 5.02, you can use the procedure below:

■ Disable floppy boot protection for EZ 5.02 and later.

■ Choose the "Save Changes" option.

■ Run your virus scan software.

NOTE: Any time a virus is suspected or found, any diskettes used in the system recently should also be suspected of infection. Discard all boot and antivirus disks used to detect and eliminate any virus.

Symptom 10: *You see the EZ-Drive error message "Unrecognized DBR."*   There is trouble with the diskette boot record of a floppy disk.

■ *Check the floppy disk.*   The DBR on the floppy diskette has been corrupted, or simply is not one that is easily recognized by the operating system (such as a language-specific version of DOS). Try to re-SYS the diskette.

■ *Accept the transfer.*   When the problem is on an important diskette (such as DOS disk 1), answer Yes to proceed with a data transfer when the "Unrecognized DBR" error appears.

■ *Check the hard drive boot files.*   If the hard drive does *not* boot with a "Non-system disk error" message, reboot the system and hold down the space bar when prompted. Insert a bootable floppy and press any key to boot to an A: prompt. Then SYS the hard drive to transfer new bootable files. The hard drive should now be able to boot without any problems.

Symptom 11: *You have trouble getting the MH32BIT.386 driver to operate in block transfer mode.*   The MH32BIT.386 driver does not support DMA Type F (or block transfer mode) data transfers. Use a different driver, or check in with Ontrack or MicroHouse resources to obtain a newer version of the driver.

Symptom 12: *You have trouble getting the MH32BIT.386 driver to work with Windows 95.*   Although the MH32BIT.386 driver *should* interact properly with Windows 95, the driver is not needed. Open the SYSTEM.INI file and comment out any references to the MH32BIT.386 driver.

Symptom 13: *You cannot get EZ-Drive to run on PS/1, PS/2, and MicroChannel systems.*   EZ-Drive does not run on all versions of PS/1 and PS/2 computers. It also will not run on MicroChannel systems. If you cannot get EZ-Drive to load or run on such a system, you should abandon the attempt.

Symptom 14: *EZ-Drive has been removed, and the hard drive is no longer accessible.*   The drive system must support large hard drives (through motherboard BIOS or drive controller BIOS) before EZ-Drive is removed.

■ *Check the CMOS Setup.*   Make sure that the CMOS Setup for your hard drive uses the same parameters as EZ-Drive. If the parameters match, your drive should remain accessible.

Symptom 15:   *You cannot recover data after invoking the EZWIPE.EXE utility.*   The EZWIPE.EXE utility erases the entire first cylinder of the hard drive completely, and all data will be inaccessible. If you invoke EZWIPE.EXE by accident, you will have to repartition and reformat the drive, then restore files from a backup.

Hard Drives and Drive Rocket

Drive Rocket is not caching software. Rather, Drive Rocket takes advantage of an IDE drive's ability to transfer data in multiple-block "chunks," and can speed the effective throughput of data across an IDE bus. However, Drive Rocket can cause several problems with memory managers or unusual system configurations.

Drive Rocket troubleshooting

Symptom 1:   *When running Drive Rocket, the QEMM Stealth ROM feature reports "Disabling Stealth ROM" and then a reference to INT 76.*   QEMM is disabling itself when Drive Rocket grabs Interrupt 13.

■ *Update the QEMM command line.*   Open CONFIG.SYS and add the following switch to the QEMM command line:

```
XSTI = 76
```

   This tells QEMM to ignore Interrupt 76.

Symptom 2:   *During installation, Drive Rocket produces an error indicating that it can't recognize the driver (i.e., "inconfigurable driver").*   Chances are that Drive Rocket is simply not compatible with your particular system. The highest probability of failure is reported on systems which already enhance drive speed, such as Pentium systems with PCI drive controllers using LBA.

■ *Update your version of Drive Rocket.*   Check with Ontrack to be sure you have the latest version of Drive Rocket.

Symptom 3:   *You have trouble removing Drive Rocket.*   Unlike other Ontrack software, Drive Rocket does not reside in the MBR.

■ *Update your CONFIG.SYS file.*   You can effectively "uninstall" Drive Rocket by removing the following line from CONFIG.SYS:

```
device = rocket.bin
```

   Also delete the ROCKET.BIN file from the root directory.

Symptom 4: *When loading, Drive Rocket does not identify the hard disk correctly.*   This usually occurs because drive ID queries are intercepted incorrectly when using OEM versions of Drive Rocket.

■ *Use a generic version of Drive Rocket.*   Replace your OEM version of Drive Rocket with a generic version.

Symptom 5: *Drive Rocket cannot be loaded into upper memory.* Chances are that this is a problem with the QEMM loadhigh statement.

■ *Try a different memory manager.*   If you absolutely cannot live with 6 kbytes less conventional memory, try a different memory manager (such as EMM386.EXE).

Symptom 6: *Drive Rocket reports that the system will experience a "negative" ($-x\%$) performance increase.*   In most cases, Drive Rocket is conflicting with another driver or device in the system. As a result, you should not use Drive Rocket on that system.

Symptom 7: *You encounter a GPF when trying to work with the Control Panel in Windows.*   You will need to tweak the Drive Rocket command line.

■ *Update your CONFIG.SYS file.*   Add the following switch to your Drive Rocket command line in the CONFIG.SYS file:

/w = 1,	if Drive Rocket is on the primary drive only, or
/w = ,1	if Drive Rocket is on the secondary drive only, or
/w = 1,1	if Drive Rocket is on both the primary and secondary drives

CD-ROM Drives

Originally designed as an audio recording medium, the CD quickly found a place in the PC with a CD-ROM drive. CDs provide two key advantages over other forms of media: (1) They hold tremendous amounts of information, and (2) they can be exchanged in the drive. The CD offers PC users access to almost unlimited information. Although CD-ROM drives are still quite slow in comparison to contemporary hard drives, CDs have become particularly popular for holding data-intensive multimedia (sound, images, and programs).

CD-ROM drive interfaces

There are two major interfaces used with CD-ROM drives: IDE/EIDE and SCSI. The IDE/EIDE interface is shown in Figure 2.4. IDE/EIDE drives are extremely popular, and most end-user systems made since 1989 carry an IDE (Integrated Drive Electronics) hard drive. EIDE (Enhanced IDE) drives and interfaces appeared in 1994 and have now largely replaced IDE in new systems, though the 40-pin interface is exactly the same. An IDE CD-ROM is typically installed to a secondary IDE channel on the drive controller or sound card. You will also need to install an ATAPI driver to use an IDE CD-ROM drive. SCSI (Small Computer System Interface) drives are outstanding in server or multitasking systems. SCSI CD-ROM drives require their own ASPI drivers. Figure 2.5 shows a standard 50-pin SCSI connection, and Fig. 2.6 shows a 68-pin SCSI connection.

CD-ROM drives and device drivers

A low-level device driver allows DOS to access the CD-ROM adapter properly at the register (hardware) level. Since most CD-ROM adapters are designed differently, they require different device drivers. If you change or upgrade the CD-ROM drive at any point, the device driver must be upgraded as well. A typical device driver uses a.SYS extension and is initiated by adding its command line to the PC's CONFIG.SYS file, such as

```
DEVICE = HITACHIA.SYS /D:MSCD000 /N:1 /P:300
```

The DEVICE command may be replaced by the DEVICEHIGH command if you have available space in the upper memory area (UMA).

A CD-ROM device driver will typically have three command-line switches associated with it. These parameters are needed to ensure that the driver installs properly. For the example command line shown above, the /D switch is the name used by the driver when it is installed in the system's device table. This name must be unique, and must be matched by the /D switch in the MSCDEX.EXE command line (covered later). The /N switch is the number of CD-ROM drives attached to the interface card. The default is 1 (which is typical for most general-purpose systems). Finally, the /P switch is the I/O port address the CD-ROM adapter card resides at. As you might expect, the port address should match the jumper settings on the adapter board. If there is no /P switch, the default is 0300h.

CD-ROM drives and MSCDEX.EXE

MS-DOS was developed in a time when no one anticipated that large files would be accessible to a PC, and it is severely limited in the file sizes that it can handle. With the development of CD-ROMs, Microsoft created an extension to MS-DOS that allows software publishers to access 650-Mbyte CDs in a standard fashion: the Microsoft CD-ROM Extensions (MSCDEX). MSCDEX is loaded in AUTOEXEC.BAT. Like most software, MSCDEX offers some vital features (and a few limitations), and it is required by a vast majority of CD-ROM products. Obtaining MSCDEX is not a problem; it is generally provided on the disk containing the CD-ROM's low-level device driver. New versions of MSCDEX can be obtained from the Microsoft Download BBS, the Microsoft forum on CompuServe (GO MSL-1), or the Microsoft Web site at http://www.microsoft.com/. You can learn more about MSCDEX and its command-line switches in Section 8.

MPC standards

The volume of sound and video information contained in "multimedia" places serious demands on the processing power and resources of a computer. Multimedia developers have outlined the requirements for a multimedia personal computer (MPC), and software developers adhering to those standards can ensure that their products will operate as expected. You can see the comparison of MPC specifications in Table 2.4.

CD-ROM drive troubleshooting

Symptom 1: *The drive has trouble accepting or rejecting a CD.* This problem is typical of motorized CD-ROM drives where the disk is accepted into a slot or placed in a motorized tray.

- *Try the tray manually.*   Turn off the PC, eject the tray manually, then gently slide the tray back and forth to see if there are any obstructions. If the tray slides smoothly, the load/unload motor may be failing, so replace the CD-ROM drive. Remember to update your low-level driver when installing a new CD-ROM model.
- *Check for obstructions.*   If the tray feels stuck or jammed, open the mechanism and check for obstructions in the mechanics.
- *Replace the drive.*   If you cannot find any obstructions, replace the CD-ROM drive.

Symptom 2: *Optical head does not seek.*   The optical head must move very slowly and smoothly to ensure accurate tracking. DOS may report this as a drive failure or an "error reading from drive x" problem. Either the head is jammed or the linear motor has failed.

- *Check for obstructions.*   Inspect the linear motor rails and see if there is any foreign matter interfering with the travel of your optical head. Remove any foreign matter.
- *Replace the CD-ROM drive.*   If problems persist, replace the drive outright. Remember to update your low-level driver when installing a new CD-ROM model.

Symptom 3: *Disk cannot be read.*   This type of problem may result in a DOS-level "sector not found" or "drive not ready" error.

- *Check the power connector.*   Make sure the 4-pin power connector is inserted properly and completely. If the drive is being powered by a Y-connector, make sure any interim connections are secure. Use a voltmeter and measure the +5-volt (pin 4) and +12-volt (pin 1) levels as shown in Table 1.3. If either voltage (especially the +12-volt supply) is unusually low or absent, replace the power supply.

TABLE 2.4 Comparison of Multimedia Standards

Component	MPC Level 1	MPC Level 2	MPC Level 3
The CPU chip and speed	386SX at 16 MHz	486SX at 25 MHz	Pentium at 75 MHz
Main system RAM	2 Mbytes	4 Mbytes	8 Mbytes
Video adapter and resolution	VGA graphics*	1.2 million pixels/s at 40% of CPU capacity	Color space conversion and scaling capability; direct access to frame buffer for video graphics subsystem with a resolution of 352 × 240 @ 30 fps, or 352 × 288 @ 25 fps—both at 15 bits/pixel unscaled, without cropping.
Video playback capability	N/A	N/A	MPEG 1
Audio	8-bit DAC and ADC linear PCM sampling; 22-kHz rate for DAC, 11-kHz rate for ADC	16-bit DAC and ADC linear PCM sampling; 44.1-kHz rate for DAC, 44.1-kHz rate for ADC	16-bit DAC and ADC linear PCM sampling; 44.1-kHz rate for DAC, 44.1-kHz rate for ADC
	Microphone input	Stereo input and output	Stereo input and output
	Synthesizer	Microphone input	Microphone input
	Multivoice	Synthesizer	MIDI playback
	Multitimbral	Multivoice	Multivoice
	6 melody/2 percussive	Multitimbral	Multitimbral
	3-channel mixer	3-channel mixer	3-channel mixer
	Stereo output	6 melody/2 percussive	6 melody/2 percussive
		Stereo output	Stereo output

Data input options	101 keyboard Two-button mouse	101 keyboard Two-button mouse	101 keyboard Two-button mouse
Input/output	9600-baud serial port Bidirectional parallel port Joystick port MIDI I/O port	9600-baud serial port Bidirectional parallel port Joystick port MIDI I/O port	9600-baud serial port Bidirectional parallel port Joystick port MIDI I/O port
Main storage (hard disk)	30-Mbyte hard disk	160-Mbyte hard disk	540-Mbyte hard disk
Floppy disk	1.44-Mbyte 3.5-in floppy	1.44-Mbyte 3.5-in floppy	1.44-Mbyte 3.5-in floppy
CD-ROM or optical audio/video storage (removable)	150-kbyte/s data transfer, 1 s maximum seek time	Double-speed 300-kbyte/s data transfer, 400 ms maximum seek time Multisession, CD - DA and XA capability	Quad-speed 600-kbyte/s data transfer, 250 ms maximum seek time Multisession, CD - DA and XA capability

*640 × 480 resolution with 16 colors

- *Check the signal connector.*   Make sure the drive's signal interface cable is connected securely at both the drive and the controller. If the cable is visibly worn or damaged, try a new one.

- *Check the compact disk.*   Make sure that the CD is the proper format (you can't start a program from an audio CD) and that it is physically clean. Try a known-good CD.

- *Check the DOS driver.*   Make sure that MSCDEX is installed and configured properly in AUTOEXEC.BAT.

- *Dust the optical head.*   Dust can obstruct the optical head. Try lightly dusting the optical head with photography-grade compressed air.

- *Check SCSI terminations.*   If the CD-ROM drive uses a SCSI interface, make sure that the SCSI bus is terminated properly— signal interference can cause the CD-ROM to malfunction.

- *Replace the drive.*   If problems persist, try replacing the CD-ROM drive.

- *Replace the controller.*   If a known-good CD-ROM drive continues to malfunction, try a new CD-ROM controller. Keep in mind that the CD-ROM controller is often integrated into a sound board or secondary EIDE controller channel.

Symptom 4: *The disk does not turn.*   This is almost always a problem with the CD-ROM drive itself (the spindle motor has failed).

- *Check the disk itself.*   Make sure that the disk is seated properly, and is not jammed or obstructed.

- *Check the power connector.*   Make sure the 4-pin power connector is inserted properly and completely. If the drive is being powered by a Y-connector, make sure any interim connections are secure. Use a voltmeter and measure the +5-volt (pin 4) and +12-volt (pin 1) levels as shown in Table 1.3. If either voltage (especially the +12-volt supply) is unusually low or absent, replace the power supply.

- *Check the signal connector.*   Make sure the drive's signal interface cable is connected securely at both the drive and the controller. If the cable is visibly worn or damaged, try a new one.

- *Replace the drive.*   If problems persist, try replacing the CD-ROM drive.

Symptom 5: *The optical head cannot focus its laser beam.*   This may often manifest itself as DOS error messages indicating that the disk cannot be read, is not ready, and so on. In almost all cases, the drive has failed.

- *Check the compact disk.*   Make sure that the CD is the proper format (you can't start a program from an audio CD) and that it is physically clean. Try a known-good CD.

- *Dust the optical head.*   Dust can obstruct the optical head. Try lightly dusting the optical head with photography-grade compressed air.

■ *Replace the drive.*   If problems persist, try replacing the CD-ROM drive.

Symptom 6:   *There is no audio being generated by the drive.*   Audio CDs can often be played in available CD-ROM drives through headphones or speakers.

■ *Check the compact disk.*   Make sure that the CD is an audio CD or contains at least one audio track.

■ *Test the front jack.*   Plug headphones and speakers into the CD-ROM audio jack, start your CD player application, and make sure that audio is being generated. You may need to adjust the front volume control.

■ *Replace the drive.*   If problems persist, try replacing the CD-ROM drive.

Symptom 7:   *Audio is not being played by the sound card.*   Audio can be channeled to the sound board for playback. Most CDs offer an audio connector that allows audio signals to be fed directly to the sound board.

■ *Check the system's mixer software.*   Most sound boards use a "mixer applet" to control input volume from sources such as line input, CD audio, and microphones. Make sure that the mixer controls have not disabled the CD-audio input or turned its volume off.

■ *Check the audio cable.*   Make sure the thin, four-wire audio cable is connected properly to the CD-ROM drive and sound board. Also make sure that the cable is wired correctly (some CD/sound card cables flip pins). Try a new audio cable. Audio cables can be obtained from SC&T International at 800-408-4084 or Advanced Multimedia Concepts at 800-428-9262.

■ *Check the sound card volume.*   Make sure that sound and MIDI files play at an acceptable volume.

■ *Test the front jack.*   Plug headphones and speakers into the CD-ROM audio jack, start your CD player application, and make sure that audio is being generated. You may need to adjust the front volume control.

■ *Check the sound drivers.*   If the audio jack at the CD-ROM drive works properly, make sure that you have installed all the necessary sound card drivers for CD audio.

■ *Replace the drive.*   If the audio jack at the CD-ROM drive does not work, replace the CD-ROM drive outright.

Symptom 8:   *You see a "Wrong DOS version" error message when attempting to load MSCDEX.*   You are running MS-DOS 4, 5, or 6 with a version of MSCDEX which does not support it. The solution is to change to the correct version of MSCDEX.

- *Update MSCDEX.*   The version compatibility for MSCDEX is shown below:

    v1.01—14,913 bytes (no ISO9660 support—High Sierra support only)

    v2.00—18,307 bytes (High Sierra and ISO9660 support for DOS 3.1 to 3.3)

    v2.10—19,943 bytes (DOS 3.1 to 3.3 and DOS 4.0 to 5.x support provided with SETVER)

    v2.20—25,413 bytes (same as above with Win 3.x support—changes in audio support)

    v2.21—25,431 bytes (DOS 3.1 to 5.0 support with enhanced control under Win 3.1)

    v2.22—25,377 bytes (DOS 3.1 to 6.0 and higher with Win 3.1 support)

    v2.23—25,361 bytes (DOS 3.1 to 6.2 and Win 3.1 support—supplied with MS-DOS 6.2)

- *Use SETVER.*   When using MS-DOS 5.x to 6.1, you will need to add the SETVER utility to CONFIG.SYS in order to use MSCDEX v2.10 or v2.20 properly—for example,

```
DEVICE = C:\DOS\SETVER.EXE
```

SETVER tells programs that they are running under a version of DOS other than DOS 5.0. This is important since MSCDEX v2.10 and v2.20 refuse to work with DOS versions higher than 4.0. SETVER is used to fool MSCDEX into working with higher versions of DOS. In some versions of DOS 5.0 (such as Compaq DOS 5.0), you will need to add an entry to SETVER for MSCDEX (i.e., SETVER MSCDEX.EXE 4.00). This entry modifies SETVER without changing the file size or date.

Symptom 9:   *You cannot access the CD-ROM drive letter.*   You may see an error message such as *"Invalid drive specification."* This is typically a problem with the CD-ROM drivers.

- *Check the CD-ROM drivers.*   Run the DOS MEM /C command and check the detailed report for both the low-level CD-ROM driver and MSCDEX. If either driver is missing, it did not load. Make sure that the command-line switches for your low-level CD-ROM driver and MSCDEX match.

- *Check your version of MSCDEX.*   You may need to use SETVER or update your version of MSCDEX (see Symptom 8).

- *Check the power connector.*   Make sure the 4-pin power connector is inserted properly and completely. If the drive is being powered by a Y-connector, make sure any interim connections are secure. Use a voltmeter and measure the +5-volt (pin 4) and +12-volt (pin 1) levels as shown in Table 1.3. If either voltage (especially the +12-volt supply) is unusually low or absent, replace the power supply.

■ *Check the signal connector.*   Make sure the drive's signal interface cable is connected securely at both the drive and the controller. If the cable is visibly worn or damaged, try a new one.

■ *Replace the drive.*   If problems persist, try replacing the CD-ROM drive.

Symptom 10:   *You see an error message when trying to load the low-level CD-ROM driver.*   This is usually the result of a driver mismatch or drive adapter failure.

■ *Check the driver version.*   Make sure that you are using the proper low-level device driver for your CD-ROM drive. If you are swapping the drive or adapter board, you probably need to load a new driver. The driver file may also be corrupted—try reinstalling the driver.

■ *Check the signal connector.*   Make sure the drive's signal interface cable is connected securely at both the drive and the controller. If the cable is visibly worn or damaged, try a new one.

■ *Replace the drive adapter.*   If problems persist, chances are that the drive adapter has failed. Try a known-good adapter. Keep in mind that many CD-ROM drives use the adapter integrated into the system's sound card.

■ *Replace the drive.*   If problems persist, try replacing the CD-ROM drive.

Symptom 11:   *You see an error message such as "Error: not ready reading from drive D:."*   In most cases, the drive and adapter hardware are recognized, but the drive cannot read from the disk.

■ *Check the power connector.*   Make sure the 4-pin power connector is inserted properly and completely. If the drive is being powered by a Y-connector, make sure any interim connections are secure. Use a voltmeter and measure the +5-volt (pin 4) and +12-volt (pin 1) levels as shown in Table 1.3. If either voltage (especially the +12-volt supply) is unusually low or absent, replace the power supply.

■ *Check the compact disk.*   Make sure that the CD is the proper format (you can't start a program from an audio CD) and that it is physically clean. Try a known-good CD.

■ *Dust the optical head.*   Dust can obstruct the optical head. Try lightly dusting the optical head with photography-grade compressed air.

■ *Replace the drive.*   If problems persist, try replacing the CD-ROM drive.

Symptom 12:   *SmartDrive is not caching the CD-ROM properly.* In most cases, you are using the wrong version of Smart Drive.

■ *Check the SmartDrive version.*   Older forms of SmartDrive (such as the ones distributed with Windows 3.1, DOS 6.0 and 6.1) will *not* adequately cache CD-ROM drives. If you are looking to SmartDrive for CD-ROM cache, you should be using the version distributed with DOS 6.2x.

■ *Check the loading order and BUFFERS.* The BUFFERS statement also does not help caching, but you should also set BUFFERS = 10,0 in the CONFIG.SYS file. Make sure to place the SmartDrive command line *after* MSCDEX. When using SmartDrive, you can change the buffers setting in the MSCDEX command line (/M) to 0—this allows you to save 2 kbytes per buffer.

Symptom 13: *The CD-ROM drivers will not install properly on a drive using compression software.* This is usually because you booted from a floppy disk and attempted to install drivers without loading the compression software first.

■ *Check the loading order.* Allow your system to boot from the hard drive before installing the drivers. This allows the compression software to assign all drive letters.

or

■ *Boot from a compression-aware floppy disk.* If you must boot the system from a floppy disk, make sure the diskette is configured to be fully compatible with the compression software being used.

Symptom 14: *You see an error message indicating that the CD-ROM drive is not found.* This type of problem may also appear as loading problems with the low-level driver.

■ *Check the power connector.* Make sure the 4-pin power connector is inserted properly and completely. If the drive is being powered by a Y-connector, make sure any interim connections are secure. Use a voltmeter and measure the +5-volt (pin 4) and +12-volt (pin 1) levels as shown in Table 1.3. If either voltage (especially the +12-volt supply) is unusually low or absent, replace the power supply.

■ *Check the signal connector.* Make sure the drive's signal interface cable is connected securely at both the drive and the controller. If the cable is visibly worn or damaged, try a new one.

■ *Check the drive adapter.* Make sure that the adapter's IRQ, DMA, and I/O address settings are correct, and that they match the command-line switches used with the low-level driver. If the adapter is for a CD-ROM alone, you may also try installing the adapter in a different bus slot.

■ *Check the SCSI termination.* If your CD-ROM uses a SCSI interface, make sure that the SCSI bus is properly terminated at both ends.

■ *Replace the drive adapter.* If problems persist, replace the drive adapter.

Symptom 15:   *After installation of the CD-ROM driver software, the system reports significantly less available RAM.*   This is usually a caching issue with CD-ROM driver software.

■ *Adjust the CD-ROM driver software.*   This type of problem has been documented with Teac CD-ROM drives and CORELCDX.COM software. If the software offers a command-line switch to change the amount of XMS allocated, reduce the number to 512 or 256. Check with tech support for your particular drive for the exact command-line switch settings.

Symptom 16:   *In a new installation, the driver fails to load successfully for the proprietary interface card.*   In almost all cases, the interface card has been configured improperly.

■ *Check the drive adapter.*   Make sure that the drive adapter is configured with the correct IRQ, DMA, and I/O address settings. In some cases, you may simply enter the drive maker (e.g., Teac) as the interface type. Make sure that the interface is set properly for the system and your particular drive.

■ *Check the driver.*   Also make sure that the driver's command-line switches correctly reflect the drive adapter's configuration.

Symptom 17:   *The CD-ROM driver loads successfully, but you see an error message such as "CDR101" (drive not ready) or "CDR103" (CDROM disk not HIGH SIERRA or ISO).*   You are using a very old version of the low-level driver or MSCDEX.

■ *Check your driver version.*   Contact the drive manufacturer's tech support and see that you have the very latest version of the low-level driver. For very old drives, there may also be a generic driver available.

■ *Check your version of MSCDEX.*   Since low-level drivers are often bundled with MSCDEX, you may also be stuck with an old version of MSCDEX. You can usually download a current version of MSCDEX from the same place you get an updated low-level driver, or download it from Microsoft at http://www.microsoft.com/.

Symptom 18:   *You are having trouble setting up more than one CD-ROM drive.*   You must be concerned about hardware and software issues.

■ *Check the drive adapter.*   Make sure that the drive adapter will support more than one CD-ROM on the same channel. If it will not, you will have to install another drive adapter to support the new CD-ROM drive.

■ *Check the low-level drivers.*   For each drive, you will need to have one copy of a low-level driver loaded in CONFIG.SYS. Make sure that the command-line switches for each driver match the hardware settings of the corresponding drive adapter.

■ *Check MSCDEX.*   You need only one copy of MSCDEX in AUTOEXEC.BAT, but the /D: switch must appear twice—once for each drive ID.

Symptom 19: *Your CD-ROM drive refuses to work with an IDE port.* It may very well be that the drive uses a nonstandard port (other than IDE).

■ *Replace the drive controller.*   You must connect the CD-ROM drive to a compatible drive adapter. If the drive is proprietary, it will not interface to an IDE port. It may be necessary to purchase a drive adapter specifically for the CD-ROM drive.

Symptom 20: *You cannot get the CD-ROM drive to run properly when mounted vertically.* CD-ROM drives with "open" drive trays cannot be mounted vertically—disk tracking simply will not work correctly. The only CD-ROM drives that can be mounted vertically are those with caddies, but even with those you should check with the manufacturer before proceeding with vertical mounting.

Symptom 21: *The SCSI CD-ROM drive refuses to work when connected to an Adaptec SCSI interface (other drives are working fine).* In most cases, the Adaptec drivers are the wrong version, or are corrupted.

■ *Try turning off Sync Negotiations.*   Turn off Sync Negotiations on the Adaptec SCSI interface and reboot the system.

■ *Check your drivers.*   Check with Adaptec technical support to determine if there are later drivers that you should use instead.

Symptom 22: *You see a "No drives found" error message when the CD-ROM driver line is executed in CONFIG.SYS.* In most cases, the driver command-line switches do not match the hardware configuration of the drive adapter.

■ *Check the low-level driver.*   Open CONFIG.SYS into a word processor and see that the low-level driver has a complete and accurate command line. Make sure that any command-line switches are set correctly.

■ *Check the MSCDEX command line.*   Open AUTOEXEC.BAT into a word processor and see that the MSCDEX command line is accurate and complete. See that any command-line switches are set correctly.

■ *Check the SmartDrive entry.*   If you are using SmartDrive with DOS 6.0 or later, try adding the /U switch to the end of your SmartDrive command line in AUTOEXEC.BAT.

■ *Check for hardware conflicts.*   Make sure that there are no other hardware devices in the system that may be conflicting with the CD-ROM drive controller.

- *Replace the drive controller.*   If problems persist, replace the drive controller.

Symptom 23:   *The LCD on your CD-ROM displays an erro r code.* Even without knowing the particular meaning of *every* possible error message, you can be assured that most CD-based error messages can be traced to the following causes (in order of ease):

- *Bad caddy.*   The CD caddy is damaged or inserted incorrectly. The CD may also be inserted into the caddy improperly.

- *Bad mounting.*   The drive is mounted improperly, or mounting screws are shorting out the drive's electronics.

- *Bad power.*   Check the +12 and +5 volts powering the CD-ROM drive. Low power may require a new or larger supply.

- *Bad drive.*   Internal diagnostics have detected a fault in the CD-ROM drive. Try replacing the drive.

- *Bad drive controller.*   Drive diagnostics have detected a fault in the drive controller. Try replacing the drive controller.

Symptom 24:   *When a SCSI CD-ROM drive is connected to a SCSI adapter, the system hangs when the SCSI BIOS starts.*   In most cases, the CD-ROM drive supports plug-and-play, but the SCSI controller's BIOS does not.

- *Disable the controller's BIOS.*   Disable the BIOS through a jumper on the controller (or remove the SCSI BIOS IC entirely) and use a SCSI driver in CONFIG.SYS instead. You may need to download a low-level SCSI driver from the adapter manufacturer.

Symptom 25:   *You see an error message such as "Unable to detect ATAPI IDE CD-ROM drive, device driver not loaded."*   You have a problem with the configuration of your IDE/EIDE controller hardware.

- *Check the signal cable.*   Make sure that the 40-pin signal cable is attached properly between the drive and the controller.

- *Check your controller configuration.*   IDE CD-ROM drives are typically installed on a secondary 40-pin IDE port. Make sure that there is no device in the system using the same IRQ or I/O address as your secondary IDE port.

- *Check the low-level driver.*   Make sure that any command-line switches for the low-level driver in CONFIG.SYS correspond to the controller's hardware settings.

Symptom 26:   *The CD-ROM drive door will not open once the 40-pin IDE signal cable is connected.*   You should need power only to operate the drive door. If the door stops when the signal cable is attached, there are some possible problems to check.

- *Check the power connector.*   Make sure that both +5 and +12 volts are available at the power connector, and that the power connector is attached securely to the back of the CD-ROM drive.

- *Check the signal cable.*   The 40-pin signal cable is probably reversed at either the drive or the controller. Try a different signal cable.

- *Check the controller type.*   Make sure that the 40-pin IDE drive is plugged into an IDE port, not a proprietary (non-IDE) port.

- *Replace the drive.*   Try a known-good CD-ROM drive.

Symptom 27: *You are using an old CD-ROM and can play CD audio, but you cannot access directories or other computer data from a CD.*   Older proprietary CD-ROM drives often used two low-level drivers—you probably only have one of the drivers installed.

- *Check your low-level drivers.*   Make sure that any necessary low-level drivers are loaded in the CONFIG.SYS file. Also make sure that any command-line switches are set properly.

- *Check the controller hardware.*   Some older sound boards with integrated proprietary CD-ROM drive controllers may not work properly with the drivers required for your older CD-ROM drive. You may have to alter the controller's IRQ, DMA, or I/O settings (and update the driver's command-line switches) until the driver and controller work together.

CD-ROM drives and Windows 95

Symptom 28: *The front panel controls of your SCSI CD-ROM drive do not appear to work under Windows 95.*   Those same controls appear to work fine in DOS. Windows 95 uses SCSI commands to poll removable media devices every 2 s in order to see if there has been a change in status. Since SCSI commands to the CD-ROM generally have higher priority than front panel controls, the front panel controls will appear to be disabled under Windows 95. Try pressing the front panel controls repeatedly.

Symptom 29: *You cannot change the CD-ROM drive letter under Windows 95.*   You need to change the drive's settings under the Device Manager.

- Open the Control Panel and select the System icon.
- Once the System Properties dialog opens, click on the Device Manager page.
- Locate the entry for the CD-ROM. Click on the "+" sign to expand the list of CD-ROM devices.
- Double-click on the desired CD-ROM.
- Once the CD-ROM drive's Properties dialog appears, choose the Settings page.

- Locate the current drive letter assignment box and enter the new drive designation. Multiple letters are needed only when a SCSI device is implementing LUN addressing (e.g., multidisk changers).

- Click on the OK button to save your changes.

- Click on the OK button to close the Device Manager.

- A System Settings Change window should appear. Click on the Yes button to reboot the system so that the changes can take effect, or click on the No button so that you can make more changes to other CD-ROMs before rebooting the system. Changes will not become effective until the system is rebooted.

Symptom 30:   *You installed Windows 95 from a CD-ROM disk using DOS drivers, but when you removed the real-mode CD-ROM drivers from CONFIG.SYS, the CD-ROM no longer works.*   You need to enable protected-mode drivers by running the Add New Hardware wizard from the Control Panel.

- Boot Windows 95 using the real-mode drivers for your CD-ROM and its interface.

- Open the Control Panel and select the Add New Hardware icon.

- Proceed to add new hardware, but do *not* let Windows 95 attempt to "auto-detect" the new hardware. Use the diskette with protected-mode drivers for the new installation.

- When the new software is installed, Windows 95 will tell you that it must reboot before the hardware will be available. Do *not* reboot yet.

- Open a word processor such as Notepad, and edit the CONFIG.SYS and AUTOEXEC.BAT files to REMark out the real-mode drivers for your CD and the reference to MSCDEX.

- Shut down Windows 95, then power down the system.

- Check to be sure that the CD-ROM interface is set to use the resources assigned by Windows 95.

- Reboot the system—your protected-mode drivers should now load normally.

Symptom 31:   *Your CD-ROM drive's parallel port-to-SCSI interface worked with Windows 3.1x, but does not work under Windows 95.* This problem is typical of the NEC CD-EPPSCSI01 interface, and is usually due to a problem with the driver's assessment of your parallel port type (e.g., bidirectional, unidirectional, or enhanced parallel port).

- *Check the CMOS Setup.*   Start your Setup routine and see what mode your parallel port is set to operate in.

- *Update your real-mode drivers.*   If you are using real-mode drivers for the interface, place a switch at the end of the interface's command line that tells the driver what mode your parallel port is operating in. For example, the Trantor T358 driver (MA358.SYS) uses the following switches:

/m02   for unidirectional mode (also known as "standard" or "output only")
/m04   for bidirectional mode (also known as PS/2 mode)
/m08   for enhanced mode

- *Update your version of MSCDEX.*   Change the MSCDEX command line in AUTOEXEC.BAT to load from the C:\WINDOWS\ CONTROL\ directory, and remove the /L:x parameter from the end of the MSCDEX command line (if present).

- *Cold boot the computer.*   Power the computer off and do a cold reboot. Since typical parallel-port-to-SCSI interfaces get their power from the SCSI device, the external drive must be powered up first.

or

- *Disable your real-mode drivers.*   Remove or REMark out any references to the interface's real-mode drivers in CONFIG.SYS, then remove or disable the MSCDEX command line in AUTOEXEC.BAT.

- *Start Windows 95.*   Open the Control Panel, select the System icon, then choose the Device Manager page.

- *Find the SCSI adapter settings.*   Expand the SCSI Controllers branch of the device tree. Select the device identification line for your parallel-port-to-SCSI interface, then click on the Properties button. Click on the Settings page.

- *Update the adapter settings.*   In the Adapter Settings dialog box, type in the same parameter that would have been used if you were using real-mode drivers.

- *Save your changes.*   Click on the OK button to save your changes, then select Yes to reboot the system.

- *Check technical support.*   If problems persist, check the technical support for your parallel-port-to-SCSI adapter and see if there are any known problems with your particular setup, or any updated drivers available for download.

Symptom 32:   *You see a message stating that the "CD-ROM can run, but results may not be as expected."*   This simply means that Windows 95 is using real-mode drivers. If protected-mode drivers are available for the CD-ROM drive, you should use those instead.

Symptom 33:   *The CD-ROM works fine in DOS or Windows 3.1x, but sound or video appears choppy under Windows 95.*   There are several factors that can affect CD-ROM performance under Windows 95:

- *Remove any real-mode drivers.*   Windows 95 is severely degraded by real-mode drivers. Try installing the protected-mode drivers for your CD-ROM drive.

- *Exit DOS or Windows 3.1x applications.* Real-mode applications run under Windows 95 can also cripple performance. Try exiting any DOS or Windows 3.1x applications that may be running on the Windows 95 desktop.

- *Exit unneeded Windows 95 applications.* Additional applications take a toll on processing power. Try exiting any Windows 95 applications that may be running in the background.

- *Try rebooting the system.* If all else fails, try rebooting the system to ensure that Windows 95 has the maximum amount of resources available before running your CD-ROM application.

Tape Drives

Tape drives date back to the early days of computing; they were the first magnetic mass-storage media. Even early IBM PCs used cassette tapes instead of floppy drives. While tape proved to be a simple and reliable medium, it was painfully slow. Tape is also a *serial* medium. That is, the entire tape must be searched from the beginning to locate desired pieces of information. Today, tape drives are relegated to the role of backup drive—a thankless but absolutely vital task.

Tape drive interfaces

There are three major interfaces used with tape drives: floppy, SCSI, and proprietary. The floppy interface is identical to the 34-pin interface shown in Fig. 2.1. In most cases, a floppy tape drive can be added as a B: drive right on the existing floppy cable. Large-capacity, high-end tape drives use a SCSI (Small Computer System Interface) approach, which is popular in server or multitasking systems. SCSI tape drives require their own ASPI drivers. Figure 2.5 shows a standard 50-pin SCSI connection, and Fig. 2.6 shows a 68-pin SCSI connection. Some tape drives continue to use proprietary interfaces, which employ a separate drive adapter board plugged into the PC. Such proprietary adapters will need their own drivers loaded into CONFIG.SYS.

Tape drive cleaning

Like floppy disk drives, tape drives bring magnetic media directly into contact with magnetic R/W heads. Over time and with use, magnetic oxides from the tape rub off onto the head surface. Oxides (combined with dust particles and smoke contamination) accumulate and act as a wedge that forces the tape away from the head surface. Even if you never have cause to actually disassemble your tape drive, you should make it a point to perform routine cleaning. Regular cleaning improves the working life of your recording media and can significantly reduce the occurrence of data errors.

In general, the objective of cleaning is remarkably simple: to remove any buildup of foreign material that may have accumulated on the R/W head. The most common cleaning method employs a prepackaged cleaning cartridge. The cartridge contains a length of slightly abrasive cleaning material. When cleaning tape is run through the drive, any foreign matter on the head is rubbed away. The cleaning tape can often be used for several cleanings before being discarded. Some cleaning tapes can be run dry, while others may have to be dampened with an alcohol-based cleaning solution. The advantage to a cleaning cartridge is *simplicity*—the procedure is quick, and you never have to disassemble the drive. Since QIC tape moves across a head much more slowly than floppy media do, you need not worry about friction damaging the R/W head. DAT (helical) heads *do* move across the tape quickly, however, so you must be cautious about cleaning times. You will probably have better results over the long term using dry cleaning cartridges that are treated with a lubricating agent to reduce friction.

You can also clean R/W heads manually, which can be convenient during a repair when the drive is already opened. Start by vacuuming away any debris that may be in the drive. Use a small, hand-held vacuum to reach tight spots. Heads can be cleaned with a fresh, lint-free swab dipped lightly in a head cleaning solution. If no head cleaning solution is available, use fresh ethyl or isopropyl alcohol. Rub the head gently but firmly to remove any debris. You may wish to use several swabs to ensure a thorough cleaning. Allow the head to dry completely before running a tape.

It is very important for you to remember that these are only general guidelines. Refer to the user's manual or reference manual for your particular drive to find the cleaning recommendations, procedures, and cautions listed by the manufacturer. Every drive has slightly different cleaning and preventive maintenance procedures. Some drives may also require periodic lubrication.

QIC standards

As tape drives have evolved, the tapes have also developed through several generations. The QIC (quarter-inch cartridge) committee is responsible for establishing tape standards, and Table 2.5 lists the important statistics for each QIC tape. Table 2.6 lists the compatibility of standard tapes in various drives.

Tape drive troubleshooting

Symptom 1: *The tape drive does not appear to power up or work at all.* In most cases, there is a problem with power provided to the drive, or the drive hardware is conflicting with other devices in the system.

■ *Check the power connector.* When the tape drive does not even appear to power up, check the power connection to the drive. Internal drives will use a 4-pin connector with +5 and +12 volts as shown in Table 1.3. External drives will use a stand-alone power pack. Make sure that any power connector is inserted completely into the drive, and see that all required voltages are present.

■ *Check the signal cable.* Make sure that the signal cable is inserted properly and completely at both ends. If the drive is internal,

TABLE 2.5   Comparison of QIC Tape Standards

Tape designation	W	L	H	Length
DC300	15.24 mm	10.16 mm	1.59 mm	91.44 mm
DC6000	15.24mm	10.16mm	1.59mm	181.88 mm
DC2000	8.26 mm	6.35 mm	1.59 mm	62.48 mm

Drive standard	Tape*	Capacity	Tracks
QIC-02	DC300	15 Mbytes	9
QIC-11†	DC300XL	30 Mbytes	9
QIC-24	DC600A	60 Mbytes	9
QIC-40	DC2000	40 Mbytes	20
QIC-80	DC2000	80 Mbytes	32
QIC-100	DC2000	40 Mbytes	12/24
QIC-120	DC600A	125 Mbytes	15
QIC-150	DC600XTD	155 Mbytes	18
QIC-150	DC6150	250 Mbytes	18
QIC-320	DC6320	320 Mbytes	26
QIC-500	QIC-143	500 Mbytes	—
QIC-525	DC6525	525 Mbytes	26
QIC-1000	DC6000	1.0 Gbyte	30
QIC-1350	DC6000	1.35 Mbytes	30
QIC-2100	DC6000	2.1 Gbytes	30

*DC300, DC600, DC2000, and DC6000 are generic series designations.

†QIC-11 is not an industry standard, and there are some incompatible versions.

TABLE 2.6   QIC Tape Read/Write Compatibility

Tapes designed for the:	Should be able to serve in the following drives:					
	QIC-11	QIC-24	QIC-120	QIC-150	QIC-320	QIC-525
QIC-11	R/W					
QIC-24	R/W	R/W	R/-			
QIC-120	R/-	R/-	R/W	R/-		
QIC-150	R/-	R/-	R/W	R/W		
QIC-320	R/-	R/-	R/W	R/W	R/W	
QIC-525	R/-	R/-	R/W	R/W	R/W	R/W

you probably have a floppy cable or a SCSI cable connection. If the drive is external, you probably have a parallel-port or external SCSI connection.

- *Check the SCSI terminations.*   For SCSI tape drives, make sure that the SCSI bus is terminated properly at both ends of the bus cable.

- *Check your parallel port.*   If you use a parallel-port tape drive, check the CMOS Setup and see that the parallel port is set to EPP or bidirectional mode.

- *Check the drive controller.*   If your tape drive uses its own drive adapter board, make sure that the adapter's resources (IRQ, DMA, and I/O address) are set correctly and do not conflict with any other devices in the system.

- *Check any driver software.*   Make sure that any drivers are loading properly, and that any command-line switches properly reflect the controller's hardware configuration.

- *Check the backup application.*   Make sure that your backup application is loading properly, and that it is configured to match the proper drive.

- *Replace the drive.*   Try the drive in another system, or try a known-good drive in the suspect system.

- *Replace the controller.*   If the drive appears to work properly in another system, replace the drive controller.

Symptom 2:   *The tape does not read or write, but the tape and head seem to move properly.*   You will probably find read/write errors indicated by your backup software.

- *Clean the tape drive.*   Excess accumulations of oxide on the R/W heads can affect the reliability of reading and writing. Try performing a head-cleaning operation.

- *Check the tape cartridge.*   Make sure that the tape is inserted into the drive correctly. Try a known-good tape. If a known-good tape works, the original tape may be defective or may need to be reformatted.

- *Replace the drive.*   If problems persist, the heads or their circuitry may have failed, so try a known-good drive.

Symptom 3:   *The R/W head does not step from track to track.*   The remainder of the drive appears to work properly. This problem may also result in tape read or write errors.

- *Check for obstructions.*   See if there are any obstructions in the head seek assembly. Some drives may require you to lubricate the assembly (check with the drive manual before attempting any lubrication).

- *Replace the drive.*   If problems persist, the head seek assembly has failed or the EOT (end of tape) sensor has failed. The drive should be replaced.

Symptom 4:   *The tape does not move, or its speed does not remain constant.*   In most cases, the drive has failed.

■ *Check the power connector.*   When the tape drive does not even appear to power up, check the power connection to the drive. Internal drives will use a 4-pin connector with +5 and +12 volts as shown in Table 1.3. External drives will use a stand-alone power pack. Make sure that any power connector is inserted completely into the drive, and that all required voltages are present. If a voltage (especially +12 volts) is low or absent, replace the power supply.

■ *Check the tape.*   Make sure that the tape is inserted properly and completely into the drive.

■ *Check for obstructions.*   Examine the tape drive motors and make sure that there are no obstructions jamming either reel.

■ *Replace the drive.*   If problems persist, the tape drive motor or encoder has failed. Try a known-good drive.

Symptom 5:   *There are problems in loading or ejecting the tape.* The ejection mechanism is probably jammed or damaged.

■ *Check the tape.*   Make sure that the tape is inserted properly and completely into the drive.

■ *Check for obstructions.*   Inspect the loading/ejection mechanism for any foreign matter that may jam or obstruct the mechanism.

■ *Replace the drive.*   If problems persist, replace the drive mechanism outright.

Symptom 6:   *The drive writes to write-protected tapes.*   If the tape is properly write-protected, your drive has probably failed.

■ *Check the tape.*   Make sure that the tape is properly write-protected.

■ *Replace the drive.*   If the drive continues to write to a write-protected tape, chances are that the drive's write-protect sensor (or circuit) has failed. Try a known-good tape drive instead.

Symptom 7:   *The drive does not recognize the beginning or end of the tape.*   In most cases, either you are using the wrong type of tape for your drive or the drive has failed.

■ *Check the tape.*   Make sure that the tape is the correct type for your drive, and that it is inserted properly and completely into the drive.

■ *Replace the drive.*   If problems persist, the drive's BOT/EOT (beginning/end of tape) sensors or circuits have failed. Try a known-good tape drive instead.

Symptom 8:   *A software program using a hardware copy protection device on the parallel port locks up.*   This symptom is typical of parallel-port tape drives. The backup software attempts to communicate with the tape drive, but it winds up communicating with the copy protection device (a.k.a. "dongle") instead.

- *Try a boot diskette.*   If the dongle relies on drivers or TSRs, try starting the PC from a boot disk that disables that software.

- *Change parallel ports.*   Try using the drive on a second parallel port. However, LPT2 often uses IRQ 5, and that is the IRQ for most sound boards.

- *Remove the copy protection device.*   Physically remove the dongle from your PC while using the tape drive. If you use the tape drive frequently, you might consider installing an A/B printer switch with the tape drive on one side and the dongle on the other.

Symptom 9:   *The backup software indicates "Too many bad sectors" on the tape.*   You may also see an error such as "Error correction failed." This type of error generally indicates that more than 5 percent of the sectors on a tape are unreadable.

- *Clean the tape drive.*   Excess accumulations of oxide on the R/W heads can affect the reliability of reading and writing. Try performing a head-cleaning operation.

- *Check the tape cartridge.*   Make sure that the tape is inserted into the drive correctly. Try a known-good tape. If a known-good tape works, the original tape may be defective or may need to be reformatted.

- *Check the signal cable.*   Make sure that the signal cable is inserted properly and completely at both ends. If the drive is internal, you probably have a floppy cable or a SCSI cable connection. If the drive is external, you probably have a parallel-port or external SCSI connection.

- *Replace the drive.*   If problems persist, the heads or their circuitry may have failed, so try a known-good drive.

Symptom 10:   *The tape backup software produces a "Tape drive error XX," where XX is a specific fault type.*   The fault type will depend on the particular drive and tape backup software you are using, so refer to the user manual for exact code meanings. The following codes are for the Colorado Tape Backup Software:

- **0Ah**—*Broken or dirty tape.*   Clean the R/W heads carefully and replace the tape (if it is broken).

- **0Bh**—*Gain error.*   Reformat the tape before attempting a backup.

- **1Ah**—*Power-on reset occurred.*   Check the drive's power and signal connections and try again.

- **1Bh**—*Software reset occurred.*   Shut down any application that might be conflicting with the tape backup software.

- **04h**—*Drive motor jammed.*   Remove the tape and make sure that there is nothing (including the tape) blocking the motor(s). Insert a new tape and try the system again.

Symptom 11: *A parallel-port tape drive does not work with a CD-ROM/sound board installed in the system.* There is a hardware conflict.

■ *Check the hardware configuration.* Chances are that your sound board is using the same IRQ as the LPT port your parallel-port tape drive is plugged into. If you remove the sound board and restart the system, your tape drive should now be available. Your solutions are to (1) use a different parallel port or (2) reconfigure the sound board hardware to use a different IRQ.

■ *Update your sound software.* If you choose to reconfigure the sound hardware, you may also need to update the sound driver command lines in CONFIG.SYS and AUTOEXEC.BAT. You may also need to update the hardware references in SYSTEM.INI (for Windows 3.1x) or in your Device Manager for Windows 95.

Symptom 12: *You cannot fit as much data on a tape as you expect.* Most drives today figure the use of compression when quoting a tape capacity.

■ *Check the backup application.* Make sure that your backup software has compression features enabled.

■ *Check the files.* Compression is not effective on files that have already been compressed (i.e., ZIP,.ARC, JPG, and so on). So if you are backing up a lot of compressed files (even with backup compression on), you simply may not achieve the quoted tape capacity.

Symptom 13: *You see an error such as "DMA conflict."* In virtually all cases, there is a hardware conflict between two or more devices in the system which is preventing the tape drive controller from running properly. You may see such problems indicated as a "DMA conflict," "Insufficient DMA buffer size," or "DMA channel conflict."

■ *Check for hardware conflicts.* Make sure that two or more devices in the system are not using the same DMA channel. You may need to reconfigure any offending hardware and the related drivers.

■ *Increase the DMA buffer size.* Start a word processor such as Notepad, open the SYSTEM.INI file, then locate the [386Enh] section. Enter a line that reads DMABufferSize = 64. Save the changes to SYSTEM.INI and restart Windows.

■ *Check your CMOS.* On some systems, shadow memory can cause DMA problems. Enter your system Setup routine and try disabling the shadow memory feature. Remember to save your changes and restart the PC.

■ *Disable your screen savers and wallpaper.* Remove any unneeded processing overhead by disabling your system screen savers and wallpaper.

- *Disable proprietary VGA drivers.* Specialized or hardware-specific VGA drivers can upset DMA activity. Try using a "standard" VGA driver under Windows 3.1x. Under Windows 95, try starting in the SafeMode.

- *Check other drivers or TSRs.* Inspect your CONFIG.SYS and AUTOEXEC.BAT files, and disable any references to unnecessary drivers or TSRs. Remember to restart your system after making any changes to your startup files.

- *Check your memory managers.* In some circumstances, specialized memory managers like QEMM can cause DMA problems. Try using HIMEM.SYS and EMM386.EXE instead of QEMM or 386MAX.

- *Check the motherboard DMA controllers.* Run a diagnostic such as CheckIt to test the DMA controllers on the motherboard. If problems are reported, you may need to replace the motherboard.

Symptom 14: *Backup software refuses to detect the tape drive.* You may see this problem indicated as "No tape drive present" or "The backup software failed to detect tape device during configuration."

- *Check the power connector.* If the drive activity light does not illuminate when a tape is inserted, or the tape does not spin, check the power connection to the drive. Internal drives will use a 4-pin connector with +5 and +12 volts as shown in Table 1.3. External drives will use a stand-alone power pack. Make sure that any power connector is inserted completely into the drive, and that all required voltages are present.

- *Check the signal cable.* Make sure that the signal cable is inserted properly and completely at both ends. If the drive is internal, you probably have a floppy cable or a SCSI cable connection. If the drive is external, you probably have a parallel-port or external SCSI connection.

- *Check for hardware conflicts.* Make sure that two or more devices in the system are not using the same DMA channel. You may need to reconfigure any offending hardware and the related drivers. (If you use a parallel-port tape drive, see Symptom 11.)

- *Check for Windows driver conflicts.* If the tape drive runs in DOS but not in Windows, chances are that the Windows driver is installed incorrectly, or is conflicting with another driver. Start Windows 3.1 in the standard mode (WIN /S). If the tape drive works, you definitely have a driver conflict. If you have Windows 95, start it in the SafeMode. Disable any unneeded tape backup drivers.

- *Check your parallel port.* If you use a parallel-port tape drive, check the CMOS Setup and make sure that the parallel port is set to EPP or bidirectional mode.

- *Check your laptop docking station.* If your trouble is with the parallel port of a docking station, try connecting the parallel-port tape drive directly to the laptop.

■ *Check the drive controller.* Floppy tape drives in two-floppy systems are often plagued with incompatible drive controllers which refuse to support a third drive. You may need to replace or update the drive controller.

■ *Replace the drive.* If your problems persist, the drive has probably failed. Try a known-good tape drive.

Symptom 15: *The tape drive experiences very slow data transfer rates.* This is often accompanied by excessive "shoe shining," where the tape is repeatedly pulled back and forth. The problem is almost always related to a throughput mismatch between the drive and system.

■ *Check your system requirements.* Make sure that your PC and operating system meet the minimum hardware and software requirements for the tape drive and backup software you are using.

■ *Check your turbo mode.* In some systems, parallel-port performance is related to the "turbo" mode. If you have throughput problems while in turbo mode, try leaving turbo mode.

■ *Check the tape cartridge.* Try the cartridge on a known-good system. If the problem follows your tape, the tape may need to be reformatted because of damaged sectors.

■ *Clean the tape drive.* Excess accumulations of oxide on the R/W heads can affect the reliability of reading and writing. Try performing a head-cleaning operation.

■ *Check DOS conventional memory.* If you're running under DOS or Windows 3.1x, try maximizing the amount of available conventional memory by loading as many drivers as possible into the UMA. It is typical for DOS backup software to demand 560 kbytes or more of conventional memory.

■ *Close background applications under Windows.* Close any background applications under Windows 3.1x or Windows 95. Also disable wallpaper, screen savers, disk caching software, and antivirus utilities.

■ *Check the backup application.* Try reinstalling and reconfiguring the backup software.

■ *Check for hardware conflicts.* If you are using a high-speed drive controller, make sure that there are no IRQ, DMA, or I/O port conflicts with other devices in the system.

Symptom 16: *Your tape backup software suffers frequent lockups.* In many cases, this problem is caused by TSR or driver conflicts.

■ *Check drivers and TSRs.* Disable any unneeded drivers or TSRs in CONFIG.SYS and AUTOEXEC.BAT.

■ *Check your version of Disk Manager.* When running hard drives with more than 528 Mbytes with Disk Manager, make sure that your backup software is compatible with Disk Manager. Also make sure that you have the latest version of Disk Manager for Windows 3.1x or Windows 95.

■ *Close background applications under Windows.*   Close any background applications under Windows 3.1x or Windows 95. Also disable wallpaper, screen savers, disk caching software, and antivirus utilities.

■ *Check the backup application.*   Try reinstalling and reconfiguring the backup software.

■ *Check your hard disk file structure.*   File structure problems can also cause software to hang up. Run CHKDSK or ScanDisk and repair any drive errors.

■ *Check the backup application.*   Try reinstalling and reconfiguring the backup software (this is also advisable if you encountered disk problems with CHKDSK or ScanDisk).

■ *Check your Windows video driver.*   Try running Windows in a standard VGA resolution (640 × 480 × 16). If you are running Windows 95, start in the SafeMode. If the problem disappears, obtain the latest video driver from your video board manufacturer.

Symptom 17:   *You encounter persistent read, write, and compare errors.*   There are a large number of error codes and messages that may indicate read, write, or compare errors. In many cases, the tape is not correct for the drive.

■ *Clean the tape drive.*   Excess accumulations of oxide on the R/W heads can affect the reliability of reading and writing. Try performing a head-cleaning operation.

■ *Retension the tape.*   Use the backup software to retension the tape cartridge.

■ *Reformat the tape.*   The tape may have corrupt blocks, or the drive may be slightly out of alignment—try reformatting the tape to the specific drive.

■ *Try a new tape.*   The tape cartridge may be defective. Try a known-good tape.

■ *Replace the drive controller.*   Try reseating the drive controller or moving it to another bus slot. Try a known-good drive controller.

■ *Replace the drive.*   The drive itself may also be defective. Try a known-good tape drive.

Other Drives

Even though floppy drives, hard drives, CD-ROM drives, and tape drives have all evolved over the years, they remain largely "standardized" media. However, the push for reliable, low-cost, high-volume storage solutions has given rise to a series of "nonstandard" drives which do not easily fit the definition of the four major drive types. Nonstandard drives are also traditionally aftermarket add-on devices attached through a parallel port or external SCSI interface.

Iomega and SyQuest are perhaps the two largest and best-respected makers of nonstandard drives.

Iomega Zip drive troubleshooting

Symptom 1: *An Iomega Zip drive displays a floppy disk icon under Windows 95.* However, the drive appears to operate properly. This is almost always due to the use of a real-mode DOS driver to support the Iomega drive and adapter.

- *Update the driver.* You will need to update the real-mode driver to an appropriate protected-mode driver for Windows 95. For SCSI adapters, you need to find the protected-mode SCSI driver for your particular SCSI adapter and install it through the Add New Hardware wizard in the Control Panel. After the protected-mode driver is installed, you can remove the obsolete real-mode driver from CONFIG.SYS. For native Iomega SCSI adapters, get the pro-tected-mode drivers directly from Iomega. For parallel-port Zip drives, uninstall the old drive software and install the new Windows 95 driver software.

Symptom 2: *There is no drive letter for the SCSI Zip drive under Windows 95.* The drive does not appear to respond. In virtually all cases, the SCSI driver has not loaded properly.

- *Check the driver.* Open the Device Manager and expand the SCSI Controllers entry, then check the Iomega Adapter line beneath it. If there is a yellow symbol with an exclamation mark on it, the Windows 95 driver did not load.
- *Check the controller.* Highlight that Iomega Adapter line and select Properties. Click on the Resources page, then verify that your I/O Range and IRQ options are set correctly—they must match the jumper settings on your adapter board. If you must update the resource settings manually, make sure the Automatic Settings box is not checked. Make sure you save any changes.
- *Update the controller.* If you allocated new resources, you may have to shut off the PC and change jumper settings on the con-troller to match the resources allocated in the Device Manager.
- *Restart the computer.* Once the system reboots, the Windows 95 driver should load normally.
- *Check the signal connector.* Make sure the SCSI cable is intact and connected to the drive properly.
- *Check your SCSI termination.* If problems persist, your SCSI adapter is probably installed correctly, but the bus may be termi-nated improperly. Make sure that you terminate both ends of the SCSI bus properly.

Symptom 3: *There is no drive letter for the parallel-port Zip drive under Windows 95.* Parallel-port drive problems can almost always be traced to faulty connections, port configuration issues, or driver problems.

- *Check the power connector.*   Parallel-port drives are powered externally. Make sure that the power pack is working, and that the power cable is connected properly to the drive. If the drive does not appear to power up, try a different power pack or drive.

- *Check the signal cable.*   Make sure that you are using a good-quality, known-good parallel-port cable which is attached securely at the PC and the drive.

- *Remove any other devices on the parallel port.*   The Zip drive is very sensitive to devices such as copy protection modules (or "dongles") and other "pass-through" devices. Try connecting the drive directly to the parallel port. Also disconnect any printers on the parallel port.

- *Check the parallel-port setup.*   Reboot the PC and enter CMOS Setup. Check to see that the parallel port is configured in EPP or bidirectional mode.

- *Check the controller.*   There is a known incompatibility between the Iomage Zip drive and the Adaptec 284x adapter—the Iomega PPA3 driver does not work with the Adaptec 284x controller. Check with Iomega for an updated driver.

- *Check the driver.*   Open the Device Manager and find the SCSI Controllers entry (even though it is a parallel-port device). If there is no such entry, the driver is not installed. If you expand the SCSI Controllers section, there should be an entry for the Iomega Parallel Port Zip Interface. If there is not, the driver is not installed.

- *Check for conflicts.*   If the Device Manager entry for the Iomega Parallel Port Zip Interface has a yellow circle with an exclamation mark on it, the interface is configured improperly and is conflicting with other devices.

- *Check the device properties.*   Highlight the Iomega Parallel Port Zip Interface entry, click on Properties, then select the Settings page. Find the box marked Adapter Settings, then type

```
/mode:nibble /speed:1
```

    Save your changes and reboot the system.

- *Try reinstalling the drivers.*   Highlight the Iomega Parallel Port Zip Interface and select Remove. Then reinstall the drivers from scratch.

- *Try running in DOS.*   Start the PC in DOS mode (command prompt only), then install the Iomega installation disk and type

```
a:\guest    ,Enter.
```

    If the Zip drive still does not receive a drive letter, the parallel port may be faulty or incompatible with the drive. Try the drive on another system. If this tactic works on another system, the problem is definitely related to your original PC hardware. If the problem follows the drive, the fault is probably in the drive. Try another drive.

Symptom 4: *The system hangs when installing drivers for Windows 95.* System hangups during installation are usually the result of hardware conflicts or problems.

- *Check the signal cable.* Make sure that you are using a good-quality, known-good cable which is attached securely at the PC and the drive.

- *Check the driver.* Open the Device Manager and find the SCSI Controllers. If there is no such entry, the driver is not installed. If you expand the SCSI Controllers section, there should be an entry for the Iomega Parallel Port Zip Interface. If there is not, the driver is not installed.

- *Check for conflicts.* If the Device Manager entry for the Iomega Parallel Port Zip Interface has a yellow circle with an exclamation mark on it, the interface is configured improperly and is conflicting with other devices.

- *Check the device properties.* Highlight the Iomega Parallel Port Zip Interface entry, click on Properties, then select the Settings page. Find the box marked Adapter Settings, then type

```
/mode:nibble /speed:1
```

Save your changes and reboot the system.

- *Try running in DOS.* Start the PC in DOS mode (command prompt only), then install the Iomega installation disk and type

```
a:\guest   ,Enter.
```

If the Zip drive still does not receive a drive letter, the parallel port may be faulty or incompatible with the drive. Try the drive on another system. If this tactic works on another system, the problem is definitely related to your original PC hardware. If the problem follows the drive, the fault is probably in the drive. Try another drive.

Symptom 5: *The Zip drive takes over the CD-ROM drive letter in Windows 95.* You may simply need to switch drive letters between the Zip drive and CD-ROM drive.

- Open Device Manager and double-click on the Disk Drives entry.
- Highlight the Iomega Zip drive entry and click on Properties.
- Click on the Settings page.
- In the Reserved Drive Letters section, there is a Start Drive Letter and an End Drive Letter setting. Enter the desired drive letter for the Zip drive in both start and end drive entries (be sure to use the same drive letter for both start and end). Click on OK.

- Double-click on the CD-ROM entry.
- Highlight your CD-ROM Drive entry and click on Properties.
- Click on the Settings page.
- In the Reserved Drive Letters section, there is a Start Drive Letter and an End Drive Letter setting. Enter the desired drive letter for the CD-ROM drive in both start and end drive entries (be sure to use the same drive letter for both start and end). Click on OK.
- Click on OK to close Device Manager, then shut down and restart the computer.

Symptom 6: *You encounter duplicate Zip drive letters.*   You notice that the Zip drive (or another drive) has been assigned a duplicate drive letter. In most cases, the problem can be traced to a third-party SCSI adapter and drivers which conflict with Iomega SCSI drivers. Do *not* use any drive before correcting this problem.

- *Check your drivers.*   Open your CONFIG.SYS file and examine each driver that scans the SCSI bus to assign drive letters. Chances are very good that you have a third-party driver which is assigning a letter to the Zip drive, as well as an Iomega-specific driver which is assigning another letter to the Zip drive. Use a command-line switch with the third-party SCSI driver to limit the number of IDs that will be assigned.

Symptom 7: *A Zip guest locks up or cannot locate the drive or adapter.*   Chances are that an ASPI manager referenced in the GUEST.INI file is conflicting with hardware in the PC. This often happens in systems with two SCSI adapters (and parallel ports).

- *Edit the GUEST.INI file.*   Open the GUEST.INI file on your Iomega install disk and specify which ASPI manager needs to load in order to access the Zip drive. Remember to make a backup copy of the GUEST.INI file before editing it.
- *Choose the Iomega SCSI adapter driver.*   If you are using a native Iomega SCSI adapter, choose the ASPI manager that applies to the adapter, as shown in Table 2.7. Once you have identified the proper ASPI manager for your adapter, REMark out all the ASPI lines in GUEST.INI other than the one that you need.
- *Choose the non-Iomega SCSI adapter driver.*   If you are using a non-Iomega SCSI adapter, you will need to add the complete path and filename for the driver to GUEST.INI, and REMark out all the other ASPI drivers.
- *Reboot the system.*   Once the GUEST.INI file is updated, save your changes and reboot the system, then run GUEST from the drive and directory containing the updated GUEST.INI file.
- *Replace the drive.*   If problems persist, try the drive on another system, or try a new drive on the suspect system.

TABLE 2.7   A Listing of Native Iomega ASPI Drivers

Iomega adapter	ASPI manager
Zip Zoom SCSI Accelerator	ASPIPC16.SYS
Jaz Jet SCSI Accelerator	ASPI2930.SYS
Parallel Port Zip Drive	ASPIPPA3.SYS or ASPIPPM1.SYS
PPA-3 Adapter	ASPIPPA3.SYS
PC1616	ASPIPC16.SYS
PC800	ASPIPC8.SYS
PC2	ASPIPC2.SYS
PC4	ASPIPC4.SYS

Symptom 8:   *You encounter Zip drive letter problems under DOS.*
The drive letters following C: may change unexpectedly when
Iomega drivers are installed to support a new device. This can interfere with applications that look at specific drives, or with access to
network resources. You will need to relocate key drives before
installing Iomega software.

- *GUEST installations are safe.*   Since the GUEST.EXE utility
  loads at the end of AUTOEXEC.BAT, the Iomega drive will be
  assigned the last drive letter.

- *Check your network drive letters.*   DOS assigns letters to network
  drives alphabetically *after* assigning letters to any internal or
  external drives connected to the computer. When a new drive is
  added, the network drive may be "pushed down" one letter (e.g.,
  from E: to F:). Applications that reference specific drive letters
  may then fail to work correctly unless they are reinstalled or
  adjusted for the drive letter change. If you use a batch file to connect to a network, it will need to be updated to the new drive letter.
  A network log-in script may also need to be revised.

- *Update your network drive letters.*   Use the DOS LASTDRIVE =
  command to relocate your first network drive letter further down
  the alphabet. This insulates your network drive letter assignment
  from future changes should you add other drives to your system.
  For example, you can make your network drive N: by adding the
  following line to the end of CONFIG.SYS:

```
LASTDRIVE = M
```

   This would allow you to add ten drives (D: through M:) to a system without pushing down your network drive letter.

> **NOTE:** Do not set your last drive to Z: or you will be unable to access any network drive. If you use multiple network drives, do not set your last drive to a letter late in the alphabet (such as X: or Y:), since that will limit the number of network drives you can use simultaneously.

■ *Check your CD-ROM drive letters.* CD-ROM drives have a specific drive letter determined by the /L option of MSCDEX in AUTOEXEC.BAT (for example, /L:E assigns the CD-ROM as drive E:). When a new drive is installed, DOS may assign the CD-ROM drive letter to the new drive, and the CD-ROM drive may seem to disappear.

■ *Update your CD-ROM drive letters.* Change the drive letter for the CD-ROM to a letter not assigned to another drive. You may want to relocate your CD-ROM drive several letters down the alphabet so that you do not have to relocate it each time you add a new drive to your system. You must have a LASTDRIVE statement in CONFIG.SYS which sets the last drive equal to or later than the CD-ROM letter.

■ *Check the overall system configuration.* When DOS does reassign drive letters, be sure to check each of the points below:

1. Edit the PATH statement in AUTOEXEC.BAT to correctly reference the new drive letters.
2. Edit any batch files (including AUTOEXEC.BAT) to correctly reference the new drive letters.
3. Edit all Windows.INI files and Windows groups to correctly reference the new drive letters.
4. Check other application setup files and rerun the application's setup if drive letters cannot be edited.
5. For networks, check your user log-in script for references to specific network drive letters.
6. Reboot the computer and check major applications—those that do not work with the new drive letter may need to be reinstalled.

Symptom 9: *The GUEST utility cannot find an available drive letter.* If all drive letters are in use, GUEST will not be able to assign a drive letter to the Zip drive.

■ *Change the last drive designation.* Use the DOS LASTDRIVE command at the end of CONFIG.SYS to increase the number of available drive letters. Do not use a letter near the end of the alphabet.

Symptom 10: *System recovery fails after the Zip Tools setup process is complete.* If the Zip Tools software for your Zip drive fails to install properly (or if the system hangs or was powered down), the Windows Startup group will have a Zip Setup icon that will attempt to run each time Windows is started.

■ *Reinstall the software.* Delete the Zip icon in your Startup group, then reinstall the Zip software.

Symptom 11: *You see error messages such as "Can't Find Zip Tools Disk" or "No Drive Letters Added" when using Zip parallel-port drives.* In most cases, you will have to manually assign the proper ASPI driver by editing your GUEST.INI file.

■ *Edit the GUEST.INI file.* Open the GUEST.INI file on your Iomega install disk. Highlight the ASPI driver line that reads ASPIPPA3.SYS, then add the following commands: /MODE = 1 /SPEED = 1. Remember to make a backup copy of the GUEST.INI file before editing it. The final command line should appear as

```
ASPI = ASPIPPA3.SYS SCAN /INFO SL360 = NO SMC = NO /MODE = 1
/SPEED = 1
```

■ *Try the new GUEST.INI file.* Save your changes to GUEST.INI, then run GUEST from the drive and directory that contains your edited GUEST.INI file. GUEST should now assign a drive letter to the Zip drive.

■ *Complete the Windows installation.* Reboot the PC, start Windows, then run the Iomega Setup routine from the drive and directory which contains your edited GUEST.INI file. The Windows installation should now proceed normally.

■ *Check the signal connector.* Make sure that the parallel-port or SCSI cable is connected properly between the drive and the system. Try a known-good working signal cable.

■ *Try a "clean" boot.* If problems persist, boot the system from a "clean" diskette and try running GUEST. If a drive letter is assigned properly, then there is a driver loading in CONFIG.SYS or AUTOEXEC.BAT which conflicts with the Zip drive. You will have to systematically locate the offending driver.

■ *Try another computer.* Try the Zip drive on another PC. If GUEST works on another PC, the original PC is using an incompatible parallel port. If the drive still refuses to work, try another Zip drive.

Symptom 12: *Windows 3.11 allows network drive letter to conflict with Zip drive letter.* You may see this as a "No Zip Tools Disk Detected" message. The drive may also no longer be accessible from the File Manager or DOS prompt. The problem is that Windows for Workgroups allows GUEST to assign a drive letter that is already used by a network drive.

■ *Remap the shared volume.* Since GUEST is typically run first, you will need to alter the network drive letter under Windows for Workgroups.

Symptom 13: *The Zip drive setup could not find a Zip Tools disk for Zip parallel-port drives.* This is usually an issue with the GUEST.INI file, which needs to be edited for proper operation.

- *Boot the system "clean."* Start the system from a clean floppy diskette, insert the Iomega installation disk, then try running the GUEST utility. If a drive letter is assigned, there may be a driver in CONFIG.SYS or AUTOEXEC.BAT conflicting with the Zip drive.

- *Edit the GUEST.INI file.* If GUEST fails to assign a Zip drive letter from a clean boot, open the GUEST.INI file in a text editor, locate the ASPI = ASPIPPA3.SYS line, then add the switches /MODE = 1 /SPEED = 1, which makes the complete command line appear as

```
ASPI = ASPIPPA3.SYS SCAN /INFO SL360 = NO SMC = NO /MODE = 1
/SPEED = 1
```

Reboot the PC and run the GUEST utility again.

- *Check the signal connector.* If GUEST *does* run, but you still cannot read the Zip Tools disk, make sure that the signal cables between the drive and the system are secure.

- *Try another computer.* If problems persist, try the Zip drive on another PC. If GUEST works on another PC, the original PC is using an incompatible parallel port. If the drive still refuses to work, try another Zip drive.

Symptom 14: *You cannot print while using a ZIP drive.* The Iomega parallel-port Zip drive works as a "pass-through" device, and the software allows the drive to share a parallel port with printers. However, some printers require two-way communication between the printer and the parallel port, which conflicts with the Zip software. This can cause data corruption and system lockups. In many cases, disabling the bidirectional communication features of the printer will clear the problem.

- *Canon BJ-610/Canon BJC 610:* These printers use drivers that are incompatible with the Zip drive—the drivers reserve the parallel port exclusively for the operation of the printer, and the Zip drive is unable to access the port. (This will usually result in a system lock-up when the drive is accessed.) The drivers for the Canon printers must be removed. The installation program for the printers will add the following lines to the [386Enh] section of your SYSTEM.INI file. These entries must be removed:

```
DEVICE = WPSRCOM.386
DEVICE = WPSCREM.386
DEVICE = WPSRBND.386
```

The following line in WIN.INI will also have to be removed:

```
LOAD = WPSLOAD.EXE
```

At this point, the Zip drive will function, but the printer will not (at least not in its high-resolution modes). To restore full printer operation, you will need to reinstall the Canon drivers.

■ *Canon Multi-Pass 1000:*   You cannot use this printer and the parallel-port Zip drive at the same time. The only way to make this printer and drive compatible is to change the output of the printer to "File" when you need to use the Zip drive, then back to "LPT1" when you want to use the printer. Use the following procedure to toggle the output from File to LPT1 under Windows 95:

1. Double-click on My Computer.
2. Double-click on Properties.
3. Right mouse button click on the Canon Printer.
4. Click on Details.
5. Click the down arrow button in the window labeled "Print to the following port."
6. Click on FILE (to switch back, choose LPT1).
7. Click on OK at the bottom of your screen.

■ *Hewlett-Packard 4S, 4+, 4V, 4SI, 4L, 4P, and 5P:*   You need to disable the bidirectional communication between the printer and the system. This can be accomplished by executing the following command from the RUN command line:

```
c:\windows\dinstall -fdinstall.ins
```

You can also use the procedure outlined below:

1. Bring up the WIN.INI file through either SYSEDIT (in Windows) or EDIT (in DOS).
2. In the first section of this file, you should see a line that reads LOAD = HPSW.EXE. You need to disable this line by inserting a semicolon (;) at the beginning of the line.
3. Now scroll down to the section labeled [Spooler] and insert a semicolon (;) at the beginning of the line that reads QP.LPT1 = HPLJ4QP.DLL.
4. Save the WIN.INI file, exit Windows, and restart the system.

You can now use the HP printer and Zip drive together. These changes will not affect the printer—they just disable the status windows that may pop up telling the current status of the printer.

■ *Hewlett-Packard 5l:*   If you installed your printer using the HOST option, you will need to uninstall the printer, then reinstall it using the PCL option. In your WIN.INI file, disable the line that reads LOAD = HPLJSW.EXE by placing a semicolon at the beginning of the line. You will need to do the same with the line that reads QP.LPT1 = ??? in the [Spooler] section of your WIN.INI file.

Symptom 15:   *You encounter problems installing a Zip SCSI drive.* In virtually all cases, SCSI problems can be traced to hardware problems or driver issues.

■ *Check the power connector.*   Make sure that power is provided to the drive (verify that the drive power light comes on).

■ *Check the signal connector.*   Make sure that the SCSI cable is intact and connected securely between the drive and the SCSI adapter. Try a new signal cable.

■ *Check the SCSI termination.* Both ends of the SCSI bus must be terminated properly. Make sure that terminators are installed in the correct places.

■ *Check the SCSI IDs.* Make sure that the Zip SCSI drive is assigned to a SCSI ID that is not in use by any other SCSI device.

■ *Check the drivers.* Make sure that the drivers for your SCSI adapter and drive are correct, that they use the right command-line switches, and that you are using the very latest versions. Also check for conflicts between SCSI drivers and other drivers in the system.

Symptom 16: *The drive letter is lost each time the PC is turned off.* In many cases, the GUEST utility does not load properly because it is at the end of AUTOEXEC.BAT.

■ *Relocate the GUEST command line.* Open the AUTOEXEC.BAT file and move the GUEST command line to a point earlier in the file. Ideally, the GUEST command line should be the entry immediately following the MSCDEX command line. Save your changes and reboot the computer. The GUEST utility should now load each time the system is rebooted.

Iomega Ditto drive troubleshooting

Symptom 1: *The internal Ditto tape drive is not detected when running from a floppy disk controller.* In most cases, the drive is not powered or is not connected properly.

■ *Check the power connector.* Internal drives are powered by a standard 4-pin mate-n-lock-type connector such as the one in Table 1.3. Make sure that +5-and +12-volt supply levels are adequate, and that the connector is securely attached to the drive.

■ *Check the signal connector.* Make sure that the signal cable is attached properly to the drive, and that the orientation of pin 1 is correct at the drive and the controller. Try a new signal cable.

■ *Check the tape.* Make sure that you have inserted a known-good tape properly into the drive. If the tape does not initialize after it is inserted, the drive may be defective. Try a new drive.

■ *Check the software.* Make sure that the backup software is installed and configured properly. Try reinstalling the software.

■ *Check the controller and drive.* Try the drive on another computer. If the drive works on another computer, the original floppy drive controller may be inadequate. Try the Ditto Dash accelerator card. If the drive does not work on another computer, the drive may be defective. Try a new drive.

Symptom 2: *The internal Ditto drive is not detected when running from a Ditto Dash accelerator card.* In most cases, the drive is not powered or is not connected properly.

- *Check the power connector.*   Internal drives are powered by a standard 4-pin mate-n-lock-type connector such as the one in Table 1.3. Make sure that +5-and +12-volt supply levels are adequate, and that the connector is securely attached to the drive.

- *Check the signal connector.*   Make sure that the signal cable is attached properly to the drive, and that the orientation of pin 1 is correct at the drive and the controller. Try a new signal cable.

- *Check the tape.*   Make sure that you have inserted a known-good tape properly into the drive. If the tape does not initialize after it is inserted, the drive may be defective. Try a new drive.

- *Check for hardware conflicts.*   Make sure that the Ditto Dash accelerator is not using an IRQ, DMA, or I/O setting used by another device in the system. Reconfigure the accelerator card if necessary.

- *Check the software.*   Make sure that the backup software is installed and configured properly. Try reinstalling the software.

- *Check the card slot.*   Make sure that the Ditto Dash accelerator card is located in a slot away from modem/fax boards or video boards. Try the accelerator in a new slot.

Symptom 3: *You notice that the internal Ditto drive takes longer to back up than expected, and the drive regularly spins back and forth.* Regular "back and forth" movement is known as *shoeshining,* and is usually accompanied by several corrected errors. The drive is probably running from a floppy controller, and the data transfer rate of your backup software is set too high.

- *Check the backup configuration.*   Check for any software settings that control the data transfer rate, and set the rate to 500 kbytes/s. Save the changes and try another backup—you should see an improvement.

- *Check your turbo mode.*   If the system is in its "turbo" mode, try disabling the turbo mode and try another backup.

- *Try a different drive.*   If the problem persists, try a Tape Accelerator II card (or a Parallel Port II tape drive) to improve data transfer rates.

Symptom 4: *The Ditto parallel-port drive is not detected under DOS or Windows 3.1x.* This is usually caused by interference with the parallel port.

- *Check the power connector.*   Parallel-port drives are powered externally. Make sure that the power pack is working, and that the power cable is connected properly to the drive. If the drive does not appear to power up, try a different power pack or drive.

- *Check the signal cable.*   Make sure that you are using a good-quality, known-good parallel-port cable which is attached securely at the PC and the drive.

- *Remove any other devices on the parallel port.*   Parallel-port drives are very sensitive to devices such as copy protection modules (or "dongles") and other "pass-through" devices. Try connecting the drive directly to the parallel port. Also disconnect any printers on the parallel port.

- *Check the parallel-port setup.*   Reboot the PC and enter CMOS Setup. Check to see that the parallel port is configured in EPP or bidirectional mode. Do *not* set the drive for ECP mode.

- *Check for hardware conflicts.*   Make sure that no other device in the system is using IRQ 7 (for LPT1) or IRQ 5 (for LPT2). If your sound board is using IRQ 7 or IRQ 5, you may need to reconfigure the device.

- *Check the tape.*   Make sure that you have inserted a known-good tape properly into the drive. If the tape does not initialize after it is inserted, the drive may be defective. Try a new drive.

- *Update the AUTOEXEC.BAT file.*   If problems persist, add the following two lines to AUTOEXEC.BAT:

```
set port_delay = 20
set ppt_flags = 16
```

- *Replace the drive.*   Try the drive on another system. If it works on another system, the original parallel port cannot support the Ditto drive. Try adding a second parallel port to the system. If the drive does not work on another PC, the drive is probably defective and should be replaced.

Symptom 5:   *The internal Ditto drive does not find any catalogs during a restore.*   The tape's catalog has been lost or corrupted. Use the steps below to rebuild a tape catalog with Iomega backup software:

- Choose the Restore option from the main menu.

- Choose the Catalog pull-down menu, then click on Rebuild.

- A screen will appear listing all the catalogs on the tape. Choose the catalog that you wish to rebuild, then choose the OK button (in DOS) or start Rebuild (in Windows).

- The software will then rebuild the catalog and write it automatically to the hard disk. The catalog will then appear in the appropriate box to select files to restore.

Symptom 6:   *The Ditto drive encounters many corrected errors during a compare.*   If a tape file does not match the same file on a hard disk, the backup software logs a read error. The software then performs a series of rereads to compare the file. If the rereads match, the software corrects the logged error. If a full tape backup produces more than 50 corrected errors, there may be a system configuration problem.

■ *Clean the tape drive.*   Clean the R/W tape heads and try the tape again.

■ *Check the tape tension.*   Use the backup software to retension the tape.

■ *Check the tape.*   The tape may be bad. Try a known-good tape. If a known-good tape works properly, the original tape may need to be reformatted. If problems persist, try another tape.

■ *Boot the system "clean."*   Try booting from a "clean" diskette, then try the DOS backup software. If the problem disappears, there may be a driver or TSR which is interfering with the Ditto drive's operation.

■ *Check the signal connector.*   Try a new parallel-port (or internal floppy drive) cable to connect the drive and the system.

■ *Check for local interference.*   Parallel-port drives may be positioned too close to monitors or high-power multimedia speakers. Try moving the drive away from strong magnetic sources. Internal drives may be positioned too close to CD-ROM drives or hard drives. Try relocating the internal Ditto drive to a more remote drive bay.

■ *Check the system DMA operation.*   The DMA operation of your computer may be too fast. Try slowing down DMA operation through the Iomega software.

Symptom 7:   *You see a "Fatal Exception Error" with the Ditto drive.* The configuration files for the drive are set up incorrectly. You will need to correct the entries.

■ *Edit the internal Ditto configuration.*   For the internal Ditto drive, you will need to edit the TAPECTRL.CFG filr located in the QBWIN directory. Delete the following lines:

```
DRIVER_TYPE:5,1 "PARALLEL Port Tape Drive," "qbwppqt.dll"
MANUFACTURER: "IOMEGA"
MODEL: "PARALLEL PORT TAPE DRIVE,"FFFF
DRIVER: 5
FEATURES: 0
I/O ADDRESS: 278, *378, 3bc
IRQ NUMBER: 5, *7
DMA NUMBER:
```

and

```
MANUFACTURER: "IOMEGA"
MODEL: "PPT (MSO chip),"FFFF
DRIVER: 5
FEATURES: 0
I/O ADDRESS: 278, *378, 3bc
```

```
IRQ NUMBER: 5, *7, 10, 11, 12, 15
DMA NUMBER:
```

Save your changes, restart the system, then run the tape backup software again.

- *Edit the external Ditto configuration.* For the external Ditto drive, you will need to add the following two lines to the AUTOEXEC.BAT file:

```
set port_delay = 20
set ppt_flags = 16
```

Save your changes, restart the system, then run the tape backup software again.

Symptom 8: *The Ditto drive is not restoring selected files.* The backup software is probably claiming that no files are selected—even though you have selected files. Take the following steps with Iomega backup software:

- Make sure there are marks next to the files listed.

- Select all files (go to the File command and use the Select All Files option).

- If the backup software still claims that no files are selected, go back into the Select Files option, then select the Special option and take the check mark out of the box that says Exclude Read-Only Files.

- Read-only files are excluded by default. This should solve the problem.

NOTE: It is very important that you perform a compare after a backup. This ensures that the data on your tape is intact. If you do not compare, data integrity cannot be guaranteed (and a restore may not be possible).

Symptom 9: *You encounter the error "The Drive Received an Invalid Command" when using a Ditto drive.* In most cases, the drive is experiencing communication problems with the controller.

- *Change the software configuration.* Go into the Configure menu of the Iomega backup software. Click on the Settings button, then change the Transfer Rate option to 500 kbytes/s. Press <Alt>+<F10> and set the option Cntr Card to bidirectional. Click on the OK button, and run another backup.

- *Update the AUTOEXEC.BAT file.* If problems persist, add the following line to AUTOEXEC.BAT:

```
set port_delay = 20
```

Restart the system and try another backup.

Iomega Bernoulli drive troubleshooting

Symptom 1: *The Iomega Bernoulli drive has a floppy icon in Windows 95.*   This is usually the result of running a real-mode driver to support the Iomega drive and adapter under Windows 95.

- *Check the Iomega driver.*   You may need to disable the real-mode driver and install the protected-mode driver under Windows 95. The Iomega software provides protected-mode drivers for Jaz Jet, Zip Zoom, PC1600, PC1616, PC800, PC2x, PPA-3, and parallel-port devices. If you are using a different adapter, you may need to upgrade and update the driver accordingly.

- *Check the non-Iomega driver.*   If you are using a non-Iomega adapter (such as a SCSI adapter), you will need protected-mode drivers from the particular SCSI vendor. However, Windows 95 does have a comprehensive library of protected-mode drivers already available.

Symptom 2: *The Iomega Bernoulli SCSI drive does not have a drive letter in Windows 95.*   The drive does not appear to respond. In virtually all cases, the SCSI driver has failed to load.

- *Check the driver.*   Open the Device Manager and expand the SCSI Controllers entry, then check the Iomega Adapter line beneath it. If there is a yellow symbol with an exclamation mark on it, the Windows 95 driver did not load.

- *Check the controller.*   Highlight that Iomega Adapter line and select Properties. Click on the Resources page, then verify that your I/O Range and IRQ options are set correctly—they must match the jumper settings on your adapter board. If you must update the resource settings manually, make sure the Automatic Settings box is not checked. Make sure you save any changes.

- *Update the controller.*   If you allocated new resources, you may have to shut off the PC and change jumper settings on the controller to match the resources allocated in the Device Manager.

- *Restart the computer.*   Once the system reboots, the Windows 95 driver should load normally.

- *Check the signal connector.*   Make sure the SCSI cable is intact and connected to the drive properly.

- *Check your SCSI termination.*   If problems persist, your SCSI adapter is probably installed correctly, but the bus may be terminated improperly. Make sure that you terminate both ends of the SCSI bus properly.

- *Check the SCSI ID.*   Make sure that the SCSI ID for your drive does not conflict with the IDs of other SCSI devices in the system.

Symptom 3: *The parallel-port (or PPA-3) adapter does not have a drive letter in Windows 95.*   Parallel-port drive problems can almost always be traced to faulty connections, port configuration issues, or driver problems.

- *Check the power connector.*   Parallel-port drives are powered externally. Make sure that the power pack is working, and that the power cable is connected properly to the drive. If the drive does not appear to power up, try a different power pack or drive.

- *Check the signal cable.*   Make sure that you are using a good-quality, known-good parallel-port cable which is attached securely at the PC and the drive.

- *Remove any other devices on the parallel port.*   Parallel-port drives are very sensitive to devices such as copy protection modules (or "dongles") and other "pass-through" devices. Try connecting the drive directly to the parallel port. Also disconnect any printers on the parallel port.

- *Check the parallel-port setup.*   Reboot the PC and enter CMOS Setup. Check to see that the parallel port is configured in EPP or bidirectional mode.

- *Check the controller.*   There is a known incompatibility between the Iomega Bernoulli drive and the Adaptec 284x adapter—the Iomega PPA3 driver does not work with the Adaptec 284x controller. Check with Iomega for an updated driver.

- *Check the driver.*   Open the Device Manager and find the SCSI Controllers entry (even though this is a parallel-port device). If there is no such entry, the driver is not installed. If there is you expand the SCSI Controllers section, there should be an entry for the Iomega Adapter. If there is not, the driver is not installed.

- *Check for conflicts.*   If the Device Manager entry for the Iomega Adapter has a yellow circle with an exclamation mark on it, the interface is configured improperly and is conflicting with other devices.

- *Check the device properties.*   Highlight the Iomega Adapter entry, click on Properties, then select the Settings page. Find the box marked Adapter Settings, then type

```
/mode:nibble /speed:1
```

Save your changes and reboot the system.

- *Try reinstalling the drivers.*   Highlight the Iomega Adapter and select Remove. Then reinstall the drivers from scratch.

- *Replace the drive.*   Try the drive on another PC. If the drive works on another system, the parallel port is incompatible (or the PPA3 is not configured properly). If the drive does not work on another PC, try a new Bernoulli drive.

Symptom 4:   *The Bernoulli drive takes over the CD-ROM's drive letter in Windows 95.*   You may simply need to switch drive letters between the Bernoulli drive and CD-ROM drive.

■ Open Device Manager and double-click on the Disk Drives entry.

■ Highlight the Iomega Bernoulli drive entry and click on Properties.

■ Click on the Settings page.

■ In the Reserved Drive Letters section, there is a Start Drive Letter and an End Drive Letter setting. Enter the desired drive letter for the Bernoulli drive in both start and end drive entries (be sure to use the same drive letter for both start and end). Click on OK.

■ Double-click on the CD-ROM entry.

■ Highlight your CD-ROM Drive entry and click on Properties.

■ Click on the Settings page.

■ In the Reserved Drive Letters section, there is a Start Drive Letter and an End Drive Letter setting. Enter the desired drive letter for the CD-ROM drive in both start and end drive entries (be sure to use the same drive letter for both start and end). Click on OK.

■ Click on OK to close Device Manager, then shut down and restart the computer.

Symptom 5: *You encounter an "Invalid Drive Specification" error after installing an Iomega SCSI drive.* Your system automatically boots into Windows, and it will not return to the installation program. The error occurs when you try to access the Iomega drive. In most cases, you need to install the Iomega SCSI software from the DOS prompt.

■ *Reinstall the SCSI software.* Boot the system from a "clean" diskette, then try installing the Iomega SCSI software again.

Symptom 6: *You encounter an "Invalid Unit Reading Drive <x>" error.* Software drivers appear to load fine, and the Bernoulli drive is assigned a drive letter as expected. In virtually all cases, there is a problem with the SMARTDRV statement in AUTOEXEC.BAT.

■ *Check the drive controller BIOS.* There may be a conflict with the BIOS on your PC1616 controller card. If you are *not* booting from the PC1616, try disabling the PC1616 BIOS with the ISACFG.COM utility accompanying the PC1616 adapter. You can also obtain the utility from Iomega at http://www.iomega.com/. Reboot the PC—the error should be corrected.

■ *Check the SMARTDRV entry.* If you *are* booting from the PC1616 controller (the Bernoulli drive), leave the controller's BIOS enabled, but try loading SMARTDRV high (i.e., into the upper memory area). If you cannot load SMARTDRV high, disable its command line in AUTOEXEC.BAT and reboot the system, then load SMARTDRV from the DOS command line once the PC initializes.

■ *Check the new GUEST utility.* If problems persist, try the new GUEST program from Iomega (http://www.iomega.com/). Once you install the GUEST.EXE and GUEST.INI files to your PC, enter the path and command line for GUEST near the end of AUTOEX-EC.BAT (before Windows starts), such as

```
c:\zinstall\guest.exe
```

■ *Remove SMARTDRV.*   If these solutions fail to correct the error, then SMARTDRV cannot be loaded and will need to be REMarked out of the AUTOEXEC.BAT file.

NOTE: If you use the GUEST program, you cannot compress the disks using DISKSPACE. Also, GUEST does not support the PC80 or PC90 adapter cards.

Symptom 7:   *You encounter problems using the Iomega parallel-port interface (PPA-3) with a Bernoulli drive.*   Problems with the PPA3 are usually related to installation issues, but drivers can also prevent the PPA3 from responding.

■ *Check the power connector.*   The external device *must* be turned on before powering up the computer. If the device refuses to power up, check the power pack and its connection to the Bernoulli drive.

■ *Check the signal connector.*   Make sure that the signal cable is the proper length, and is connected securely to the drive and system. Unusually long cables may cause read/write errors.

■ *Check the printer.*   Try disconnecting the printer or other parallel-port devices from the system, so that the PPA3 is the only parallel-port device attached to the parallel port.

■ *Check the drive termination.*   The PPA3 is terminated, and the last drive attached to the PPA3 must also be terminated. If the Bernoulli drive is the last device attached to the PPA3, make sure it is terminated properly.

■ *Check the driver installation.*   You need either OAD 1.3 (or higher) or Iomega SCSI 2.0 (or higher) to use the PPA3. Once the drivers are installed, you should see several lines in CONFIG.SYS, such as

```
REM OAD 1.3 or later:
DEVICE = C:\OADDOS\ASPIPPA3.SYS /L = 001
DEVICE = C:\OADDOS\DOSCFG.EXE /M1 /V /L = 001
DEVICE = C:\OADDOS\DOSOAD.SYS /L = 001
```

or

```
REM Iomega SCSI 2.0 or later:
DEVICE = C:\IOMEGA\ASPIPPA3.SYS /L = 001
DEVICE = C:\IOMEGA\SCSICFG.EXE /V /L = 001
DEVICE = C:\IOMEGA\SCSIDRVR.SYS /L = 001
```

■ *Try some ASPIPPA3.SYS command-line options.*   The ASPIP-PA3.SYS driver provides several important command-line options

TABLE 2.8   Command-Line Options for ASPIPPA3.SYS

/MODE = n
   /MODE = 1 is the most compatible mode.
   /MODE = 2 is the Bidirectional Transfer Mode—your PC must have a
   bidirectional parallel port.
   /MODE = 3 is Enhanced Mode, which requires an Intel SL series
   microprocessor (i.e., 80386SL, 80486SL, or 82360SL).

/SL360 = Yes/No
   This tells the ASPIPPA3.SYS driver whether or not the computer uses
   an Intel SL microprocessor chipset. If you're not sure (or if a divide
   overflow occurs during loading), set to /SL360 5 No.

/SPEED = n
   Values 1 to 10 are available. Start by setting /SPEED = 1. If that
   solves the problem, continue to increase the value until the problem
   recurs, then use the highest value that functioned properly. If you are
   still not sure which value to use, set /SPEED = 1.

/SCAN
   This forces the ASPIPPA3.SYS driver to check all parallel-port
   addresses. There are three addresses possible: 278h, 378h, and 3BCh.

/Busy_Retry = Yes
   This option forces the driver to retry several times when a device is
   busy (instead of just reporting an error).

/Port = <Address>
   This is used to manually specify the port address of the parallel port.

(see Table 2.8) that can be employed to streamline its operation. If
the ASPIPPA3.SYS command line generates any errors, you can
decipher the errors with Table 2.9.

Symptom 8:   *The Iomega PPA3 locks up on installation.*   Chances
are that the ASPIPPA3.SYS driver is causing the computer to lock up
or is causing a "Divide by zero overflow" error.

■ *Check the power connector.*   The external device *must* be turned
on before powering up the computer. If the device refuses to power
up, check the power pack and its connection to the Bernoulli drive.

■ *Check the signal connector.*   Make sure that the signal cable is the
proper length, and is connected securely to the drive and the system. Unusually long cables may cause read/write errors.

■ *Check the drive termination.*   The PPA3 is terminated, and the
last drive attached to the PPA3 must also be terminated. If the
Bernoulli drive is the last device attached to the PPA3, make sure
it is terminated properly by setting the termination switch on the
back of the drive to "I." If the switch is set to "O," turn off the drive,
set the switch to "I," turn on the drive, and reboot the PC.

TABLE 2.9   ASPIPPA3.SYS Error Messages

Error code	Possible cause
4001	Command-line syntax error.
4002	Adapter initialization failed—possible problem with the adapter or the parallel port.
4003	User specified a port address and there was no adapter there.
4004	No adapter found.
4005	User pressed both SHIFT keys to bypass this driver.
4006	Current DOS version is not supported by this driver.
4100	Conflicting port address was detected in command line.
4107	Improper speed value. Acceptable range is 0 to 10 decimal.
4108	Bad value—value outside limits.

■ *Update the ASPIPPA3.SYS driver.*   Try adding the /SL360 = NO switch to the command line, such as

```
DEVICE = C:\IOMEGA\ASPIPPA3.SYS /SL360 = NO
```

Save your changes to CONFIG.SYS and reboot the computer.

■ *Check the hardware.*   Try the PPA3 and Bernoulli drive on another PC. If they work on another system, the original parallel port is probably incompatible. If the PPA3 and drive do not work on another system, try another set of cables. If problems persist, try the Bernoulli drive directly on a SCSI adapter. If the drive works directly, the PPA3 has probably failed. If the drive does not work, it has probably failed.

Symptom 9:   *You encounter SCSI communication problems.*   In virtually all cases, SCSI problems can be traced to hardware problems or driver issues.

■ *Check the power connector.*   Make sure that power is provided to the drive (verify that the drive power light comes on).

■ *Check the signal connector.*   Make sure that the SCSI cable is intact, and is connected securely between the drive and the SCSI adapter. Try a new signal cable.

■ *Check the SCSI termination.*   Both ends of the SCSI bus must be terminated properly. Make sure that terminators are installed in the correct places.

■ *Check the SCSI IDs.*   Make sure that the Bernoulli SCSI drive is assigned to a SCSI ID that is not used by any other SCSI device.

■ *Check the drivers.*   Make sure that the drivers for your SCSI adapter and drive are correct, that they use the right command-line switches, and that you are using the very latest versions. Also check for conflicts between SCSI drivers and other drivers in the system.

Symptom 10:   *Your IDE Bernoulli drive receives two drive letters.* Your plug-and-play (PnP) BIOS is detecting the Bernoulli drive as a fixed drive and assigning one drive letter, but the Iomega drivers detect the Bernoulli drive again and assign a second drive letter.

■ *Disable PnP support for the Bernoulli drive.*   Enter your system CMOS Setup and disable the PnP support for the Bernoulli drive. Save your changes and reboot the system.

■ *Initialize without the Bernoulli cartridge.*   If you cannot disable BIOS support for the Bernoulli drive, power up the system with the Bernoulli disk removed. This causes BIOS to overlook the drive, but the Iomega drivers will still assign the drive letter properly.

SyQuest drive troubleshooting

Symptom 1:   *You encounter problems with SyQuest drives and Future Domain SCSI adapters.*   Although SyQuest drives should perform properly with Future Domain SCSI adapters, there are some issues that might cause problems.

■ *Check the SCSI ID.*   Future Domain SCSI adapters install drives from the highest SCSI ID (6) to the lowest (0)—this is opposite to the way the majority of HBA manufacturers, which assign drives from ID 0. Make sure that any hard disk drives have a higher SCSI ID number than the SyQuest drives when you install a removable drive on the SCSI bus. That way, the hard drives will be assigned the lower DOS drive letter (i.e., C: then D:).

■ *Check the boot device.*   Future Domain controllers will not allow the SyQuest drive to serve as a boot device. If you must make the SyQuest drive bootable, contact Future Domain for a firmware upgrade.

■ *Check the PowerSCSI software.*   Future Domain PowerSCSI software works with cartridges prepared and used on the same PC. When the cartridge is exchanged with one of a different format, size, or partition, the PowerSCSI driver will not handle the new cartridge properly. You might need different SCSI drivers.

■ *Check your SCSI drivers.*   In order for the SyQuest utilities to work properly with Future Domain adapters (and handle nonnative cartridges), the CONFIG.SYS file must contain the following drivers:

```
DEVICE = C:\PWRSCSI!\DCAM18XX.EXE
DEVICE = C:\PWRSCSI!\ASPIFCAM.SYS
DEVICE = C:\SYQUEST\SCSI\SQDRIVER.SYS
```

The correct CAM.EXE driver for your particular adapter must be used in the CONFIG.SYS file (such as CAM950.EXE). Do not use FDBIOS.SYS or INT4BCAM.SYS with SQDRIVER.SYS (only one driver can be used to control the SyQuest drive). The SyQuest DOS formatting program SQPREP will partition and format DOS cartridges with Future Domain adapters if the drivers are correctly installed in CONFIG.SYS as shown above.

Symptom 2: *You encounter problems with SyQuest drives and NCR SCSI adapters.* SyQuest drives work well with NCR adapters, but you must be using version 3.12 or later SyQuest utilities.

■ *Check your SCSI drivers.* To make the SyQuest cartridges removable under DOS, the following three entries must be present in CONFIG.SYS:

```
DEVICE = C:\SDMS\DOSCAM.SYS     (10-08-93 or later)
DEVICE = C:\SDMS\ASPICAM.SYS    (10-08-93 or later)
DEVICE = C:\SyQuest\SCSI\SQDRIVER.SYS
```

If you choose to use the NCR driver SCSIDISK.SYS instead of SQDRIVER.SYS, the ability to remove cartridges and use nonnative cartridges will be lost. Make sure that both drivers are *not* loaded together, or data corruption will result.

■ *Check the SCSI ID.* Typical NCR SCSI priority is from lowest (0) to highest (6), and the NCR adapter is SCSI ID 7. The SyQuest DOS partition and format utility (SQPREP) works well with NCR adapters as long as the drivers are loaded in CONFIG.SYS as shown above.

Symptom 3: *You encounter problems with SyQuest drives and Rancho Technology SCSI adapters.* SyQuest SCSI drives work properly with Rancho Technology SCSI adapters, but there are some issues that you must be aware of.

■ *Check the SyQuest cartridge.* Rancho Technology SCSI BIOS requires that a cartridge be installed in the SyQuest drive at boot time (the Rancho Technology BIOS will hang if no cartridge is installed and the drive is ready).

■ *Check your SCSI drivers.* SyQuest utilities will work through the ASPICAM driver supplied with Rancho Technology adapters. To make the cartridges removable under DOS, the CONFIG.SYS file must have drivers loaded in this order:

```
REM For the Rancho Technology 1600:
DEVICE = C:\RT1600\DOSCAM.SYS     (12-14-94 or later)
DEVICE = C:\RT1600\ASPICAM.SYS    (12-14-94 or later)
DEVICE = C:\SyQuest\SCSI\SQDRIVER.SYS
```

or

```
REM For the Rancho Technology 1000:
DEVICE = C:\RT1000\RTASPI10.SYS   (01-26-93 or later)
```

```
DEVICE = C:\SyQuest\SCSI\SQDRIVER.SYS
```

If you choose to use the Rancho Technology driver SCSIDISK.SYS instead of SQDRIVER.SYS, the ability to remove cartridges and use nonnative cartridges will be lost. Make sure that both drivers are *not* loaded together, or data corruption will result.

■ *Check the SCSI ID.*   Typical Rancho Technology SCSI priority is from lowest (0) to highest (6), and the Rancho Technology adapter is SCSI ID 7. The SyQuest DOS partition and format utility (SQPREP) works well with Rancho Technology adapters as long as the drivers are loaded in CONFIG.SYS as shown above.

Symptom 4:   *You encounter problems with Packard Bell multimedia PCs and SyQuest drives.*   Packard Bell systems often use unusual IRQ assignments which may interfere with the default settings of many SCSI adapters.

■ *Check the hardware settings.*   Many Packard Bell PCs use IRQ 11 and IRQ 12 for the CD-ROM drive, sound board, and mouse. When installing a SCSI adapter, make sure to use IRQ 10 and the I/O address of 340h. If there is any other 16-bit card (especially a network card) in the system, use IRQ 15 instead.

Symptom 5:   *You encounter problems using BusLogic SCSI adapters and SyQuest drives.*   The BusLogic ASPI driver (BTDOSM.SYS) will operate with the SyQuest device driver SQDRIVER.SYS.

■ *Check the SCSI drivers.*   Install the BusLogic driver first, then install the SyQuest software. Once the drivers are installed, the CONFIG.SYS file should be in this order:

```
DEVICE = C:\BUSLOGIC\BTDOSM.SYS /D
DEVICE = C:\SYQUEST\SCSI\SQDRIVER.SYS
```

Remove the BusLogic disk driver BTMDISK.SYS:

```
REM DEVICE = C:\BUSLOGIC\BTMDISK.SYS
```

Relocate any other Buslogic device drivers *after* SQDRIVER.SYS. Reboot the system after making any changes to CONFIG.SYS.

■ *Check the driver dates.*   Make sure that you are using SQDRIVER.SYS version 7.72 or higher, or the SyQuest software release 3.12 or higher (01-27-95 or later).

Symptom 6:   *You encounter problems using Qlogic SCSI adapters and SyQuest drives.*   While SyQuest SCSI drives will operate properly with Qlogic SCSI adapters, there are some issues that can cause problems.

■ *Check the FastSCSI software.*   Qlogic FastSCSI software does not

support SyQuest cartridge exchange unless the SyQuest SQDRIV-
ER.SYS driver is installed. Install the two Qlogic drivers, then
install the SyQuest drivers. Make sure that the QL00DISK.SYS
driver is *not* installed in CONFIG.SYS. A typical CONFIG.SYS file
will appear, such as

```
DEVICE = C:\QLOGIC\QL41DOS.SYS
DEVICE = C:\QLOGIC\QL00ASPI.SYS
DEVICE = C:\SyQuest\SCSI\SQDRIVER.SYS
```

Make sure to use the correct QLxxDOS.SYS driver for your particular Qlogic SCSI adapter.

■ *Check CorelSCSI software.*   CorelSCSI software is often shipped
with Qlogic SCSI adapters. If a CorelSCSI driver is installed to
support a SyQuest drive, do *not* install the SQDRIVER.SYS driver.

■ *Disable unneeded Qlogic drivers.*   Disable or REMark out the
QL00DISK.SYS driver if it is entered in the CONFIG.SYS file. If
the QL00DISK.SYS driver is allowed to coexist with SQDRIV-
ER.SYS, data corruption will result.

Symptom 7:   *You encounter problems using an IBM MicroChannel
SCSI controller and SyQuest drive.*   This note applies to the /A and
/2A MicroChannel SCSI adapters. The IBM ASPI driver
(ASPI4B.SYS) will operate with the SyQuest driver SQDRIVER.SYS
only under DOS—not under Windows.

■ *Try a third-party driver.*   The MSDRVR.ZIP shareware has been
known to circumvent this incompatibility. For current pricing and
availability, contact the shareware maker:

Micro Staff Co., Ltd.
1-46-9 Matsubara, Setagaya-ku, Tokyo, Japan 156
Tel: 011-81-3-3325-8128
Fax: 011-81-3-3327-7037
CompuServe ID: 100157,1053

Symptom 8:   *You encounter problems using Data Technology
Corporation (DTC) SCSI adapters and SyQuest drives.*   The DTC
SCSI adapters will operate with SyQuest drives, but there are sever-
al points that can cause problems.

■ *Check the SCSI drivers.*   Install the DTC ASPI driver first, then
install the SyQuest utility software. Once all the drivers are
installed, the CONFIG.SYS file should appear in this order:

```
REM For the DTC 3280AS ISA version and the DTC 3290AS EISA
version:
DEVICE = C:\DTC\ASPI3xxx.SYS
DEVICE = C:\SYQUEST\SCSI\SQDRIVER.SYS
```

Remember to remove the DTC device driver ASCSI.SYS in the
CONFIG.SYS file:

```
REM DEVICE = C:\DTC\ASCSI.SYS
```

Also, in the AUTOEXEC.BAT file:

```
REM C:\DTC\ASCSI.EXE
```

Load any other DTC device drivers after SQDRIVER.SYS.
Or

```
REM For the DTC 3130 PCI version:
DEVICE = C:\DTC\DOSCAM.SYS
DEVICE = C:\DTC\ASPICAM.SYS
DEVICE = C:\SYQUEST\SCSI\SQDRIVER.SYS*
```

Remember to remove the DTC device driver SCSIDISK.SYS in the CONFIG.SYS file:

```
REM DEVICE =
C:\DTC\SCSIDISK.SYS
```

Load any other DTC device drivers after SQDRIVER.SYS. Remember to reboot the PC after making any changes to your CONFIG.SYS or AUTOEXEC.BAT files.

- *Check the driver dates.* Make sure that you are using SQDRIVER.SYS version 7.72 or higher or the SyQuest software release 3.12 or higher (01-27-95 or later).

Symptom 9: *The lights on the SyQuest drive are blinking in a regular pattern.* The drive has suffered a fault, and generally must be replaced.

- *Check the light pattern.* Use Table 2.10 to find the specific error code. In most cases, you will have to replace the drive outright.

TABLE 2.10   SyQuest Error Codes for SQ555, SQ5110C, and 5200C Drives

Green flashes	Amber flashes	Problem	Action
0	3	Microprocessor problems	Replace drive
1	1, 2, 3	PCBA (drive circuitry) failure	Replace drive
2	1, 2, 3, 4, 5, 6	PCBA (drive circuitry) failure	Replace drive
3	0, 3	Microprocessor problems	Replace drive
3	1, 2, 4, 5	PCBA (drive circuitry) failure	Replace drive
4	1, 2, 3	Drive motor problem	Replace drive
4	4, 5	Drive motor speed problem	Replace cartridge
4	6	Cannot find servo	Reinsert cartridge
5	1	Power failure	Check power supply
5	2	Drive motor speed problem	Replace cartridge
5	3, 4, 5, 6, 7, 8, 9	Power-up initialization incomplete	Reinsert cartridge Replace cartridge
6	0, 1, 2, 3	PCBA (drive circuitry) failure	Replace drive
6	4	Drive motor speed problem	Replace cartridge
6	5	Excessive runout failure	Reinsert cartridge Clean spindle motor Replace cartridge
6	6	Incompatible cartridge	Use proper cartridge
6	7	PCBA (drive circuitry) failure	Replace drive
7	1, 2, 3, 4, 5	PCBA (drive circuitry) failure	Replace drive
OFF	Solid ON or flashing light	Power fault	Replace drive
		Defective cartridge	Replace cartridge
		Head loading failure	Replace drive
Solid ON	Solid ON	Microprocessor problem	Reinitialize the drive Replace the drive

3

Input Device Troubleshooting

All computers require at lease one input device—a means of getting commands and instructions into the system. Input devices present the technician with special problems. In order to translate physical keystrokes and movement into digital signals, there must be a reliable mechanical mechanism at work. As a result, input devices eventually wear out with regular use. In the real world, input devices can also be damaged by accumulations of dust and debris, physical abuse, and liquid spills. This section examines the most common types of input devices: keyboards, mice, and joysticks. Other more exotic input devices are also covered at the end of the section.

Keyboard

The keyboard is the classic input device. In spite of the advances that have taken place in the PC industry over the last 20 years, the keyboard remains a direct and reliable means of typing commands and text into an operating system. The greatest problem with keyboards is their susceptibility to dust, spills, and foreign matter (e.g., staples and paper clips).

Keyboard assembly

The keyboard assembly is remarkably straightforward. A single printed circuit board containing a matrix of keys is sandwiched between two plastic housings. To access the printed circuit, you must remove the screws holding the plastic housings together (located on the underside of the keyboard). You must then separate the two housings, which are held together by plastic tabs. A single thin cable known as a *keyboard connector* connects the keyboard assembly to the keyboard controller on the motherboard. When a key is pressed, circuitry in the keyboard generates a key code which is passed to the PC.

Keyboards and key codes

When a key is pressed, the row and column signals that are generated are interpreted by a *keyboard interface* IC (typically located on the keyboard assembly itself). The keyboard interface converts the row and column signals into a single-byte code (called a *key code* or *scan code*). Two unique scan codes are produced during a keystroke cycle. When the key is depressed, a *make code* byte is sent along to the system. When the key is released, a *break code* byte is generated. Both codes are transmitted to the host computer in a serial fashion. By using two individual codes, the computer can determine when a key is held down or when keys are held in combinations. Table 3.1 illustrates the make and break codes for conventional keyboards used in the United States.

TABLE 3.1   Typical Make and Break Codes for U.S. Keyboards

Key	Make code*	Break code*		Key	Make code*	Break code*
A	1E	9E		B	30	B0
C	2E	AE		D	20	A0
E	12	92		F	21	A1
G	22	A2		H	23	A3
I	17	97		J	24	A4
K	25	A5		L	26	A6
M	32	B2		N	31	B1
O	18	98		P	19	99
Q	10	90		R	13	93
S	1F	9F		T	14	94
U	16	96		V	2F	AF
W	11	91		X	2D	AD
Y	15	95		Z	2C	AC
0/)	0B	8B		1/!	02	82
2/@	03	83		3/#	04	84
4/$	05	85		5/%	06	86
6/^	07	87		7/&	08	88
8/*	09	89		9/(	0A	8A
./>	29	A9		-/_	0C	8C
= /+	0D	8D		[	1A	9A

TABLE 3.1   Typical Make and Break Codes for U.S. Keyboards (Continued)

Key	Make code*	Break code*		Key	Make code*	Break code*
]	1B	9B	|	;/:	27	A7
'/"	28	A8	|	,/<	33	B3
//?	35	B5	|	L Sh	2A	AA
L Ctrl	1D	9D	|	L Alt	38	B8
R Sh	36	B6	|	R Alt	E0 38	E0 B8
R Ctrl	E0 1D	E0 9D	|	Caps	3A	BA
BK SP	0E	8E	|	Tab	0F	8F
Space	39	B9	|	Enter	1C	9C
ESC	01	81	|	F1	3B	BB
F2	3C	BC	|	F3	3D	BD
F4	3E	BE	|	F5	3F	BF
F6	40	C0	|	F7	41	C1
F8	42	C2	|	F9	43	C3
F10	44	C4	|	F11	57	D7
F12	58	D8	|	Up Ar	E0 48	E0 C8
Dn Ar	E0 50	E0 D0	|	Lt Ar	E0 4B	E0 CB
Rt Ar	E0 4D	E0 CD	|	Ins	E0 52	E0 D2
Home	E0 47	E0 C7	|	Pg Up	E0 49	E0 C9
Del	E0 53	E0 D3	|	End	E0 4F	E0 CF
Pg Dn	E0 51	E0 D1	|	ScrLk	46	C6

*All make and break codes are given in hexadecimal (hex) values. Alphabetic characters represent both upper- and lowercase.

Dvorak keyboards

Most technicians are familiar with QWERTY-style keyboards—this is the standard format for typewriters that was adopted in the late 1800s. A popular alternative to the QWERTY keyboard is the *Dvorak keyboard*. Mechanically and electronically, the Dvorak keyboard is identical to a conventional keyboard. Only the key order is different: All of the vowels are located on the left side of your *home row* (the middle row of letters) in the pattern AOEUIDHTNS.

Dvorak keyboards have several advantages over QWERTY models. Most letters typed (about 70 percent) are on the home row, so finger (and wrist) strain can be reduced. Since there is less reach to deal with, typing can be accomplished faster, and with fewer errors. The vast majority of words use both hands for typing, which spreads out the strain on your hands more evenly, whereas there are thousands of words that demand one-handed typing on QWERTY keyboards.

Converting to Dvorak keyboards

There are two classical methods of implementing Dvorak keyboards: dedicated keyboards and keyboard conversions. Dedicated keyboards are just what the name implies—you buy a ready-made keyboard and plug it in. Although the keys are located in different places, the key codes are the same, so your PC doesn't know the difference. As a result, you can interchange QWERTY and Dvorak keyboards at will without any changes to the PC or operating system. You can also convert your existing QWERTY keyboard to Dvorak under Windows 95:

- Open the Control Panel and double-click on the Keyboard icon.
- Select the Language page and double-click on the English (United States) entry (or your own default entry).
- Select United States (Dvorak) from the list that appears.
- Save your changes—you may need to install a diskette with the proper drivers.
- It may be necessary to reboot the system.

Under DOS, you will need a DOS TSR to handle the conversion. For MS-DOS 5.0 through 6.22, you can find the Dvorak TSR on the MS-DOS Supplemental Disk. You can obtain the driver files from Microsoft's FTP or Web site, or from the Microsoft forum on CompuServe (GO MSDOS). Download the file DOS62S.EXE.

NOTE: If you do download and extract these supplemental DOS files, make *very* sure to extract them to a new directory. Under no circumstances should you allow DOS files to overwrite files in the DOS directory or anywhere in your Windows directory.

Once the software conversion has been made, you will need to exchange the keys on your QWERTY keyboard. Figure 3.1 illustrates the differences between a QWERTY key layout and a Dvorak key layout. You can use a key-pulling tool to physically exchange the key caps, or get key stickers or overlays from Hooleon Corporation at (602) 634-7515 or Keytime at (206) 522-8973. You can also obtain more detailed information directly from Dvorak International at (802) 287-2434.

Keyboard interface

The actual transfer of scan codes between the keyboard and the PC is accomplished serially using one of the interfaces shown in Fig. 3.2.

QWERTY

```
Q  W  E  R  T  Y  U  I   O  P

A  S  D  F  G  H  J  K  L  ;  '

Z  X  C  V  B  N  M  ,  .  /
```

Dvoark

```
"  ,  .  P  Y  F  G  C  R  L  /

A  O  E  U  I  D  H  T  N  S  -

;  Q  J  K  X  B  M  W  V  Z
```

Figure 3.1   QWERTY and Dvorak keyboards.

Note that there are three important signals in a keyboard interface: the keyboard clock (KBCLOCK), the keyboard data (KBDATA), and the signal ground. Unlike most serial communication, which is asynchronous, the transfer of data from keyboard to controller is accomplished synchronously—data bits are returned in sync with the clock signals. It is also important for you to note that most XT-style systems are designed with a unidirectional data path (from keyboard to system). AT-style keyboard interfaces are bidirectional. This feature allows AT keyboards to be controlled and programmed from the PC.

Keyboard cleaning and maintenance

Virtually all computer keyboards are open to the air. Over time, everyday dust, pet hair, water vapor, cigar/cigarette smoke, and debris from hands and ordinary use will settle into the keyboard. Eventually, accumulations of this foreign matter will cause keys to stick or will prevent keys from making proper contact (i.e., a key does not work every time it is pressed). In either case, keyboard problems will develop. Fortunately, treating a finicky keyboard is a relatively straightforward process.

■ *Get a key removal tool.*   Your local computer store should have a very inexpensive key removal tool. If you cannot find one (or if you

6 pin Mini DIN Connector

1	KBDATA
2	nc
3	Ground
4	+5 Vdc (or +3.0 or +3.3 Vdc)
5	KBCLOCK
6	nc

IBM PC/XT/AT Configuration

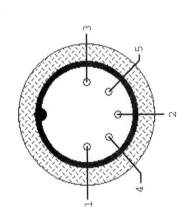

1	KBCLOCK
2	KBDATA
3	nc
4	Ground
5	+5 Vdc (or +3.0 or +3.3 Vdc)

Figure 3.2 Keyboard interfaces.

need one in a hurry), bend an ordinary paper clip into the shape of a U and bend small tabs inward at the tips.

■ *Remove the key cap of the offending key(s).*   Use the key removal tool or slip the tabs under the key and pull up gently. Do not struggle with the key cap, and avoid removing the space bar unless absolutely necessary. Be sure to note the location of each key as in Fig. 3.1.

■ *Dislodge foreign matter.*   Turn the keyboard upside down and rap on the case gently. This should dislodge staples, paper clips, and other "stuff" that might have dropped into the keyboard.

■ *Sweep out the dust.*   Use a soft-bristled brush to sweep out any stubborn dust or debris. Use a can of compressed air and a thin nozzle to blow out any dust between the keys (you may want to do this in an open or outdoor area).

■ *Clean the key contacts.*   Squirt a bit of good-quality electronic contact cleaner into the key switch and work the switch to distribute the cleaner. Allow the cleaner to dry completely, then test the key before reinstalling the key cap.

NOTE: If you choose to use a vacuum cleaner for keyboard cleaning, make sure that the vacuum is "static-safe."

Keyboard troubleshooting

Symptom 1:   *During initialization, you see an error message indicating that there is no keyboard connected.*   Virtually all keyboard problems are due to keyboard failures or connection problems.

■ *Check the keyboard connection.*   Make sure that the keyboard connector is installed properly.

■ *Check the keyboard switch setting.*   If the keyboard has a switch to select between XT and AT mode, make sure the switch is set properly. The switch is located underneath the keyboard (maybe under a small door). Most keyboards made since around 1988 will not have this switch.

■ *Replace the keyboard.*   Try a new keyboard. If a new keyboard works, there is probably a fault in the original keyboard. Simply replace the keyboard.

■ *Check the motherboard.*   Inspect the keyboard connector in the PC itself. Make sure that any cable between the connector and the motherboard is installed properly. If the keyboard connector is hard-soldered to the motherboard, check to see that none of the solder points are broken or "cold."

■ *Replace the keyboard controller.*   In most cases, a keyboard controller fault manifests itself as something other than a "no keyboard" problem, but it may be worth replacing the keyboard controller IC (if possible). Try using a POST board to isolate the error code. Otherwise, you should try replacing the motherboard.

Symptom 2: *During initialization, you see an error message indicating that the keyboard lock is on.*   The detection of a locked keyboard will halt system initialization. This is usually just a simple oversight.

■ *Check the keyboard lock.*   Make sure that the keyboard switch is in the "unlocked" position. If the switch is unlocked, but the system detects it as locked, the switch may be defective. Check continuity across the switch in the locked and unlocked positions. If the switch continuity does not respond, the switch is defective.

■ *Replace the motherboard.*   If the switch continuity responds as expected, there is a fault on the motherboard. You may have to replace the motherboard.

Symptom 3: *The keyboard is completely dead—no keys appear to function at all.*   All other computer operations are normal, but the keyboard does not respond when touched. Keyboard status LEDs may or may not be working properly.

■ *Replace the keyboard.*   Try a known-good keyboard in the system. If a known-good keyboard works, the original keyboard is probably defective and should be replaced. Try the suspect keyboard on another system. If the keyboard works on another system, the fault lies on the motherboard.

■ *Check the motherboard.*   Inspect the keyboard connector in the PC itself. Make sure that any cable between the connector and the motherboard is installed properly. If the keyboard connector is hard-soldered to the motherboard, check to see that none of the solder points are broken or "cold."

■ *Replace the motherboard.*   If problems persist, you should replace the motherboard.

Symptom 4: *The keyboard is acting erratically—one or more keys appear to work intermittently or are inoperative.*   The computer operates normally and most keys work just fine, but one or more keys do not respond when pressed. Extra force or repeated strikes may be needed to operate these keys.

■ *Clean the keyboard.*   Inspect the offending keys, clean out any accumulations of dust and debris, then use contact cleaner to clean the keys.

■ *Replace the keyboard.*   If you cannot clean the keys, or if problems persist, try replacing the keyboard with a known-good working keyboard.

Symptom 5: *The keyboard is acting erratically—one or more keys are stuck or repeating.*   Suspect a shorted or jammed key.

■ *Check for foreign objects.*   Paper clips and other small objects that slide into the keyboard can easily short out keys and cause erratic keyboard operation.

■ *Try some contact cleaner.* If you need to remove any key caps, clean the key contacts with good-quality electronic cleaner.

■ *Replace the keyboard.* If problems persist, replace the keyboard outright.

Symptom 6: *You see a message such as "KBC Error" displayed during system startup.* Either the keyboard is not connected properly or the keyboard controller (KBC) has failed.

■ *Check the keyboard connection.* Make sure that the keyboard connector is installed properly.

■ *Replace the keyboard.* Try a new keyboard. If a new keyboard works, there is probably a fault in the original keyboard. Simply replace the keyboard. Try the keyboard on another system. If the keyboard works on another system, the fault lies on the motherboard.

■ *Replace the keyboard controller.* If the KBC is mounted on a socket (like a BIOS), try replacing the keyboard controller IC.

■ *Replace the motherboard.* If you can't replace the KBC (or if a new keyboard controller fails to correct the problem), replace the motherboard outright.

Symptom 7: *You cannot clear macros from a programmable keyboard.* In most cases, you need to use the right key combination.

■ *Clear the keyboard programming.* If the keyboard has a <Remap> key, press that first (a Program light will start blinking). Press the <Ctrl> key twice to map the key to itself. Press <Alt> twice to map the key to itself. Press the <Suspend Macro> key (the Program light should stop blinking). Press the <Ctrl> and <Alt> keys while pressing <Suspend Macro>—this will clear all of the keyboard's programming. (The key sequence used for your keyboard may be different, so be sure to check the procedure for your own keyboard.)

■ *Replace the keyboard.* If problems persist, replace the keyboard.

Mouse

Although the keyboard is ideal for entering long sequences of text or instructions, it is very poor at designating selections. PC designers developed a *pointing device* that could streamline making selections, thus paving the way for graphics-based operating systems like Windows 95. The development of computer pointing devices has been ongoing since the early 1970s, but the first commercial pointing device for IBM-compatible systems was widely introduced in the early 1980s. The device's small size, long taillike cord, and quick scurrying movements immediately earned it the label of *mouse.*

Mouse assembly

A mouse has four major parts: the plastic housing, the mouse ball, the electronics PC board, and the signal cable. The *housing* assembly will vary a little depending on the manufacturer and vintage of your particular mouse, but the overall scheme is almost always identical. The *mouse ball* is a hard rubber ball situated inside the mouse body just below a small *PC board*. When the mouse is positioned on a desktop, the ball contacts two actuators that register the mouse ball's movement in the x (left-to-right) and y (up-and-down) directions. Each of the two sensors generates a series of pulses which represents movement in one of the two axes. Pulses equate to mouse movement—more pulses mean more movement. The pulses from both axis are amplified by the PC board and sent back to the computer along with information on the condition of each mouse button.

The *trackball* is basically an inverted mouse. Instead of your using your hand to move a mouse body around on a desk surface, your hand or fingertips move the ball itself, which is mounted through the top of the device; the trackball remains stationary. For the purposes of this book, a mouse and a trackball are the same thing.

Mice and device drivers

All pointing devices require a device driver (usually loaded in the CONFIG.SYS or AUTOEXEC.BAT file during system startup). The device driver is responsible for interpreting the x and y signals generated by a pointing device, then adding to (or subtracting from) the current cursor position. When an application queries the device driver, it can determine the exact position of the cursor, as well as the state of any mouse buttons. Windows 3.1x and Windows 95 use their own device drivers, which are independent of the drivers loaded in CONFIG.SYS or AUTOEXEC.BAT.

Every mouse or trackball uses its own unique device driver, so when you install a new pointing device, you will have to update the driver also. However, virtually all pointing devices use similar program code to interrogate the cursor position and buttons. As a result, you may be able to use a mouse from one manufacturer and a driver from another—but this is not recommended, and you will invariably lose some of the functionality of the pointing device.

Cleaning a pointing device

Pointing devices are perhaps the simplest peripheral available for your computer. While they are reasonably resistant to wear and tear, trackballs and mice can easily be fouled by dust, debris, and foreign matter introduced from the ball. Contamination of this sort is almost never damaging, but it can cause some maddening problems when using the pointing device. A regimen of routine cleaning will help to prevent contamination problems. Turn your small computer off before performing any cleaning procedures.

- *Remove the ball.*   A ball is held in place by a retaining ring. For a mouse, the retaining ring is on the bottom. For a trackball, the ring is on the top. Rotate the ring and remove it gently—the ball will fall out. Place the retaining ring in a safe place.

■ *Clean the ball.*   Wash the ball in warm, soapy water, then dry it thoroughly with a clean, lint-free towel. Place the ball in a safe place.

■ *Blow out the dust.*   Use a can of photography-grade compressed air to blow out any dust or debris that has accumulated inside the pointing device. You may want to do this in an open or outdoor area.

■ *Clean the rollers.*   Notice that there are three rollers in the mouse: an x roller, a y roller, and a small pressure roller the keeps the ball pressed against the x and y rollers. Use a cotton swab dipped in iso-propyl alcohol to clean off any layer of gunk that may have accu-mulated on the rollers.

■ *Reassemble and test.*   Allow everything to dry completely, then replace the ball and retaining ring. You should then test the point-ing device to be sure that it is performing as expected.

NOTE: Do *not* use harsh solvents, wood alcohol, or chemicals inside the pointing device or on the ball. Chemicals can easily melt the plastic and result in permanent damage to the pointing device.

Pointing device troubleshooting

Symptom 1:   *The cursor appears, but it moves only erratically (if at all) as the ball moves.*   This symptom may occur in either the hori-zontal or the vertical axis, and suggests that there is an intermittent condition occurring somewhere in the pointing device.

■ *Check the signal connector.*   Make sure that the mouse cable is not cut or damaged anywhere, and that it is attached securely to the serial or PS/2 port.

■ *Clean the pointing device.*   Chances are that the x or y roller (or both) is fouled. Use the procedure in the previous section to disas-semble and clean the trackball or mouse.

■ *Check for hardware conflicts.*   Make sure that there are no other devices in your system using the same IRQ or I/O address range used by your COM port or PS/2 port. Also make sure that you are not using COM ports that share resources—for example, avoid using COM1 and COM3 (or COM2 and COM4) at the same time. Try the pointing device on a different port. Update the driver's command-line switches if necessary.

■ *Try a new pointing device.*   If all else fails, try a known-good point-ing device. You may have to update the drivers to accommodate the new pointing device.

Symptom 2: *One or both buttons function erratically (if at all).*
Buttons are prone to problems caused by dust accumulation and general contact corrosion.

- *Check the signal connector.*   Make sure that the mouse cable is not cut or damaged anywhere, and that it is attached securely to the serial or PS/2 port.
- *Clean the switch contacts.*   It is possible that your switch contacts may have become fouled through dust accumulation or contact corrosion. Spray some good-quality contact cleaner into the switch contacts, work the cleaner around, let the cleaner dry, then try the mouse again.
- *Check the driver.*   Make sure that the driver is appropriate for your particular pointing device. If you have installed a new pointing device, check that the new driver is installed properly. If the driver uses command-line switches, make sure that the switches are configured properly. You might also check to see that the driver is the latest revision.
- *Try a new pointing device.*   If all else fails, try a known-good pointing device. You may have to update the drivers to accommodate the new pointing device.

Symptom 3: *The screen cursor appears on the display, but it does not move.*   If the cursor appears, the device driver has loaded correctly and the application program is communicating with the driver. In most cases, you have a connection problem.

- *Check the signal connector.*   Make sure that the mouse cable is not cut or damaged anywhere, and that it is attached securely to the serial or PS/2 port.
- *Clean the pointing device.*   Both the *x* and *y* rollers may be completely fouled. Use the procedure in the previous section to disassemble and clean the trackball or mouse.
- *Check for hardware conflicts.*   Make sure that there are no other devices in your system using the same IRQ or I/O address range used by your COM port or PS/2 port. Also make sure that you are not using COM ports that share resources—for example, avoid using COM1 and COM3 (or COM2 and COM4) at the same time. Try the pointing device on a different port. Update the driver's command-line switches if necessary.
- *Try a new pointing device.*   If all else fails, try a known-good pointing device. You may have to update the drivers to accommodate the new pointing device.

Symptom 4: *The mouse or trackball device driver fails to load.*   In most cases, the driver did not load because the pointing device was simply not detected.

- *Check the signal connector.* Make sure that the mouse cable is not cut or damaged anywhere, and that it is attached securely to the serial or PS/2 port.

- *Check the driver.* If the driver is not written for your particular pointing device, it may not detect the device properly, so the driver will not load. If you see a "File not found" error when the device driver attempts to load, the driver may be corrupt or accidentally erased. You might try reinstalling the driver software.

- *Check the CMOS Setup.* Many newer system BIOS versions provide an option in the CMOS Setup for a mouse port. Check the CMOS Setup to see that any entries for your mouse are enabled.

- *Check for hardware conflicts.* Make sure that there are no other devices in your system using the same IRQ or I/O address range used by your COM port or PS/2 port. Also make sure that you are not using COM ports that share resources—for example, avoid using COM1 and COM3 (or COM2 and COM4) at the same time. Try the pointing device on a different port. Update the driver's command-line switches if necessary.

- *Try a new pointing device.* If all else fails, try a known-good pointing device. You may have to update the drivers to accommodate the new pointing device.

Symptom 5: *When installing a new mouse and driver, you see a "General protection fault" when trying to use the mouse with one or more applications under Windows.* In most cases, the new mouse driver is conflicting with one or more applications.

- *Check the driver.* Make sure that the driver for your pointing device is the latest version which is the proper driver for your particular device. If a new driver is causing problems, try an older version if one is available.

- *Try a new pointing device.* If all else fails, try a known-good pointing device. You may have to update the drivers to accommodate the new pointing device.

Symptom 6: *You see an error message such as "This pointer device requires a newer version."* In virtually all cases, you have the wrong driver for your pointing device installed on the system.

- *Check the driver.* Make sure that the driver you are using is appropriate for the particular mouse. For example, selecting a Logitech or Genius mouse in Windows setup will cause this kind of problem if you have a Microsoft mouse on the system. Change the mouse type under Windows.

Symptom 7: *You see an error message such as "Mouse port disabled or mouse not present."* This is almost always a connection problem or a setup problem.

- *Check the signal connector.* Make sure that the mouse cable is not cut or damaged anywhere, and that it is attached securely to the serial or PS/2 port.

- *Check the CMOS Setup.* Many newer system BIOS versions provide an option in the CMOS Setup for a mouse port. Check the CMOS Setup to see that any entries for your mouse are enabled.

Joystick

One of the first game applications for the PC was "flight simulation." However, keyboard and mouse control did not lend itself well to flight controls. PC designers developed the *analog joystick,* which provided both x- and y-axis signals simultaneously. For game players, this translated to smooth left-right and up-down motion. Through the years, the joystick has become an enduring icon of computer entertainment.

Inside the joystick

Each analog joystick is assembled with two separate potentiometers (typically 100 kΩ) arranged perpendicular to one another; one potentiometer represents the x axis, and the other potentiometer represents the y axis. The two potentiometers are linked together mechanically and attached to a movable stick. As the stick is moved left or right, one potentiometer is moved. As the stick is moved up or down, the other potentiometer is moved. Of course, the stick can be moved along both the x and y axes simultaneously, with the proportions of resistance reflecting the stick's position. The wiring scheme for a standard 15-pin dual joystick port is shown in Fig. 3.3.

A joystick also has one or two buttons. The buttons are typically open, and their closed state can be detected by reading the byte at I/O port 201h. Since a game port is capable of supporting two joysticks simultaneously (each with two buttons), the upper four bits of 201h indicate the on/off status of the buttons.

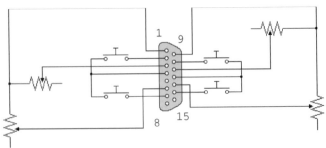

Figure 3.3   15-pin joystick wiring.

Joystick drift

The term *drift* (or *rolling*) indicates a loss of control by the joystick. There are three possible reasons for this.

- *Drift can be the result of a system conflict.*   Since a game port does not generate an interrupt, conflicts rarely result in system crashes or lockups, but another device feeding data to port 201h can easily upset joystick operation. If you have sound boards or multiport I/O boards in your system that are equipped with game ports, be sure to disable any unused ports (check the user instructions for individual boards to determine how to disable extra game ports).

- *Drift can be due to heat.*   Once PCs are started up, it is natural for the power used by most components to be dissipated as heat, and heating tends to change the value of components. For logic circuits, this is typically not a problem, but for analog circuits, the consequences can be much more pronounced. As heat changes the values of a game port's timing circuit, the joystick center values will shift—the circuit warms up, and error creeps into the joystick. It is interesting to note that the joystick itself is rarely the cause of drift. If you can compensate for drift by recalibrating the joystick, try a better-quality game port adapter board.

- *Drift can also be a result of application problems.*   A poor or inaccurate routine will tend to calibrate the joystick incorrectly. Try another application. If another application can calibrate and use the joystick properly, you should suspect a bug in the particular application. Try contacting the application manufacturer to find out if there is a patch or fix available.

Cleaning a joystick

Ordinarily, the typical joystick should not require routine cleaning or maintenance. Most joysticks use reasonably reliable potentiometers which should last for the life of the joystick. The two major enemies of a joystick are wear and dust. Wear occurs during normal use as potentiometer sliders move across the resistive surface—it can't be avoided. Over time, wear will affect the contact resistance values of both potentiometers. Uneven wear will result in uneven performance. When this becomes noticeable, it is time to buy a new joystick. Dust presents another problem. The aperture at the top of a joystick gives an opening for dust and other debris. Since dust is conductive, it can adversely affect potentiometer values and interfere with slider contacts. This produces jumpy or nonlinear responses.

Turn off the computer and disconnect the joystick. Open the joystick, which is usually held together by two screws in the bottom housing. Remove the bottom housing and locate the two (*x*- and *y*-axis) potentiometers. Most potentiometers have small openings somewhere around their circumference. Dust out the joystick area with photography-grade compressed air, and spray a small quantity of good-quality electronic contact cleaner into each potentiometer. Move the potentiometer through its complete range of motion a few times, and allow several minutes for the cleaner to dry. Reassemble the housing and try the joystick again. If problems persist, replace the joystick.

Joystick troubleshooting

Symptom 1: *The joystick does not respond.* In most cases, the joystick is not installed properly.

- *Check the signal connector.* Make sure that the joystick cable is not cut or damaged anywhere, and that it is attached securely to the game port.
- *Check the application.* It is the application which interrogates the joystick port. Examine the "options" or "setup" sections of your application and make sure that the control method is set to "joystick" rather than "mouse" or "keyboard."
- *Check the game port.* Virtually all recent sound boards provide a 15-pin MIDI/joystick port in addition to the sound connections. If you are using the sound board port, make sure that the port is jumpered for use with a joystick (not MIDI). If you prefer to use a stand-alone joystick controller instead of the sound board's controller, make sure that the sound board's port is jumpered as a MIDI port or disable the port outright. Also be sure that the game port's I/O address is set properly (i.e., 201h).

Symptom 2: *The basic X/Y, two-button features of the joystick work, but the hat switch, throttle controls, and supplemental buttons do not seem to respond.* In virtually all cases, the joystick is configured wrong.

- *Check the application.* Many new applications provide several different joystick options, and even allow you to define the particular use of each feature from within the application itself.
- *Check the joystick files.* Your joystick probably requires a supplemental definition file (i.e., an FCS file) in order to use all of the joystick's particular features.
- *Check the game port.* You may need a "dual-port" game port adapter. Some enhanced joysticks use *both* joystick positions (i.e., the *xy* axes and fire buttons make up one joystick, while the throttle and other buttons take up the other position). You may need to install a dual-port game port card.

Symptom 3: *Joystick performance is erratic or choppy.* This is usually a mechanical issue within the joystick itself.

- *Check the signal connector.* Make sure that the joystick cable is not cut or damaged anywhere, and that it is attached securely to the game port.

- *Try a new joystick.*   Test a known-good joystick on the system. If a new joystick works as expected, the original joystick is worn out or damaged internally.

- *Check the application.*   Try recalibrating the joystick through the particular application.

- *Check the hardware setup.*   Make sure that no other devices in the system are using the I/O address assigned to your game port (i.e., 201h).

- *Replace the game port.*   It is possible that the game port may be too slow for your particular system—this frequently occurs when older game port boards are used in very fast computers. Try a "speed-adjusting" game port if you can.

Symptom 4:   *The joystick is sending incorrect information to the system—the joystick appears to be drifting.*   Either the application is not calibrating the joystick properly or the game port is not adequate.

- *Check the application.*   Try recalibrating the joystick using your particular application. If the problem persists, try calibrating the joystick through a different application. If calibration works through one application, but problems persist in another, you may have a buggy application which needs a patch to update it.

- *Check the hardware setup.*   Make sure that no other devices in the system are using the I/O address assigned to your game port (i.e., 201h).

- *Replace the game port.*   If drift continues with different applications, you may need to replace the game port adapter with a "low-drift" or "speed-adjusting" model.

Symptom 5:   *You see an error such as "Joystick Not Connected" under Windows 95.*   Windows 95 does not recognize the game port hardware.

- *Check the game port driver.*   Use the Device Manager under Windows 95 to examine the resources assigned to the game port driver. Typically, the resource range should be set to 201h through 201h (only one address location). If the game port entry has a yellow icon next to it, there is a hardware conflict in the system, and other hardware is also trying to use the same I/O location.

- *Check the game port hardware.*   The game port card should be installed properly into its bus slot. Make sure that the game port is enabled (this is typical of game ports integrated onto sound cards or multi-I/O cards). If a sound card enables you to switch a 15-pin port between MIDI and joystick, make sure that the jumper is set to the "joystick" position.

- *Check the signal connector.*   Make sure that the joystick cable is not cut or damaged anywhere, and that it is attached securely to the game port.

- *Try a new joystick.* Test a known-good joystick on the system. If a new joystick works as expected, the original joystick is probably suffering from internal wiring damage.

Symptom 6: *The joystick drifts frequently and requires recalibration.* This type of symptom is usually the result of problems with the game port adapter.

- *Replace the game port.* Try a different game port adapter and see if the problem persists. If problems disappear, you simply need a better-quality or speed-adjusting game port.
- *Try a new joystick.* Test a known-good joystick on the system. If a new joystick works as expected, the original joystick is probably suffering from internal wiring damage.

Symptom 7: *The joystick handle has lost tension—it no longer "snaps" back to the center.* This problem may be accompanied by a rattling sound within the joystick. In most cases, a spring has popped out of place inside the joystick.

- *Check the joystick.* Open the joystick and see if any springs or clips have slipped out of place. Replace any springs or clips (if possible).
- *Replace the joystick.* If you cannot locate or correct the problem, simply replace the joystick outright.

Symptom 8: *The joystick responds, but refuses to accept a calibration.* In virtually all cases, the problem is with your game port adapter.

- *Check the hardware setup.* Make sure that no other devices in the system are using the I/O address assigned to your game port (i.e., 201h). If more than one adapter in your system has game port capability, make sure that only one game port is enabled.
- *Replace the game port.* If drift continues with different applications, you may need to replace the game port adapter with a "low-drift" or "speed-adjusting" model.

Symptom 9: *The hat switch and buttons on a joystick work only intermittently (if at all). This problem also applies to stand-alone pedals.* In most cases, erratic behavior of a joystick's "enhanced features" is a symptom of game port speed problems.

- *Check the joystick.* Before going too far, try a known-good joystick. If the problems disappear, the original joystick may in fact be defective. If the problems persist, you have a game port problem.
- *Check the hardware setup.* Make sure that no other devices in the system are using the I/O address assigned to your game port (i.e., 201h). If more than one adapter in your system has game port capability, make sure that only one game port is enabled.

■ *Replace the game port.* If drift issues continue with different applications, you may need to replace the game port adapter with a "low-drift" or "speed-adjusting" model.

Symptom 10: *When downloading FCS (or calibration) files to a joystick, the line saying "put switch into calibrate" doesn't change when the download switch is moved.* This is a typical problem with advanced joysticks. In most cases, the joystick needs to be "cleared."

■ *Clear the joystick.* Rock the download switch back to analog, then to calibrate—this should clear the joystick for a new calibration download.

■ *Replace the joystick.* If problems persist, the actual switch may be defective. Try a known-good joystick instead.

Symptom 11: *To download a calibration file, you need to rock the red switch back and forth a number of times (or hit the <Enter> key a number of times) to get it to 100 percent.* This is virtually always the result of a keyboard controller (keyboard BIOS) problem.

■ *Upgrade the keyboard controller (keyboard BIOS).* Some advanced joystick products do not interact well with the host computer's keyboard controller. For example, Thrustmaster's Mark II experiences known microcode problems with a few of the keyboard controller chips on the market. These include AMI versions (D, B, 8, 0), Acer, and Phoenix. You may need to replace the keyboard controller with a later version.

Modem Troubleshooting

The PC has evolved tremendously over the last few years, and few parts have undergone a more radical transformation than the *modem*. The plain, old 9600-bps workhorses of just a few years ago have progressed to 14.4 kbytes, to 28.8 kbytes, to 33.6 kbytes and ISDN capability seemingly overnight. The great advantage of this speed increase is that on-line sources such as the Internet can now offer content like graphics, animation, video, and audio, which was traditionally far too data-intensive to be practical. Along with these advances, however, there have also been some problems. This chapter covers modem standards, initialization issues, and troubleshooting.

Internal modem assembly

There are basically three types of modems: internal, external, and PCMCIA. For this chapter, a PCMCIA modem should be regarded as an internal modem. An *internal* modem is a stand-alone board which plugs directly into a PC expansion bus; each major modem function is detailed in Figure 4.1. The internal modem contains its own universal asynchronous receiver/transmitter (UART). It is the UART which manipulates data into and out of serial form. A UART forms the foundation of a serial port, and this can represent a serious hardware conflict for your PC—when installing an internal modem, be sure that the IRQ line and I/O address chosen for the UART "serial port" do not conflict with other serial ports already in the system. It may be necessary to disable conflicting ports.

Before being transmitted over telephone lines, serial data is converted into audio signals. This process is carried out by a *modulator* circuit. The modulated audio is then coupled to the telephone line using a circuit very similar to that used by ordinary telephones to couple voice. Audio signals are made available to a single RJ11-type (telephone line) connector at the rear of the modem. Internal modems often provide a second RJ11 jack for a separate telephone. Signals received from the telephone line must be translated back into serial data. The telephone interface separates the received sig-

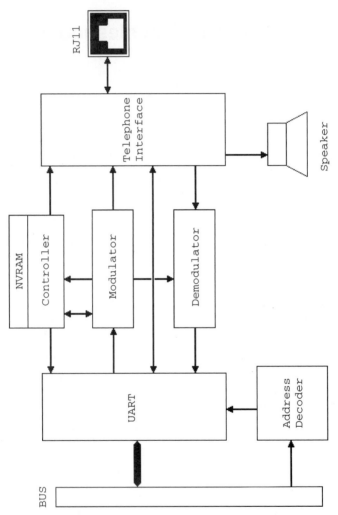

Figure 4.1 Block diagram of an internal modem.

nals and passes them to the *demodulator*. After demodulation, the resulting serial data is passed to the UART, which in turn converts the serial bits into parallel words that are placed on the system's data bus.

Besides combining and separating modulated audio data, the *telephone interface* generates the dual-tone multifrequency (DTMF) dialing signals needed to reach a remote modem—in much the same way as a touch-tone telephone operates. When a remote modem dials in, the telephone interface detects the incoming ring and alerts the UART to begin negotiating a connection. Finally, the telephone interface drives a small speaker. During the first stages of modem operation, the speaker is often used to hear dial tone, dialing signals, and audio negotiation between the two modems. Once a connection is established, the speaker is usually disabled.

A *controller* circuit manages the overall operation of the modem, but in a more general sense, it switches the modem between its control and data operating modes. The controller accepts commands from the modulator, which allows modem characteristics and operating parameters to be changed. In the event of power loss or reset conditions, default modem parameters can be loaded from NVRAM. Permanent changes to modem parameters are stored in NVRAM.

External modem assembly

For all practical intents and purposes, the *external* modem (Fig. 4.2) provides virtually all the essential functions offered by an internal modem. Many of the external modem's functions are identical to those of an internal modem. The major difference between modems is that the external modem does not include a built-in UART to provide a serial port. Instead, the external modem relies on a serial port already configured in the PC. A 9-pin or 25-pin serial cable connects the PC serial port to the modem. This often makes external modems faster and easier to set up than internal modems, since you need not worry about interrupt lines and I/O address settings—hardware conflicts are rare with external modems.

The other practical difference in an external modem is the way it is powered. While internal modems are powered from the expansion bus, external modems must be powered from a small ac adapter. In locations where ac outlets are scarce, this may be a problem. On the other hand, external modems provide a series of signal status LEDs. The LEDs allow you to easily check the state of serial communications.

One of the appealing attributes of external modems is the series of lights that typically adorns the front face. By observing these lights and the sequence in which they light, you can often follow the progress of a communication—or quickly discern the cause of a communication failure. The following markings are typical of many modems, but keep in mind that your particular modem may use fewer indicators (or be marked differently).

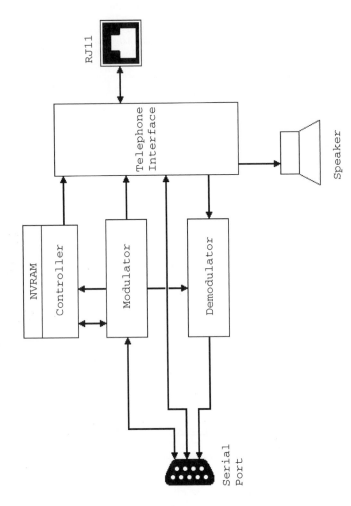

Figure 4.2 Block diagram of an external modem.

136

- *HS* (*high speed*).   When this indicator is lit, the modem is operating at its very highest transfer rate.

- *AA* (*auto answer*).   When illuminated, your modem will answer any incoming calls automatically. This feature is vital for unattended systems such as bulletin boards.

- *CD* (*carrier detect*).   This lights whenever the modem detects a carrier signal. This means it has successfully connected to a remote computer. This LED will go out when either one of the modems drops the line.

- *OH* (*off-hook*).   This LED lights any time the modem takes control of the telephone line—equivalent to taking the telephone off the hook.

- *RD* (*receive data*).   Also marked Rx. This LED flickers as data is received by the modem from a remote modem.

- *SD* (*send data*).   Also marked Tx. This LED flickers as data is sent from your modem to the remote modem.

- *TR* (*terminal ready*).   This light illuminates when the modem detects a DTR signal from the communication software.

- *MR* (*modem ready*).   This is simple power-on light that indicates that the modem is turned on and ready to operate.

Modems and UART types

Whether a modem is internal or external, the UART is clearly its heart. It is the modem which converts bus data into serial data (and vice versa). However, the UART must be able to keep pace with the modem's data transfer rate. As modem speeds have increased, UARTs have become faster also. When a new external modem is installed on an older PC, the PC's serial port may simply not be fast enough to deal with the modem. The result is often limited modem performance (if the modem works at all). Today, the 16550A UART is the device of choice. Table 4.1 compares the major UART types. When faced with an older UART, it is often possible to replace the UART IC outright; otherwise, it is a simple matter to disable the existing serial port and install a newer serial adapter using a new UART.

Modem Standards

Nowhere is the need for standards more acute than in communication. As modems have evolved, the United States and the international community have developed a suite of standards to outline the modem. Standards focus on three areas: data transfer, error correction, and data compression. Table 4.2 highlights Bell, ITU (formerly CCITT), and MNP standards.

AT command set

Modern modems are programmable devices—that is, they can be highly configured in order to optimize their performance. Modem

TABLE 4.1   Comparison of Popular UARTs

UART	Description
8250	This is the original PC/XT serial-port UART. There are several minor bugs in the UART, but the original PC/XT BIOS corrected for them. The 8250 was replaced by the 8250B.
8250A	This slightly updated UART fixed many of the problems of the 8250, but it would not work in PC/XT systems because the BIOS was written to circumvent the 8250's problems. In either case, the 8250A will not work adequately at over 9600 bps.
8250B	The last of the 8250 series reinserted the bugs that existed in the original 8250 so that the PC/XT BIOS would function properly. The 8250B also does not run at above 9600 bps.
16450	This higher-speed UART was the desired choice for AT (i286) systems. Stable at 9600 bps, the 16450 laid the groundwork for the first "high-speed" modems. However, the 16450 will not work in PC/XT systems. This IC should be replaced by the 16550A.
16550	The 16550 was faster than the 16450, allowing operation above 9600 bps, but its performance was still limited by internal design problems. This IC should be replaced by the 16550A.
16550A	The fastest of the UARTs, a 16550A eliminates many of the serial-port problems encountered when using a fast modem.

TABLE 4.2   Comparison of Modem Standards

Bell Standards

The Bell System largely dictated North American telecommunications standards before it was broken up into AT&T and seven regional operating companies in 1984. In that period, two major standards were developed that set the stage for future modem development. Today, the Bell standards are completely obsolete.

- *BELL103.*   This was the first widely accepted modem standard; it used simple FSK modulation at 300 baud. This is the *only* standard where the data rate matches the baud rate. It is interesting to note that many modems today *still* support BELL103 as a lowest common denominator when all other modulation techniques fail.
- *BELL212A.*   This represents a second widely accepted modem standard in North America; it used PSK modulation at 600 baud to transmit 1200 bps. Many European countries ignored BELL212A in favor of the similar (but not entirely identical) European standard called V.22.

TABLE 4.2   **Comparison of Modem Standards (*Continued*)**

ITU (CCITT) Standards

After the Bell System breakup, AT&T no longer wielded enough clout to dictate standards even in North America—and certainly not to the international community, which had developed serious computing interest. It was at this time that the ITU (International Telecommunications Union, formally the CCITT) gained prominence and acceptance in the United States. All U.S. modems have been built to ITU standards ever since. ITU specifications are characterized by the symbol V (e.g., V.17). The "V" simply means *standard* (rather like the "RS" in RS-232). The subsequent number denotes the particular standard. Some standards also add the term "bis," which means the *second version* of a particular standard, or the term "terbo," which is the *third version* of a standard. The list below provides a comprehensive look at ITU standards. Only the bolded standards relate to modems in particular, but all are related to communications. This index may aid you in understanding the broad specifications that are required to fully characterize the computer communications environment.

- *V.1* is a very early standard that defines binary 0/1 bits as space/mark line conditions and voltage levels.
- *V.2* limits the power levels [in decibels (dB)] of modems used on phone lines.
- *V.3* defines an international alphabet.
- *V.4* describes the sequence of bits within a character as transmitted (the data frame).
- *V.5* describes the standard synchronous signaling rates for dial-up lines.
- *V.6* describes the standard synchronous signaling rates for leased lines.
- *V.7* provides a list of modem terms in English, Spanish, and French.
- *V.10* describes unbalanced high-speed electrical interface characteristics (RS-423).
- *V.11* describes balanced high-speed electrical characteristics (RS-422).
- *V.13* explains simulated carrier control (with a full-duplex modem used as a half-duplex modem).
- *V.14* explains the procedure for asynchronous-to-synchronous conversion.
- *V.15* describes the requirements and designs for telephone acoustic couplers. This is largely unused today, since most telephone equipment is modular and can be plugged into telephone adapters directly rather than being loosely attached to the telephone handset.
- *V.16* describes medical analog data transmission modems.
- *V.17* describes an application-specific modulation scheme for Group 3 fax which provides two-wire half-duplex trellis-coded transmission at 7200, 9600, 12,000, and 14,400 bps. In spite of the low number, this is a fairly recent standard.
- *V.19* describes early DTMF modems using low-speed parallel transmission. This standard is largely obsolete.

TABLE 4.2   Comparison of Modem Standards (*Continued*)

ITU (CCITT) Standards (*Continued*)

- **V.20** explains modems with parallel data transmission. This standard is largely obsolete.
- **V.21** provides the specifications for 300-bps FSK serial modems (based upon BELL103).
- **V.22** provides the specifications for 1200-bps (600-baud) PSK modems (based upon BELL212A).
- **V.22bis** describes 2400-bps modems operating at 600 baud using QAM.
- **V.23** describes the operation of a rather unusual type of FM modem working at 1200/75 bps. That is, the host transmits at 1200 bps and receives at 75 bps. The remote modem transmits at 75 bps and receives at 1200 bps. V.23 is used in Europe to support some videotext applications.
- **V.24** (known as EIA RS-232 in the United States) defines *only* the functions of the serial-port circuits. EIA-232-E (the current version of the standard) also defines electrical characteristics and connectors.
- **V.25** defines automatic answering equipment and parallel automatic dialing. It also defines the answer tone that modems send.
- **V.25bis** defines serial automatic calling and answering, which is the ITU (CCITT) equivalent of AT commands. This is the current ITU standard for modem control by computers via serial interface. The Hayes AT command set is used primarily in the United States.
- **V.26** defines a 2400-bps PSK full-duplex modem operating at 1200 baud. **V.26bis** defines a 2400-bps PSK half-duplex modem operating at 1200 baud.
- **V.26terbo** defines a 2400/1200-bps switchable PSK full-duplex modem operating at 1200 baud.
- **V.27** defines a 4800-bps PSK modem operating at 1600 baud.
- **V.27bis** defines a more advanced 4800/2400-bps switchable PSK modem operating at 1600/1200 baud.
- **V.27terbo** defines a 4800/2400-bps switchable PSK modem commonly used in half-duplex mode at 1600/1200 baud to handle Group 3 fax rather than computer modems.
- **V.28** defines the electrical characteristics and connections for V.24 (RS-232). Where the RS-232 specification defines all necessary parameters, the ITU (CCITT) breaks the specifications down into two separate documents.
- **V.29** defines a 9600/7200/4800-bps switchable PSK/QAM modem operating at 2400 baud. This type of modem is often used to implement Group 3 fax rather than computer modems.
- **V.31** defines electrical characteristics for single-current interchange circuits controlled by contact closure.
- **V.32** defines the first of the truly modern modems, a 9600/4800-bps switchable QAM full-duplex modem operating at 2400 baud. This standard also incorporates trellis coding and echo cancellation to produce a stable, reliable, high-speed modem.

TABLE 4.2   Comparison of Modem Standards (*Continued*)

ITU (CCITT) Standards (*Continued*)

- **V.32bis** is a fairly new standard extending the V.32 specification to define a 4800/7200/9600/12,000/14,400-bps switchable TCQAM full-duplex modem operating at 2400 baud. Trellis coding, automatic transfer rate negotiation, and echo cancellation make this type of modem one of the most popular and least expensive for everyday PC communication.

- **V.32terbo** continues to extend the V.32 specification by using advanced techniques to implement a 14,400/16,800/19,200-bps switchable TCQAM full-duplex modem operating at 2400 baud. Unlike V.32bis, V.32terbo is not widely used because of the rather high cost of components.

- **V.32fast** is the informal name for a standard that the ITU has not yet completed. When the standard is finished, a V.32fast modem with speeds up to 28,800 bps will probably replace V.32bis. It is anticipated that this will be the last *analog* protocol, as such protocols will eventually give way to all-digital protocols as local telephone services become entirely digital. V.32fast will probably be renamed V.34 upon completion and acceptance.

- **V.33** defines a specialized 14,400-bps TCQAM full-duplex modem operating at 2400 baud.

- **V.34** defines the finalized 28.8-kbyte ITU-T protocol. V.34 has more carrier speeds that it can negotiate to (from 28,800 bps all the way down to 2400 bps, in 2400-bps steps).

- **V.35** defines data transmission at 48 kbytes using 60- to 108-kHz group band circuits.

- **V.36** defines a specialized 48,000-bps "group" modem which is rarely (if ever) used commercially. This type of modem uses several conventional telephone lines.

- **V.37** defines a specialized 72,000-bps "group" modem which combines several telephone channels.

- **V.40** provides error indication with electromechanical equipment.

- **V.41** defines a code-independent error control system.

- **V.42** is the only ITU error-correcting procedure for modems using the V.22, V.22bis, V.26terbo, V.32, and V.32bis protocols. The standard is also defined as a link access procedure for Modems (LAPM) protocol. ITU V.42 is considered very efficient, and is about 20 percent faster than MNP4. If a V.42 connection cannot be established between modems, V.42 automatically provides fallback to the MNP4 error correction standard.

- **V.42bis** provides a Lempel-Ziv-based data-compression scheme for use in conjunction with V.42 LAPM (error correction). V.42bis is a data-compression standard for high-speed modems which can compress data by as much as 4:1 (depending on the type of file you send). Thus, a 9600-baud modem can transmit data at up to 38,400 bps using V.42bis. A 14.4-kbps modem can transmit at up to a startling 57,600 bps.

TABLE 4.2   Comparison of Modem Standards (*Continued*)

ITU (CCITT) Standards (*Continued*)

- ***V.50*** sets standard telephony limits for modem transmission quality.
- ***V.51*** outlines required maintenance of international data circuits.
- ***V.52*** describes apparatus for measuring data transmission distortion and error rates.
- ***V.53*** outlines impairment limits for data circuits.
- ***V.54*** describes loop test devices for modem testing.
- ***V.55*** describes impulse noise measuring equipment for line testing.
- ***V.56*** outlines the comparative testing of modems.
- ***V.57*** describes comprehensive test equipment for high-speed data transmission.
- ***V.100*** describes the techniques for interconnection between PDNs (public data networks) and PSTNs (public switched telephone networks).

MNP Standards

The *Microcom Networking Protocol* (MNP) is a complete hierarchy of standards developed during the mid-1980s which are designed to work with other modem technologies for error correction and data compression. While most ITU standards refer to modem data transfer, MNP standards concentrate on providing error correction and data compression when your modem is communicating with another modem that supports MNP. For example, MNP class 4 is specified by ITU V.42 as a backup error control scheme for LAPM in the event that V.24 cannot be invoked. Out of nine recognized MNP levels, your modem probably supports the first five. Each MNP class has all the features of the previous class plus its own.

- *MNP class 1 (block mode):*   An old data transfer mode which sends data in only one direction at a time—about 70 percent as fast as data transmissions using no error correction. This level is now virtually obsolete.
- *MNP class 2 (stream mode):*   An older data transfer mode which sends data in both directions at the same time—about 84 percent as fast as data transmissions using no error correction.
- *MNP class 3:*   The sending modem strips start and stop bits from the data block before sending it, while the receiving modem adds start and stop bits before passing the data to the receiving computer. About 8 percent faster than data transmissions using no error correction. The increased throughput is realized only if modems on both ends of the connection are operating in a *split speed* (or *locked COM port*) fashion—that is, the rate of data transfer from computer to modem is *higher* than the rate of data transfer from modem to modem. Also, data is being transferred in big blocks (e.g., 1 kbyte) or continuously (e.g., using the Zmodem file transfer protocol).

TABLE 4.2   Comparison of Modem Standards (*Continued*)

MNP Standards (*Continued*)

- *MNP class 4:*   A protocol (with limited data compression) which checks telephone connection quality and uses a transfer technique called *adaptive packet assembly*—on a noise-free line, the modem sends larger blocks of data. If the line is noisy, the modem sends smaller blocks of data (less data will have to be resent). This means more successful transmissions on the first try. It is about 20 percent faster than data transmissions using no error correction at all, so most current modems are MNP4-compatible.

- *MNP class 5:*   Classical MNP data compression. MNP5 provides data compression by detecting redundant data and recoding it to fewer bits, thus increasing effective data throughput. A receiving modem decompresses the data before passing it to the receiving computer. MNP5 can send data transmissions up to two times as fast as transmissions using no data compression or error correction (depending on the kind of data transmitted). In effect, MNP5 gives a 2400-bps modem an effective data throughput of as much as 4800 bps, and a 9600-bps system as much as 19,200 bps.

- *MNP class 6:*   Uses *universal link negotiation* to let modems get maximum performance out of a line. Modems start at low speeds, then move to higher speeds until the best speed is found. MNP6 also provides *statistical duplexing* to help half-duplex modems simulate full-duplex modems.

- *MNP class 7:*   Offers a much more powerful data compression process (Huffman encoding) than MNP5. MNP7 modems can increase the data throughput by as much as three times in some cases. Although MNP7 is more efficient than MNP5, not all modems are designed to handle the MNP7 protocol. Also, MNP7 is faster than MNP5, but MNP7 is still generally considered slower than the ITU's V.42bis.

- *MNP class 9:*   Reduces the data overhead (the "housekeeping bits") encountered with each data packet. MNP9 also improves error correction performance because only the data that was in error, not the entire data packet, has to be resent.

- *MNP class 10:*   Uses a set of protocols known as *adverse channel enhancements* to help modems overcome poor telephone connections by adjusting data packet size and transmission speed until the most reliable transmission is established. This is a more powerful version of MNP4.

programming is accomplished by sending ASCII text strings during the initialization, dialing, and disconnect phases of the modem's operation. The codes used to program a modem are called the "command set," and since a programming string is typically started by the letters "AT," the codes are usually referred to as the *AT command set* (not to be confused with the IBM PC AT). The advantage of a standard code set is software compatibility. Any generic communications software can work with almost any modem simply by using the correct AT command string. Table 4.3 provides an extensive listing of AT commands. This can be particularly helpful when trying to interpret command strings.

TABLE 4.3   Index of the AT Command Set

Basic AT Commands

NOTE: Settings that are underlined (e.g., *F0*) are the default settings for an entry.

(A/) *Repeat last command.*

(A) *Answer.*

(Bx) *CCITT or Bell modulation.*

- B0—CCITT operation at 300 or 1200 bps.
- B1—BELL operation at 300 or 1200 bps.
- B2—V.23 with originate mode: receive 1200 bps, transmit 75 bps; answer mode: receive 75 bps, transmit 1200 bps.
- B3—V.23 with originate mode: receive 75 bps, transmit 1200 bps; answer mode: receive 1200 bps, transmit 75 bps.

(Dx) *Dial.* The valid dial string parameters are described below. Punctuation characters may be used for clarity, with parentheses, hyphens, and spaces being ignored:

0–9	*DTMF digits:* The numbers 0 to 9.
*	*The "star" digit* (Tone dialing only).
#	*The "pound" digit* (Tone dialing only).
!	*Flash:* The modem will go on-hook for a time defined by the value of S29.
,	*Dial pause:* The modem will pause for a time specified by S8 before dialing the digits that follow.
;	*Return to command state:* Added to the end of a dial string, this causes the modem to return to the command state after it processes the portion of the dial string preceding the symbol. This allows the user to issue additional AT commands while remaining off-hook. The additional AT commands may be placed in the original command line following the ";" or may be entered on subsequent command lines. The modem will enter call progress only after an additional dial command is issued without the ";" terminator. Use "H" to abort the dial in progress and go back on-hook.

TABLE 4.3   Index of the AT Command Set (*Continued*)

Basic AT Commands (*Continued*)

^   *Enable calling tone:* Applicable to current dial attempt only. The calling tone is a 1800-Hz tone every 3 to 4 s that alerts recipient of automatic calling equipment (as defined in CCITT V.25).

>   *Ground pulse:* If enabled by a country-specific parameter, the modem will generate a grounding pulse on the EARTH relay output.

@   *Wait for silence:* The modem will wait for at least 5 s of silence in the call progress frequency band before continuing with the next dial string parameter. If the modem does not detect these 5 s of silence before the expiration of the call abort timer (S7), the modem will terminate the call attempt with a NO ANSWER message. If busy detection is enabled, the modem may terminate the call with the BUSY result code. If an answer tone arrives during execution of this parameter, the modem handshakes.

A–D   *DTMF letters:* A, B, C, and D.

J   *Fastest speed:* Perform MNP10 link negotiation at the highest supported speed for this call only.

K   *Power adjustment:* Enable power-level adjustment during MNP10 link negotiation for this call only.

L   *Redial last number:* The modem will redial the last valid telephone number. This command must be immediately after the "D," with all the following characters ignored.

P   *Select pulse dialing:* Pulse dial the numbers that follow until a "T" is encountered. Affects current and subsequent dialing.

R   *Delay:* This command will cause the modem to wait 10 s after dialing, then go into answer mode. This command must be placed at the end of the dial string.

T   *Select tone dialing:* Tone dial the numbers that follow until a "P" is encountered. Affects current and subsequent dialing.

W   *Wait for dial tone:* The modem will wait for a dial tone before dialing the digits following "W." If no dial tone is detected within the time specified by S6, the modem will abort the rest of the sequence, return on-hook, and generate an error message.

(Ex) *Command echo.*

- E0 Disables command echo.
- E1 Enables command echo.

(Fx) *Select line modulation.*

- F0—Selects auto-detect mode—all connect speeds are possible.
- F1—Selects V.21 or Bell 103 according to the "B" setting.
- F2—Not supported (some modems use this setting for 600 bps).
- F3—Originator is at 75 bps and answerer is at 1200 bps.
- F4—Selects V.22 1200 bps or Bell 212A according to the "B" setting.

TABLE 4.3   Index of the AT Command Set (*Continued*)

Basic AT Commands (*Continued*)

- F5—Selects V.22bis as the only acceptable line modulation.
- F6—Selects V.32bis 4800 bps or V.32 4800 bps as the only acceptable line modulation.
- F7—Selects V.32bis 7200 bps as the only acceptable line modulation.
- F8—Selects V.32bis 9600 bps or V.32 9600 bps as the only acceptable line modulation.
- F9—Selects V.32bis 12,000 bps as the only acceptable line modulation.
- F10—Selects V.32bis 14,400 bps as the only acceptable line modulation.

(Hx) *Disconnect [hangup].*

- H0—The modem will release the line if the modem is currently on-line, and will terminate any test (AT&T) that is in progress.
- H1—If on-hook, the modem will go off-hook and enter command mode. The modem will return on-hook after a period of time determined by S7.

(Ix) *Identification.*

- I0—Reports product code.
- I1—Reports precomputed checksum from ROM.
- I2—The modem will respond "OK."
- I3—Reports firmware revision.
- I4—Reports modem identifier string.
- I5—Reports country code parameter (e.g., "022").
- I6—Reports modem data pump model and internal code revision.

(Lx) *Speaker volume.*

- L0—Low speaker volume.
- L1—Low speaker volume.
- <u>L2</u>—Medium speaker volume.
- L3—High speaker volume.

(Mx) *Speaker control.*

- M0—Speaker is always off.
- <u>M1</u>—Speaker is on during call establishment, but off when receiving carrier.
- M2—Speaker is always on.
- M3—Speaker is off when receiving carrier and during dialing, but on during answering.

(Nx) *Automode enable.*

- N0—Automode detection is disabled.
- <u>N1</u>—Automode detection is enabled.

(Ox) *Return to on-line data mode.*

- O0—Enters on-line data mode without a retrain.

TABLE 4.3   Index of the AT Command Set (*Continued*)

Basic AT Commands (*Continued*)

- O1—Enters on-line data mode with a retrain before returning to on-line data mode.
- O3–14—Forces the modem to a new rate that is user-defined (defined in S62).

(P) *Set pulse dial default.*
(Qx) *Quiet results codes.*

- Q0—Enables result codes to the DTE.
- Q1—Disables result codes to the DTE.

(Sn) *Read/write S-registers.*

- n = v—Sets S-register *n* to the value *v*.
- n?—Reports the value of S-register *n*.

(T) *Set tone dial default.*
(Vx) *Result code form.*

- V0—Enables short-form (terse) result codes.
- V1—Enables long-form (verbose) result codes.

(Wx) *Error correction message control.*

- W0—Upon connection, the modem reports only the DTE speed.
- W1—Upon connection, the modem reports the line speed, the error-correction protocol, and the DTE speed, respectively.
- W2—Upon connection, the modem reports the DCE speed.

(Xx) *Extended result codes.*

- X0—Sends only OK, CONNECT, RING, NO CARRIER, ERROR, and NO ANSWER result codes.
- X1—Sends only OK, CONNECT, RING, NO CARRIER, ERROR, NO ANSWER, and CONNECT XXXX.
- X2—Sends only OK, CONNECT, RING, NO CARRIER, ERROR, NO DIAL TONE, NO ANSWER, and CONNECT XXXX.
- X3—Sends only OK, CONNECT, RING, NO CARRIER, ERROR, NO ANSWER, CONNECT XXXX, and BUSY.
- X4—Enables monitoring of busy tones; sends all messages.

(Yx) *Long space disconnect.*

- Y0—Disables long space disconnect.
- Y1—Enables long space disconnect.

(Zx) *Soft reset and restore profile.*

- Z0—Soft reset and restore stored profile 0.
- Z1—Soft reset and restore stored profile 1.

(&Bx) *Autoretrain.*

- &B0—Hang up on a poor received signal.

TABLE 4.3   Index of the AT Command Set (*Continued*)

AT& Commands

- &B1—Retrain on a poor received signal. Hang up if the condition persists.
- &B2—Do not hang up; do not retrain (i.e., tolerate any line).

(&Cx) *RLSD (DCD) option.*

- &C0—RLSD remains ON at all times.
- &C1—RLSD follows the state of the carrier.

(&Dx) *DTR option.*

- &D0—DTR drop is interpreted according to the current &Q setting as follows:

    (&Q0, 5, 6)—DTR is ignored (assumed to be ON). Allows operation with DTEs which don't provide DTR.

    (&Q1, 4)—DTR drop causes the modem to hang up. Auto-answer is not affected.

    (&Q2, 3)—DTR drop causes the modem to hang up. Auto-answer is inhibited.

- &D1—DTR drop is interpreted according to the current &Q setting as follows:

    (&Q0, 1, 4, 5, 6)—DTR drop is interpreted by the modem as if the asynchronous escape sequence had been entered. The modem returns to asynchronous command state without disconnecting.

    (&Q2, 3)—DTR drop causes the modem to hang up. Auto-answer is inhibited.

- &D2—DTR drop is interpreted according to the current &Q setting as follows:

    (&Q0–6)—DTR drop causes the modem to hang up. Auto-answer is inhibited.

- &D3—DTR drop is interpreted according to the current &Q setting as follows:

    (&Q0, 1, 4, 5, 6)—DTR drop causes the modem to perform a soft reset as if the Z command were received. The &Y setting determines which profile is loaded.

    (&Q2, 3)—DTR drop causes the modem to hang up. Auto-answer is inhibited.

(&Fx) *Restore factory configuration.*

- &F0—Restore factory configuration 0.
- &F1—Restore factory configuration 1.

(&Gx) *Select guard tone.*

- &G0—Disables guard tone.
- &G1—Disables guard tone.
- &G2—Selects 1800-Hz guard tone.

(&Jx) *Telephone jack type.*

- &J0—RJ11 telephone jack.

TABLE 4.3   **Index of the AT Command Set (*Continued*)**

AT& Commands (*Continued*)

- &J1—RJ12 or RJ13 telephone jack.

(&Kx) *Flow control.*

- &K0—Disables flow control.
- &K3—Enables RTS/CTS flow control.
- &K4—Enables XON/XOFF flow control.
- &K5—Enables transparent XON/XOFF flow control.
- &K6—Enables both RTS/CTS and XON/XOFF flow control.

(&Lx) *Dial-up/leased line option.*

- &L0—Dial-up line.
- &L1—Leased line.

(&Mx) *Asynchronous/synchronous mode selection.*

- &M0—Selects direct asynchronous operation.
- &M1—Selects synchronous connect mode with asynchronous off-line command mode.
- &M2—Selects synchronous connect mode with asynchronous off-line command mode.
- &M3—Selects synchronous connect mode.
- &M4—Hayes AutoSync mode.

(&Px) *Dial pulse ratio.*

- &P0—Make = 39%, break = 61% (at 10 pps for the U.S.).
- &P1—Make = 33%, break = 67% (at 10 pps for Europe).
- &P2—Make = 33%, break = 67% (at 20 pps for Japan).

(&Qx) *Sync/async mode.*

- &Q0—Selects direct asynchronous operation.
- &Q1—Selects synchronous connect mode with asynchronous off-line command mode.
- &Q2—Selects synchronous connect mode with asynchronous off-line command mode.
- &Q3—Selects synchronous connect mode.
- &Q4—Selects AutoSync operation.
- &Q5—The modem will try to negotiate an error-corrected link.
- &Q6—Selects asynchronous operation in normal mode (speed buffering).

Starting AutoSync.   Set registers S19, S20, and S25 to the desired values before selecting AutoSync operation with &Q4. After the CONNECT message is issued, the modem waits the period of time specified by S25 before examining DTR. If DTR is on, the modem enters the synchronous operating state; if DTR is off, the modem terminates the line connection and returns to the asynchronous command state.

TABLE 4.3   Index of the AT Command Set (*Continued*)

AT& Commands (*Continued*)

Stopping AutoSync.   AutoSync operation is stopped upon loss of carrier or the ON-to-OFF transition of DTR. Loss of carrier will cause the modem to return to the asynchronous command state. An ON-to-OFF transition of DTR will cause the modem to return to the asynchronous command state and either not terminate the line connection (&D1 active) or terminate the line connection (any other &Dn command active).

(&Rx) *RTS / CTS option.*

- &R0—In sync mode, CTS tracks the state of RTS; the RTS-to-CTS delay is defined by S26. In async mode, CTS acts according to the V.25bis handshake.
- &R1—In sync mode, CTS is always ON (RTS transitions are ignored). In async mode, CTS will drop only if required by flow control.

(&Sx) *DSR override.*

- &S0—DSR will remain ON at all times.
- &S1—DSR will become active after answer tone has been detected and inactive after the carrier has been lost.

(&Tx) *Test and diagnostics.*

- &T0—Terminates the test in progress. Clears S16.
- &T1—Initiates local analog loopback, V.54 Loop 3.
- &T2—Returns an ERROR message.
- &T3—Initiates local digital loopback, V.54 Loop 2.
- &T4—Enables digital loopback acknowledgment for remote request.
- &T5—Disables digital loopback acknowledgement for remote request.
- &T8—Initiates local analog loopback, V.54 Loop 3, with self-test.

(&Vx) *Display current configuration and stored profiles.*

- &V0—View active file, stored profile 0, and stored phone numbers.
- &V1—View active file, stored profile 1, and stored phone numbers.

(&Wx) *Store current configuration.*

- &W0—Store the current configuration as profile 0.
- &W1—Store the current configuration as profile 1.

(&Xx) *Sync transmit clock source option.*

- &X0—The modem generates the transmit clock.
- &X1—The DTE generates the transmit clock.
- &X2—The modem derives the transmit clock.

(&Yx) *Designate a default reset profile.*

- &Y0—The modem will use profile 0.

TABLE 4.3 **Index of the AT Command Set (*Continued*)**

AT& Commands (*Continued*)

- &Y1—The modem will use profile 1.

(&Zn = x) *Store telephone number.*

- &Zn = x—(*n* = 0 to 3, and *x* = dial string)

AT% Commands

(%BAUD) *Bit-rate multiplier.*
(%Cx) *Enable/disable data compression.*

- %C0—Disables data compression. Resets S46 bit 1.
- %C1—Enables MNP 5 data compression negotiation. Resets S46 bit 1.
- %C2—Enables V.42bis data compression. Sets S46 bit 1.
- %C3—Enables both V.42bis and MNP 5 data compression. Sets S46 bit 1.

(%CCID) *Enable caller ID.*
(%CD) *Carrier detect lamp.*
(%CDIA) *Display last DIAG.*
(%CIDS) *Store ID numbers.*
(%CRID) *Repeat last ID.*
(%CSIG) *Store SIG numbers.*
(%CXID) *XID enable.*
(%Dx) *V.42bis dictionary size.*

- %D0—Dictionary set to 512.
- %D1—Dictionary set to 1024.
- %D2—Dictionary set to 2048.
- %D3—Dictionary set to 4096.

(%Ex) *Enable/Disable Line Quality Monitor and Auto-Retrain Fallback/Fallforward.*

- %E0—Disable line quality monitor and auto-retrain.
- %E1—Enable line quality monitor and auto-retrain.

- %E2—Enable line quality monitor and fallback/fallforward.
- %E3—Enable line quality monitor and auto-retrain, but hang up when EQM reaches threshold.

(%Gx) *Auto fallforward/fallback enable.*

- %G0—Disabled.
- %G1—Enabled.

(%L) *Line signal level.*
(%Mx) *Compression type.*

- %M0—Compression disabled.
- %M1—Transmit compression only.
- %M2—Receive compression only.

TABLE 4.3   Index of the AT Command Set (*Continued*)

AT% Commands (*Continued*)

- %M3—Two-way compression.

(%P) *Clear encoder dictionary.*
(%Q) *Line signal quality.*
(%Sx) *Set maximum string length in V.42bis.*
(%SCBR) *Call back reference outgoing calls.*
(%SKEY) *Store authentication key outgoing call.*
(%SPRT) *Security mode—outgoing calls.*
(%SPNP) *Serial plug-and-play control.*
(%SPWD) *Password outgoing calls.*
(%SSPW) *Supervisor password outgoing calls.*
(%SUID) *User ID outgoing calls.*
(%TTx) *PTT testing utilities.*

- %TT00–%TT09—DTMF tone dial digits 0 to 9.
- %TT0A—DTMF digit *.
- %TT0B—DTMF digit A.
- %TT0C—DTMF digit B.
- %TT0D—DTMF digit C.
- %TT0E—DTMF digit #.
- %TT0F—DTMF digit D.
- %TT10—V.21 channel no. 1 mark (originate) symbol.
- %TT11—V.21 channel no. 2 mark symbol.
- %TT12—V.23 backward channel mark symbol.
- %TT13—V.23 forward channel mark symbol.
- %TT14—V.22 originate (call mark) signaling at 600 bps (*not supported*).
- %TT15—V.22 originate (call mark) signaling at 1200 bps.
- %TT16—V.22bis originate (call mark) signaling at 2400 bps.
- %TT17—V.22 answer signaling (guard tone if PTT required).
- %TT18—V.22bis answer signaling (guard tone if required).
- %TT19—V.21 channel no. 1 space symbol.
- %TT20—V.32, 9600 bps.
- %TT21—V.32bis, 14,400 bps.
- %TT1A—V.21 channel no. 2 space symbol.
- %TT1B—V.23 backward channel space symbol.
- %TT1C—V.23 forward channel space symbol.
- %TT30—Silence (on-line), i.e., go off-hook.
- %TT31—V.25 answer tone.
- %TT32—1800-Hz guard tone.
- %TT33—V.25 calling tone (1300 Hz).
- %TT34—Fax calling tone (1100 Hz).
- %TT40—V.21 channel 2.
- %TT41—V.27ter, 2400 bps.
- %TT42—V.27ter, 4800 bps.
- %TT43—V.29, 7200 bps.

TABLE 4.3   Index of the AT Command Set (*Continued*)

AT% Commands (*Continued*)

- %TT44—V.29, 9600 bps.
- %TT45—V.17, 7200 bps long train.
- %TT46—V.17, 7200 bps short train.
- %TT47—V.17, 9600 bps long train.
- %TT48—V.17, 9600 bps short train.
- %TT49—V.17, 12,000 bps long train.
- %TT4A—V.17, 12,000 bps short train.
- %TT4B—V.17, 14,400 bps long train.
- %TT4C—V.17, 14,400 bps short train.

AT\ Commands

(\Ax) *Select maximum MNP block size.*

- \A0—64 characters
- \A1—128 characters
- \A2—192 characters
- \A3—256 characters
- \A4—Maximum 32 characters (for ETC enhanced throughput cellular).

(\Bx) *Transmit break to remote.*

- \B1–\B9—Break length in 100-ms units (default = 3—non-error-corrected mode only).

(\Cx) *Set autoreliable buffer.*

- \C0—Does not buffer data.
- \C1—Buffers data on the answering modem for 4 s.
- \C2—Does not buffer data on the answering modem.

(\Ex) *Optimize local echo.*
(\Gx) *Modem-to-modem flow control (XON/XOFF).*

- \G0—Disables modem-to-modem XON/XOFF flow control.
- \G1—Enables modem-to-modem XON/XOFF flow control.

(\Jx) *Constant DTE speed option.*

- \J0—DCE and DTE rates are independent.
- \J1—DTE rate adjusts to DCE connection rate after on-line.

(\Kx) *Break control.* If the modem receives a break from the DTE when the modem is operating in data transfer mode:

- \K0—Enter on-line command mode, no break sent to the remote modem.
- \K1—Clear data buffers and send break to remote modem.
- \K2—Same as \K0.
- \K3—Send break to remote modem immediately.

TABLE 4.3   Index of the AT Command Set (*Continued*)

AT\ Commands (*Continued*)

- \K4—Same as \K0.
- \K5—Send break to remote modem in sequence with transmitted data.

If the modem is in the on-line command state (waiting for AT commands) during a data connection, and the \B command is received in order to send a break to the remote modem:

- \K0—Clear data buffers and send break to remote modem.
- \K1—Clear data buffers and send break to remote modem (same as \K0).
- \K2—Send break to remote modem immediately.
- \K3—Send break to remote modem immediately (same as \K2).
- \K4—Send break to remote modem in sequence with data.
- \K5—Send break to remote modem in sequence with data (same as \K4).

If there is a break received from a remote modem during a non-error-corrected connection:

- \K0—Clear data buffers and send break to the DTE.
- \K1—Clear data buffers and send break to the DTE (same as \K0).
- \K2—Send a break immediately to DTE.
- \K3—Send a break immediately to DTE (same as \K2).
- \K4—Send a break in sequence with received data to DTE.
- \K5—Send a break in sequence with received data to DTE (same as \K4).

(\Lx) *MNP block / stream mode select.*

- \L0—Use stream mode for MNP connection.
- \L1—Use interactive block mode for MNP connection.

(\Nx) *Operating mode.*

- \N0—Selects normal-speed buffered mode.
- \N1—Selects direct mode.
- \N2—Selects reliable (error-correction) mode.
- \N3—Selects auto reliable mode.
- \N4—Selects LAPM error-correction mode.
- \N5—Selects MNP error-correction mode.

(\O) *Originate reliable link control.*
(\Qx) *DTE flow control options.*

- \Q0—Disables flow control.
- \Q1—XON/XOFF software flow control.
- \Q2—CTS flow control to the DTE.
- \Q3—RTS/CTS hardware flow control.

TABLE 4.3   Index of the AT Command Set (*Continued*)

AT\ Commands (*Continued*)

(\S) *Report active configuration.*
(\Tx) *Set inactivity timer.*

- $\underline{n = 0}$—Disable the inactivity timer.
- n = 1–90—Length in minutes.

(\U) *Accept reliable link control.*
(\Vx) *Protocol result code.*

- \V0—Disable protocol result code (e.g., CONNECT 9600).
- \V1—Enable protocol result code (e.g., CONNECT 9600/LAPM).

(\Xx) *Set XON/XOFF pass-through option.*

- \X0—If XON/XOFF flow control enabled, do not pass XON/XOFF to remote modem or local DTE.
- \X1—Always pass XON/XOFF to the remote modem or local DTE.

(\Y) *Switch to reliable operation.*
(\Z) *Switch to normal operation.*

AT-Commands

(-Jx) *Set V.42 detection phase.*

- -J0—Disables the V.42 detection phase.
- -J1—Enables the V.42 detection phase.

(-Kx) *MNP extended services.*

- -K0—Disables V.42 LAPM–to–MNP10 conversion.
- -K1—Enables V.42 LAPM–to–MNP10 conversion.
- -K2—Enables V.42 LAPM–to–MNP10 conversion; inhibits MNP Extended Services.

(-Qx) *Enable fallback to V.22bis/V.22.*

- -Q0—Disables fallback to 2400 bps (V.22bis) and 1200 bps (V.22). Fallback only to 4800 bps.
- -Q1—Enables fallback to 2400 bps (V.22bis) and 1200 bps (V.22).

(-SDR = n) *Distinctive ring reporting.*

- -SDR = 1—Type 1 distinctive ring detect
- -SDR = 2—Type 2 distinctive ring detect
- -SDR = 3—Type 1 and Type 2 distinctive ring detect
- -SDR = 4—Type 3 distinctive ring detect
- -SDR = 5—Type 1 and Type 3 distinctive ring detect
- -SDR = 6—Type 2 and Type 3 distinctive ring detect
- -SDR = 7—Types 1, 2, and 3 distinctive ring detect

TABLE 4.3 Index of the AT Command Set (*Continued*)

AT-Commands (*Continued*)						
Distinctive Ring Types						
Type	On	Off	On	Off	On	Off	Sound
1	2.0	4.0					Rinnnnnnnnnng
2	0.8	0.4	0.8	4.0			Ring Ring
3	0.4	0.2	0.4	0.2	0.8	4.0	Ring Ring Rinnng

(-SEC = n) *LAPM and MNP link control.*

- -SEC = 0—Disable LAPM or MNP10. EC transmit level set in register S91.
- -SEC = 1, 0–30—Enable LAPM or MNP10. EC transmit level set to value after comma (0 to 30).
- (-SKEY) *Program key.*
- (-SPRT) *Remote security mode.*
- (-SPWD) *Program password.*
- (-SSE) *Simultaneous voice data.*
- (-SSG) *Set DSVD receive gain.*
- (-SSKY) *Program supervisor key.*
- (-SSP) *Select DVSD port.*
- (-SSPW) *Supervisor password.*
- (-SUID) *Program user ID.*
- (-V) *Display root firmware version number.*

AT" Commands

("Hx) *V.42bis compression control.*

- "H0—Disable V.42bis.
- "H1—Enable V.42bis only when transmitting data.
- "H2—Enable V.42bis only when receiving data.
- "H3—Enable V.42bis for both directions.

("Nx) *V.42bis dictionary size.*

- "N0—512 bytes.
- "N1—1024 bytes.
- "N2—1536 bytes.

("Ox) *Select V.42bis maximum string length.*

- n = 6–64
- n = 32

AT~ Commands

(~Dx) *Factory-configured operating profile.*

- ~D0—Disable (no error correction, no data compression).
- ~D1—MNP4.
- ~D2—MNP5.

TABLE 4.3   Index of the AT Command Set (*Continued*)

AT~ Commands (*Continued*)

- ~D3—V.42.
- ~D4—V.42bis.

AT~~ Commands

(~~Lx) *Digital line current sensing on/off.*

- ~~L0—Turn off digital line current sensing.
- ~~L1—Turn on digital line current sensing.

(~~S = m) *Digital line overcurrent sense time set.*

- m = 0 through 9
- m = 4

(~~S?) *Display line overcurrent sense time display.*

AT + Fax Commands

Some modems support fax commands conforming to EIA standard 578. These commands are given here with short descriptions; they also typically support error correction and V.17terbo at 19.2 kbytes.

(+FAA) *Auto-answer mode parameter.*
(+FAXERR = x) *Fax error value parameter.*
(+FBOR = x) *Phase C data bit order parameter.*
(+FBUF?) *Read the buffer size.*
(+FCLASS?) *Service class indication.*

- + FCLASS?—000 if in data mode; 001 if in fax class 1.

(+FCLASS = x) *Service class capabilities.*

- + FCLASS = ?—0, modem is set up for data mode.

  0,1, modem is capable of data and fax class I services.

(+FCLASS = n) *Service class selection.*

- + FCLASS = 0—Select data mode
- + FCLASS = 1—Select fax class 1

(+FCR) *Capability to receive.*
(+FDCC = x) *Modem capabilities parameter.*
(+FDCS = x) *Current session results.*
(+FDIS = x) *Current session negotiation parameters.*
(+FDR) *Begin or continue phase C receive data.*
(+FDT = x) *Data transmission.*
(+FET = x) *Transmit page punctuation.*
(+FK) *Terminate session.*
(+FLID = x) *Local ID string parameter.*
(+FMDL?) *Request modem model.*
(+FMFR?) *Request modem IC manufacturer.*
(+FPHCTO) *Phase C time out.*

TABLE 4.3   Index of the AT Command Set (*Continued*)

AT + Fax Commands (*Continued*)

(+FPTS = x) *Page transfer status.*
(+FREV?) *Request modem revision.*
(+FRH = ?) *FAX SDLC receive capabilities.*
(+FRH = n) *Modem accept training (SDLC).*
(+FRM = ?) *FAX normal-mode receive capabilities.*
(+FRM = n) *Modem accept training.*
(+FRS = ?) *FRS range capabilities.*
(+FRS = n) *Receive silence.*

- + FRS = 4—e.g., wait 40 ms for silence.

(+FTH = ?) *FAX SDLC mode transmit capabilities.*
(+FTH = n) *Modem initiate training (SDLC).*
(+FTM = ?) *FAX normal-mode transmit capabilities.*
(+FTM = n) *Modem initiate training.*
(+FTS = ?) *FTS range capabilities.*
(+FTS = n) *Transmission silence.*

- + FTS = 5—e.g., fax transmission silence for 50 ms.

(+VCID) *Caller ID service.*

Other AT Commands

(_+BRC+_) *Remote escape into BRC state (from host on-line data mode).*
($BRC) *Enable/disable host.*
(#CID) *Enable caller ID detection.*
(:E) *Compromise equalizer enable.*

- :E0—Disables the equalizer.
- :E1—Enables the equalizer.

($GIVEBRC) *Enter BRC state (from target on-line command state).*
(*Hx) *Link negotiation speed.*

- *H0—Link negotiation occurs at the highest supported speed.
- *H1—Link negotiation occurs at 1200 bps.
- *H2—Link negotiation occurs at 4800 bps.

()Mx) *Enable cellular power level adjustment.*

-)M0—Disables power level adjustment during MNP10 link negotiation.
-)M1—Enables power level adjustment during MNP10 link negotiation.

(@Mx) *Initial cellular power level setting.*

- @M0—−26 dBm.
- @M1—−30 dBm.
- @M2—−10 dBm.
- @M26—−26 dBm

NOTE: Table 4.3 represents a compendium of commands compiled from a variety of modem manufacturers over several generations. Some modems may not be capable of every function or mode listed here.

Virtually all AT command strings start with the prefix "AT" (attention). For example, the command string ATZE1Q0V1 contains five separate commands: attention (AT), reset the modem to its power-up defaults (Z), enable the command echo to send command characters back to the sender (E1), send command result codes back to the PC (Q0), and select text result codes, which causes words to be used as result codes. While this may seem like a mouthful, a typical modem can accept command strings up to 40 characters long. The term *result codes* is used for the messages that the modem generates when a command string is processed. Either numbers (default) or words (using the V1 command) can be returned. For example, when a command is processed correctly, a result code OK is produced, or CONNECT when a successful connection is established. Table 4.4 shows an index of modem result codes.

TABLE 4.4   List of Typical Modem Result Codes

Response code		Definition
#	Verbose	
0	OK	The OK code is returned by the modem to acknowledge execution of a command line.
1	CONNECT	Sent alone when speed is 300 bps.
2	RING	The modem sends this result code when incoming ringing is detected on the line.
3	NO CARRIER	No modem carrier signal is detected.
4	ERROR	Generated from AT command string errors if a command cannot be executed or if a parameter is outside of range.
5	CONNECT 1200	Connection at 1200 bps.
6	NO DIAL TONE	No dial tone was received from the local line.
7	BUSY	A busy tone has been detected.
8	NO ANSWER	The remote modem does not answer properly.
9	CONNECT 600	Connection at 600 bps.
10	CONNECT 2400	Connection at 2400 bps.
11	CONNECT 4800	Connection at 4800 bps.
12	CONNECT 9600	Connection at 9600 bps.

TABLE 4.4 **List of Typical Modem Result Codes (*Continued*)**

Response code #	Verbose	Definition
13	CONNECT 14400	Connection at 14,400 bps.
14	CONNECT 19200	Connection at 19,200 bps.
15	CONNECT 16800	Connection at 16,800 bps.
16	CONNECT 19200	Connection at 19,200 bps.
17	CONNECT 38400	Connection at 38,400 bps.
18	CONNECT 57600	Connection at 57,600 bps.
22	CONNECT 1200TX/75RX	Connection at 1200 bps/75 bps.
23	CONNECT 75TX/1200RX	Connection at 75 bps/1200 bps.
24	CONNECT 7200	Connection at 7200 bps.
25	CONNECT 12000	Connection at 12,000 bps.
26	CONNECT 1200/75	Connection at 1200 bps/75 bps (V.23).
27	CONNECT 75/1200	Connection at 75 bps/1200 bps (V.23).
28	CONNECT 38400	Connection at 38,400 bps.
29	CONNECT 21600	Connection at 21,600 bps.
30	CONNECT 24000	Connection at 24,000 bps.
31	CONNECT 26400	Connection at 26,400 bps.
32	CONNECT 28800	Connection at 28,800 bps.
33	CONNECT 115200	Connection at 115.2 kbps.
35	DATA	Modem data is present.
40	CARRIER 300	A V.21 or Bell 103 carrier has been detected on the line.
42	CARRIER 75/1200	A V.23 backward channel carrier has been detected on the line.
43	CARRIER 1200/75	A V.23 forward channel carrier has been detected on the line.
44	CARRIER 1200/75	A V.23 forward channel carrier has been detected on the line.
45	CARRIER 75/1200	A V.23 backward channel carrier has been detected on the line.
46	CARRIER 1200	The high or low channel carrier in either V.22 or Bell 212 mode has been detected on the line.
47	CARRIER 2400	The high or low channel carrier in V.22bis or V.34 mode has been detected on the line.
48	CARRIER 4800	The channel carrier in V.32, V.32bis, or V.34 has been detected on the line.
49	CARRIER 7200	The channel carrier in V.32bis or V.34 has been detected on the line.
50	CARRIER 9600	The channel carrier in V.32, V.32bis, or V.34 mode has been detected on the line.

TABLE 4.4   List of Typical Modem Result Codes (*Continued*)

Response code #	Verbose	Definition
51	CARRIER 12000	The channel carrier in V.32bis or V.34 mode has been detected on the line.
52	CARRIER 14400	The channel carrier in V.32bis or V.34 mode has been detected on the line.
53	CARRIER 16800	The channel carrier in V.32terbo or V.34 mode has been detected on the line.
54	CARRIER 19200	The channel carrier in V.32terbo or V.34 mode has been detected on the line.
55	CARRIER 21600	The channel carrier in V.34 mode has been detected on the line.
56	CARRIER 24000	The channel carrier in V.34 mode has been detected on the line.
57	CARRIER 26400	The channel carrier in V.34 mode has been detected on the line.
58	CARRIER 28800	The channel carrier in V.34 mode has been detected on the line.
66	COMPRESSION: CLASS 5	The modem has connected with MNP class 5 data compression.
67	COMPRESSION: V.42bis	The modem has connected with V.42bis data compression.
69	COMPRESSION: NONE	The modem has connected without data compression.
70	PROTOCOL: NONE	The modem has connected without any form of error correction.
76	PROTOCOL: NONE	The modem has connected without any form of error correction.
77	PROTOCOL: LAP-M	The modem has connected with V.42 LAPM error correction.
80	PROTOCOL: MNP	The modem has connected with MNP error correction.
81	PROTOCOL: MNP 2	The modem has connected with MNP error correction.
82	PROTOCOL: MNP 3	The modem has connected with MNP error correction.
83	PROTOCOL: MNP 2, 4	The modem has connected with MNP error correction.
84	PROTOCOL: MNP 3, 4	The modem has connected with MNP error correction.

Besides simply selecting modem commands, you can program many attributes of the modern modem. To accommodate this feature, each different parameter must be held in a series of memory locations (called *S-registers*). Each S-register is described in Table 4.5. For example, the default escape sequence for the AT command set is a series of three pluses: +++. You could change this character by writing an new ASCII character to S2. For the most part, default S-register values are fine for most work, but you can often optimize the modem's operation by experimenting with the register values. Since S-register contents must be maintained after power is removed from the modem, the registers are stored in nonvolatile RAM (NVRAM).

Modem initialization strings

One of the most difficult steps in configuring a new modem (or new modem software) is the proper use of initialization strings. Initialization strings (or *init strings,* as they are sometimes called) are vital in setting up the modem properly before each use—if they are wrong or absent, the modem will not behave as expected (if it works at all). There are strings for CCITT and ISDN modems. Keep in mind that initialization strings are not absolute—except for the "AT" at the start of each line, you can modify each string as required for your own system and telephone line.

NOTE: A few AT command strings are so long that they "run over" into a second line. When you enter these strings into communication software, you should be sure to enter all of the commands on the same line, without spaces or carriage returns.

Modem negotiation

The connection of two modems is not an instantaneous occurrence—each "connection" is the result of a carefully planned process of negotiation. Modems must decide on their speed, data compression, error correction, and so on. Faster modems must recognize slower modems and revise their speed downward. The negotiation process is perhaps the most important part of a modem's operation (and the most prone to problems). This part of the chapter outlines the negotiation sequence for a V.22bis (2400-bps) and a V.32 (4800/9600-bps) modem.

- **Step 1:** *Pickup.* The receiving modem picks up the ringing line (goes "off-hook"). It then waits at least 2 s. This is known as a *billing delay*; it is required by the telephone company to ensure that the connection has been properly established. No data transfer is allowed during the billing delay.

- **Step 2:** *Answer tone.* The receiving modem transmits an answer tone back to the network, a 2100-Hz tone that lasts for about 3.3 s. An answer tone serves two purposes. First, you can hear this tone in the receiving modem's speaker, so manual modem users know when to place the modem into data mode. Even more important, the answer tone is used by the telephone network to disable echo

TABLE 4.5   Index of S-register Assignments

Register	Function	Range	Units	Default
S0	Rings to auto-answer	0–255	Rings	0
S1	Ring counter	0–255	Rings	0
S2	Escape character	0–255	ASCII	43
S3	Carriage return character	0–127	ASCII	13
S4	Line feed character	0–127	ASCII	10
S5	Backspace character	0–255	ASCII	8
S6	Wait time for dial tone	2–255	Seconds	4
S7	Wait for carrier	1–255	Seconds	50
S8	Pause time for comma (,)	0–255	Seconds	2
S9	Carrier detect response time	1–255	1/10 seconds	6
S10	Carrier loss disconnect time	1–255	1/10 seconds	14
S11	Touch tone (DTMF) duration	50–255	1/1000 seconds	95
S12	Escape code guard time	0–255	2/100 seconds	50
S13	Reserved	—	—	138 (8Ah)
S14	General bit-mapped options	—	—	0
S15	Reserved	—	—	—
S16	Test mode bit map options (&T)	—	—	0
S17	Reserved	—	—	—
S18	Test timer	0–255	Seconds	0
S19	AutoSync bit map register			0
S20	AutoSync HDLC address or BSC sync character	0–255	—	0
S21	V.24/general bit map options			4 (04h)
S22	Speaker/results bit map options			118 (76h)
S23	General bit map options	—	—	55 (37h)
S24	Sleep inactivity timer	0–255	Seconds	1
S25	Delay to DTR off	0–255	1/100 seconds	5
S26	RTS-to-CTS delay	0–255	1/100 seconds	1

TABLE 4.5   Index of S-register Assignments (*Continued*)

Register	Function	Range	Units	Default
S27	General bit map options	—	—	73 (49h) with ECC 74 (4Ah) without ECC
S28	General bit map options	—	—	0
S29	Flash dial modifier time	0–255	10 ms	70
S30	Disconnect activity timer	0–255	10 seconds	0
S31	General bit map options			194 (C2h)
S32	XON character	0–255	ASCII	17 (11h)
S33	XOFF character	0–255	ASCII	19 (13h)
S34	Reserved	—	—	—
S35	Reserved	—	—	—
S36	LAPM failure control	—	—	7
S37	Line connection speed	—	—	0
S38	Delay before forced hangup	0–255	Seconds	20
S39	Flow control	—	—	3
S40	General bit map options	—	—	105 (69h) No MNP10 107 (6Bh) MNP10
S41	General bit map options	—	—	131 (83h)
S43	Auto fallback character for MNP negotiation	0–255	—	13
S44	Data framing	—	—	—
S46	Data compression control	—	—	136 (no compression) 138 (with compression)
S46*	Automatic sleep timer	0–255	100 ms	100
S47	Forced sleep timer with powerdown mode in PCMCIA	0–255	100 ms	10
S48	V.42 negotiation control	—	—	7
S49	Buffer low limit	—	—	—
S50	Buffer high limit	—	—	—

TABLE 4.5   Index of S-register Assignments (*Continued*)

Register	Function	Range	Units	Default
S50*	Fax/data mode selection	—	—	0 (data mode) 1 (fax mode)
S53	Global PAD configuration	—	—	—
S55	AutoStream protocol request	—	—	—
S56	AutoStream protocol status	—	—	—
S57	Network options register	—	—	—
S58	BTLZ string length	6–64	Bytes	32
S59	Leased-line failure alarm	—	—	—
S60	Leased-line failure action	—	—	—
S61	Leased-line retry number	—	—	—
S62	Leased-line restoral options	—	—	—
S62*	DTE rate status	0–17	—	16 (57,600 bps)
S63	Leased-line transmit level	—	—	—
S64	Leased-line receive level	—	—	—
S69	Link layer k protocol	—	—	—
S70	Maximum number of retransmissions	—	—	—
S71	Link-layer timeout	—	—	—
S72	Loss of flag idle timeout	—	—	—
S72*	DTE speed select	0–18	—	0 (last auto-baud)
S73	No activity timeout	—	—	—
S74	Minimum incoming LCN	—	—	—
S75	Minimum incoming LCN	—	—	—
S76	Maximum incoming LCN	—	—	—
S77	Maximum incoming LCN	—	—	—
S78	Outgoing LCN	—	—	—
S79	Outgoing LCN	—	—	—

TABLE 4.5   Index of S-register Assignments (*Continued*)

Register	Function	Range	Units	Default
S80	X.25 packet-level N20 parameter	—	—	—
S80*	Soft switch functions	—	—	1
S81	X.25 packet-level T20 parameter	—	—	—
S82	LAPM break control	—	—	128 (40h)
S84	ASU negotiation	—	—	—
S85	ASU negotiation status	—	—	—
S86	Call failure reason code	0–255	—	—
S87	Fixed-speed DTE interface	—	—	—
S91	PSTN transmit attenuation level	0–15	-dBm	10
S92	Fax transmit attenuation level	0–15	-dBm	10
S92*	MI/MIC options	—	—	—
S93	V.25bis async interface speed	—	—	—
S94	V.25bis mode control	—	—	—
S95	Result code messages control	—	—	0
S97	V.32 late connecting handshake timing	—	—	—
S99	Leased-line transmit level	0–15	-dBm	10
S101	Distinctive ring reporting	0–63	—	0
S105	Frame size	—	—	—
S108	Signal quality selector	—	—	—
S109	Carrier speed selector	—	—	—
S110	V.32/V.32bis selector	—	—	—
S113	Calling tone control	—	—	—
S116	Connection timeout	—	—	—
S121	Use of DTR	—	—	—
S122	V.13 selection	—	—	—
S141	Detection phase timer	—	—	—
S142	On-line character format	—	—	—
S143	KDS handshake mode	—	—	—
S144	Autobaud group selection	—	—	—
S150	V.42 options	—	—	—

TABLE 4.5 **Index of S-register Assignments (*Continued*)**

Register	Function	Range	Units	Default
S151	Simultaneous voice data control	—	—	—
S154	Force port speed	—	—	—
S157	Timeout result code	—	—	—
S201	Cellular transmit level (MNP10)	10–63	—	58 (3Ah)
S202	Remote access escape character	0–255	ASCII	170

*The register may be used for different purposes by some modems.

suppressers in the connection in order to allow optimum data throughput. If echo suppressers remain active, data transfer will be half-duplex (one direction at a time). The answering modem then goes silent for about 75 ms to separate the answer tone from data.

- **Step 3:** *The USB1 signal.* The receiving modem then transmits alternating binary 1s at 1200 bps (known as the *USB1 signal*). This results in the static sound you hear just after the answer tone. The sending modem detects the USB1 signal in about 155 ms, then falls silent for about 456 ms.

- **Step 4:** *The S1 signal.* After the 456-ms silence, the sending modem transmits double digits (i.e., 00 and 11) at 1200 bps for 100 ms (the *S1 signal*). An older Bell 212 or V.22 modem does not send the S1 signal, so if the S1 signal is absent, the receiving V.22bis modem will fall back to 1200 bps. The receiving modem (still generating a USB1 signal) receives the S1 signal. It responds by sending a 100-ms burst of S1 signal so that the sending modem knows that the receiving modem can handle 2400-bps operation. At this point, both modems know whether they will be operating in 1200-bps or 2400-bps mode.

- **Step 5:** *The SB1 signal.* At this point, the sending modem sends scrambled 1s at 1200 bps (the *SB1 signal*). The "scrambling" creates white noise which checks power across the whole audio bandwidth. The receiving modem then replies with the SB1 signal for 500 ms.

- **Step 6:** *Ready to answer.* After 500 ms, the receiving modem switches starts sending scrambled 1s at 2400 bps for 200 ms. A full 600 ms after getting the SB1 signal from the receiving modem, the sending modem also sends scrambled 1s at 2400 bps for 200 ms. After both modems have finished their final 200-ms transmissions, they are ready to pass data.

The negotiation process for a V.32 modem is remarkably similar to that for the V.22bis modem. However, the V.32 negotiation is more involved because of the error-correction elements that must be configured. Still, let's look at each step in the procedure.

- **Step 1:** *Pickup.*   The receiving modem picks up the ringing line (goes "off-hook"). It then waits at least 2 s. This is known as a *billing delay*; it is required by the telephone company to ensure that the connection has been properly established. As with the V.22bis modem, no data transfer is allowed during the billing delay.

- **Step 2:** *Answer tone.*   The receiving modem transmits an answer tone back to the network. A V.25 answer tone (a 2100-Hz tone with a duration of about 3.3 s) is returned to the calling modem. However, the V.32 modem uses a modified answer tone in which the signal phase is reversed every 450 ms; this sounds like little "clicks" in the signal. An answer tone serves two purposes. First, you can *hear* this tone in the receiving modem's speaker, so manual modem users know when to place the modem into data mode. Even more important, the answer tone is used by the telephone network to disable echo suppressers in the connection in order to allow optimum data throughput. The modems themselves will handle echo suppression.

- **Step 3:** *Signal AA.*   The sending modem waits about 1 s after receiving the answer tone, then generates an 1800-Hz tone (known as *signal AA*). When the receiving modem interprets this signal, it knows (quite early on) that it is communicating with another V.32 modem.

- **Step 4:** *The USB1 Fallback.*   If the answering modem heard signal AA, it will immediately try to establish a connection; otherwise, it will reply to the sending modem with a *USB1 signal* (alternating binary 1s at 1200 bps). This causes the connection to "fall back" to a V.22bis connection. This fallback attempt will continue for 3 s. If the sending modem does not respond to the USB1 signal within 3 s, the receiving modem will continue trying the connection as a V.32.

- **Step 5:** *Signals AC and CA.*   During a V.32 connection, the receiving modem sends *signal AC* (a mixed 600-Hz and 3000-Hz tone signal) for at least 1/2400 s, then it reverses the signal phase, creating *signal CA*.

- **Step 6:** *Signal CC.*   When the sending modem detects the phase change in signal AC/CA, it reverses the phase of its own signal AA, creating a new signal (called *signal CC*).

- **Step 7:** *Echo canceller configuration.*   Once the answering modem receives the phase-changed signal CC, it again changes the phase of CA, returning it to signal AC. This multitude of phase changes may seem like a ridiculous waste of time, but this exchange between the two modems is vital for approximating the round-trip (propagation) delay of the communication circuit so that the modem's echo canceller circuitry may be set properly.

■ **Step 8:** *Agreeing on specifics.* Once the exchange of phase changes sets the echo cancellers, both modems exchange data in half-duplex mode in order to set up adaptive equalizers, test the phone line quality, and agree on an acceptable data rate. In actual practice, the answering modem sends first (from 650 ms to 3525 ms). The sending modem responds, but leaves the signal on while the answering modem sends another burst of signals (this is when the final data rate is established).

■ **Step 9:** *Passing data.* Once the data rate is established, both modems proceed to send scrambled binary 1s for at least 1/1200 s (a brief white-noise sound), then they are ready to pass data.

Modem Installation Issues

Modems are among the most versatile and diverse devices in the PC market. As a result, it can be extremely difficult and time-consuming to install and configure a modem properly. While installation problems almost never damage a new modem, they can seriously degrade the modem's performance (if the modem works at all). The most common problems with new installations are outlined below.

■ *Incorrect hardware resources.* An internal modem must be set with a unique IRQ line and I/O port. If the assigned resources are also used by another serial device in the system (such as a mouse), the modem or the conflicting device (or perhaps both) will not function properly. Remove the modem and use a diagnostic to check available resources. Reconfigure the internal modem to clear the conflict. External modems make use of existing COM ports, so the COM port must be configured with the proper IRQ.

■ *Defective telecommunication resources.* All modems need access to a telephone line in order to establish connections with other modems. If the telephone jack is defective or hooked up improperly, the modem may work fine, but no connection is possible. Remove the telephone line cord from the modem and try the line cord on an ordinary telephone. When you lift the receiver, you should draw a dial tone. Try dialing a local number—if the line rings, chances are good that the telephone line is working. Check the RJ11 jack on the modem. One or more bent connector pins can break the line even though the line cord is inserted properly. If the modem displays "partial" behavior (e.g., the fax features work but the modem features do not), the two telephone wires may be reversed at the jack—try reversing the red and green wires.

■ *Improper cabling.* An external modem must be connected to the PC serial port with a cable. Traditional serial cables were 25-pin assemblies. Later, 9-pin serial connectors and cables became common. Of those 9 wires, only three are really vital. As a result, quite a few cable assemblies may be incorrect or otherwise specialized.

Make sure that the serial cable between the PC and the modem is a "straight-through" type cable. Also check to see that both ends of the cable are intact (installed evenly, no bent pins, and so on). Try a new cable if necessary.

■ *Improper power.* External modems must receive power from batteries or from an ac eliminator. Make sure that any batteries are fresh and installed completely. If an ac adapter is used, see that it is connected to the modem properly.

■ *Incorrect software settings.* Both internal and external modems must be initialized with an AT ASCII command string before a connection is established. If these settings are absent or incorrect, the modem will not respond as expected (if it responds at all). Check the communication software and make sure that the AT command strings are appropriate for the modem being used—different modems often require slightly different command strings.

■ *Suspect the modem itself.* Modems are typically quite reliable in everyday use. If there are jumpers or DIP switches on the modem, check to see that each setting is correct. Perhaps modems' most vulnerable point is the telephone interface, which is particularly susceptible to high-voltage spikes that might enter through the telephone line. If all else fails, try another modem.

Checking the command processor

The *command processor* is the controller which manages the modem's operation in the command mode. It is the command processor which interprets AT command strings. When the new modem installation fails to behave as it should, you should first check the modem command processor using the procedure outlined below. Make sure you have the modem's user guide on hand (if possible). If the command processor checks out, but the modem refuses to work under normal communication software operations, the software may be refusing to save settings such as COM port selection, speed, and character format.

■ *Check the installation.* Make sure the modem is installed properly and connected to the desired PC serial port. If the modem is internal, you should check the IRQ and I/O port settings.

■ *Start your software.* Open your communication software package and select a "direct connection" to establish a path from your keyboard to the modem. A dialog box with a blinking cursor will probably appear. If the modem is working and installed properly, you should now be able to send commands directly to the modem's command processor.

■ *Check the command processor.* Type the command AT and then press the <ENTER> key. The modem should return an "OK" result code. When an "OK" is returned, chances are that the modem is working correctly. If you see double characters being displayed, try using the command ATE0 to disable the command-mode echo. If you do not see an "OK," try issuing an ATE1 command to enable the command-mode echo. If there is still no response, commands are not reaching the modem, or the modem is defective. Check the connections between the modem and the serial port. If the modem is internal, check that it is installed correctly and that all jumpers are placed properly.

■ *Reset the modem.*   Try resetting the modem with the ATZ command and the <ENTER> key. This should reset the modem. If the modem now responds with "OK," you may have to adjust the initialization command string in the communication software.

■ *Try the factory defaults.*   Load factory default settings by typing the command AT&F, then pressing the <ENTER> key. This should restore the factory default values for each S-register. You may also try the command AT&Q0 and <ENTER> to deliberately place the modem into asynchronous mode. You should see "OK" responses to each attempt, which indicate the modem is responding as expected; if you do not, it may be necessary to update the modem's initialization command string. If the modem still does not respond, the communication software may be incompatible, or the modem is defective.

Checking the dialer and telephone line

After you are confident that the modem's command processor is responding properly, you can also check the telephone interface by attempting a call; this also can verify that you have an active telephone line. When the telephone interface checks out, but the modem refuses to work under normal communication software operations, the software may be refusing to save settings such as COM port selection, speed, and character format.

■ *Check the installation.*   Make sure that the modem is installed properly and connected to the desired PC serial port. If the modem is internal, you should check the IRQ and I/O port settings.

■ *Start your software.*   Open your communication software and select a "direct connection" to establish a path from your keyboard to the modem. A dialog box with a blinking cursor will probably appear. If the modem is working and installed properly, you should now be able to send commands directly to the modem.

■ *Check the dialer.*   Dial a number by using the DT (dial using tones) command followed by the full number being called—for example, ATDT15088297683—followed by the <ENTER> key. If your local telephone line supports only rotary dialing, use the modifier R after the D. If you are calling from a PBX, be sure to dial 9 or whatever is the outside-access code. Listen for a dial tone, followed by the tone dialing beeps. You should also hear the destination phone ringing. These sounds confirm that your telephone interface dials correctly, and that the local phone line is responding properly.

- *Check the telephone interface.* If there is no dial tone, check the phone line by dialing with an ordinary phone. Note that some PBX systems must be modified to produce at least 48 volts dc for the modem to work. If there is no dial tone, but the modem attempts to dial, the telephone interface is not grabbing the telephone line correctly (the dialer is working). If the modem draws dial tone, but no digits are generated, the dialer may be defective. In either case, try another modem.

Symptoms

Symptom 1: *The modem appears to be functioning properly, but you cannot see what you are typing.* The modem is not configured properly, or is operating in half-duplex mode.

- *Switch to full-duplex mode.* Full-duplex systems "receive" what they transmit, echoing the data back to the sender. Since half-duplex systems do not echo, what is being sent is typically not shown on the screen. Most terminal programs have an option to enable LOCAL ECHO so that what is transmitted is also displayed. You can often enable the modem's local echo by typing the ATE1 command during a direct connection or adding the E1 entry to the modem's initialization string. When local echo is not an option, switching to full duplex will often do the same thing.

Symptom 2: *The modem appears to be functioning properly, but you see double characters print while typing.* The full-duplex modem is probably operating in local echo mode.

- *Disable local echo.* Full-duplex modem connections usually produce an echo. If local echo is enabled also, you will see what you are transmitting. But that character will also be echoed, creating a double display—when you hit "A," you'll see "AA." Double-letter problems are usually solved by turning off local echo by using the ATE0 command during direct connection or adding the E0 command to the modem's initialization string.

Symptom 3: *The modem will not answer at the customer's site, but it works fine in the shop.* This type of symptom is often due to user error, but it may also be the result of excessive line load.

- *Check the installation.* Make sure that the modem is installed properly into its expansion bus (internal modems), that any cabling is connected securely (external modems), and that the modem is powered properly (external modems). Something may be loose.
- *Check the auto-answer mode.* Make sure that the customer is starting any communication software properly before an incoming call, and that the modem is in the auto-answer mode.
- *Check the ringer equivalence.* If there are too many devices attached to the customer's phone line, there may not be enough

TABLE 5.16   POST Codes for AMI BIOS (Prior to April 1990)

Hex code	Description
01	NMI is disabled and the i286 register test is about to start
02	i286 register test has passed
03	ROM BIOS checksum test (32 kbytes from F8000h) passed OK
04	8259 PIC has initialized OK
05	CMOS interrupt disabled
06	Video system disabled and the system timer checks OK
07	8253/4 programmable interval timer test OK
08	Delta counter channel 2 OK
09	Delta counter channel 1 OK
0A	Delta counter channel 0 OK
0B	Parity status cleared
0C	The refresh and system timer check OK
0D	Refresh check OK
0E	Refresh period checks OK
10	Ready to start 64 kbytes base memory test
11	Address line test OK
12	64 kbytes base memory test OK
13	System interrupt vectors initialized
14	8042 keyboard controller checks OK
15	CMOS read/write test OK
16	CMOS checksum and battery OK
17	Monochrome video mode OK
18	CGA color mode set OK
19	Attempting to pass control to video ROM at C0000h
1A	Returned from video ROM
1B	Display memory R/W test OK
1C	Display memory R/W alternative test OK
1D	Video retrace test OK
1E	Global equipment byte set for proper video operation
1F	Ready to initialize video system
20	Video test OK
21	Video display OK
22	The power-on message is displayed
30	Ready to start the virtual-mode memory test
31	Virtual-mode memory test started
32	CPU has switched to virtual mode
33	Testing the memory address lines
34	Testing the memory address lines
35	Lower 1 Mbyte of RAM found
36	Memory size computation checks OK
37	Memory test in progress
38	Memory below 1 Mbyte is initialized
39	Memory above 1 Mbyte is initialized
3A	Memory size is displayed
3B	Ready to test the lower 1 Mbyte of RAM

TABLE 5.16 **POST Codes for AMI BIOS (Prior to April 1990)** (*Continued*)

Hex code	Description
3C	Memory test of lower 1 Mbyte OK
3D	Memory test above 1 Mbyte OK
3E	Ready to shut down for real-mode testing
3F	Shutdown OK—now in real mode
40	Ready to disable gate A20
41	A20 line disabled successfully
42	Ready to start DMA controller test
4E	Address line test OK
4F	System still in real mode
50	DMA page register test OK
51	Starting DMA controller 1 register test
52	DMA controller 1 test passed; starting DMA controller 2 register test
53	DMA controller 2 test passed
54	Ready to test latch on DMA controllers 1 and 2
55	DMA controllers 1 and 2 latch test OK
56	DMA controllers 1 and 2 configured OK
57	8259 PIC initialized OK
58	8259 PIC mask register check OK
59	Master 8259 PIC mask register OK
5A	Ready to check timer interrupts
5B	Timer interrupt check OK
5C	Ready to test keyboard interrupt
5D	Error detected in timer or keyboard interrupt
5E	8259 PIC controller error
5F	8259 PIC controller OK
70	Start of keyboard test
71	Keyboard controller OK
72	Keyboard test OK
73	Keyboard global initialization OK
74	Floppy setup ready to start
75	Floppy controller setup OK
76	Hard disk setup ready to start
77	Hard disk controller setup OK
79	Ready to initialize timer data
7A	Verifying CMOS battery power
7B	CMOS battery verified OK
7D	Analyzing CMOS RAM size
7E	CMOS memory size updated
7F	Send control to adapter ROM
80	Enable the SETUP routine if <Delete> is pressed
81	Return from adapter ROM
82	Printer data initialization is OK
83	RS-232 data initialization is OK

TABLE 5.16   POST Codes for AMI BIOS (Prior to April 1990)
(*Continued*)

Hex code	Description
84	80×87 check and test OK
85	Display any soft-error message
86	Give control to ROM at E0000h
87	Return from system ROM
00	Call the Int. 19 boot loader

TABLE 5.17   POST Codes for AMI BIOS (after April 1990)

Hex code	Description
01	NMI is disabled and the i286 register test is about to start
02	i286 register test has passed
03	ROM BIOS checksum test (32 kbytes from F8000h) passed OK
04	Passed keyboard controller test with and without mouse
05	Chipset initialized; DMA and interrupt controller disabled
06	Video system disabled and system timer checks OK
07	8254 programmable interval timer initialized
08	Delta counter channel 2 initialization complete
09	Delta counter channel 1 initialization complete
0A	Delta counter channel 0 initialization complete
0B	Refresh started
0C	System timer started
0D	Refresh check OK
10	Ready to start 64 kbytes base memory test
11	Address line test OK
12	64 kbytes base memory test OK
15	ISA BIOS interrupt vectors initialized
17	Monochrome video mode OK
18	CGA color mode set OK
19	Attempting to pass control to video ROM at C0000h
1A	Returned from video ROM
1B	Shadow RAM enabled
1C	Display memory R/W test OK
1D	Alternative display memory R/W test OK
1E	Global equipment byte set for proper video operation
1F	Ready to initialize video system
20	Finished setting video mode
21	ROM type 27256 verified
22	The power-on message is displayed
30	Ready to start the virtual-mode memory test
31	Virtual-mode memory test started
32	CPU has switched to virtual mode

TABLE 5.17   POST Codes for AMI BIOS (after April 1990)
(*Continued*)

Hex code	Description
33	Testing the memory address lines
34	Testing the memory address lines
35	Lower 1 Mbyte of RAM found
36	Memory size computation checks OK
37	Memory test in progress
38	Memory below 1 Mbyte is initialized
39	Memory above 1 Mbyte is initialized
3A	Memory size is displayed
3B	Ready to test the lower 1 Mbyte of RAM
3C	Memory test of lower 1 Mbyte OK
3D	Memory test above 1 Mbyte OK
3E	Ready to shut down for real-mode testing
3F	Shutdown OK—now in real mode
40	Cache memory now on; ready to disable gate A20
41	A20 line disabled successfully
42	i486 internal cache turned on
43	Ready to start DMA controller test
50	DMA page register test OK
51	Starting DMA controller 1 register test
52	DMA controller 1 test passed; starting DMA controller 2 register test
53	DMA controller 2 test passed
54	Ready to test latch on DMA controller 1 and 2
55	DMA controller 1 and 2 latch test OK
56	DMA controller 1 and 2 configured OK
57	8259 PIC initialized OK
70	Start of keyboard test
71	Keyboard controller OK
72	Keyboard test OK; starting mouse interface test
73	Keyboard and mouse global initialization OK
74	Display SETUP prompt; floppy setup ready to start
75	Floppy controller setup OK
76	Hard disk setup ready to start
77	Hard disk controller setup OK
79	Ready to initialize timer data
7A	Timer data area initialized
7B	CMOS battery verified OK
7D	Analyzing CMOS RAM size
7E	CMOS memory size updated
7F	Enable SETUP routine if <Delete> is pressed

TABLE 5.17   POST Codes for AMI BIOS (after April 1990) (Continued)

Hex code	Description
80	Send control to adapter ROM at C800h to DE00h
81	Return from adapter ROM
82	Printer data initialization is OK
83	RS-232 data initialization is OK
84	80 × 87 check and test OK
85	Display any soft-error message
86	Give control to ROM at E0000h
A0	Program the cache SRAM
A1	Check for external cache
A2	Initialize EISA adapter card slots
A3	Test extended NMI in EISA system
00	Call the Int. 19 boot loader

TABLE 5.18   POST Codes for AMI BIOS Version 2.2x

Hex code	Description
00	Flag test (the CPU is being tested)
03	Register test
06	System hardware initialization
09	Test BIOS ROM checksum
0C	Page register test
0F	8254 timer test
12	Memory refresh initialization
15	8237 DMA controller test
18	8237 DMA controller initialization
1B	8259 PIC initialization
1E	8259 PIC test
21	Memory refresh test
24	Base 64 kbytes address test
27	Base 64 kbytes memory test
2A	8742 keyboard test
2D	MC146818 CMOS IC test
30	Start the protected-mode test
33	Start the memory sizing test

TABLE 5.18 **POST Codes for AMI BIOS Version 2.2x** (*Continued*)

Hex code	Description
36	First protected-mode test passed
39	First protected-mode test failed
3C	CPU speed calculation
3F	Reading the 8742 hardware switches
42	Initializing the interrupt vector area
45	Verifying the CMOS configuration
48	Testing and initializing the video system
4B	Testing unexpected interrupts
4E	Starting second protected-mode test
51	Verifying the LDT instruction
54	Verifying the TR instruction
57	Verifying the LSL instruction
5A	Verifying the LAR instruction
5D	Verifying the VERR instruction
60	Address line A20 test
63	Testing unexpected exceptions
66	Starting the third protected-mode test
69	Address line test
6A	Scan DDNIL bits for null pattern
6C	System memory test
6F	Shadow memory test
72	Extended memory test
75	Verify the memory configuration
78	Display configuration error messages
7B	Copy system BIOS to shadow memory
7E	8254 clock test
81	MC46818 real-time clock test
84	Keyboard test
87	Determining the keyboard type
8A	Stuck key test
8D	Initializing hardware interrupt vectors
90	Testing the math coprocessor
93	Finding available COM ports
96	Finding available LPT ports
99	Initializing the BIOS data area
9C	Fixed/floppy disk controller test
9F	Floppy disk test
A2	Fixed disk test
A5	Check for external ROMs
A8	System key lock test
AE	F1 error message test
AE	System boot initialization
B1	Call Int. 19 boot loader

TABLE 5.19   POST Codes for AMI Plus BIOS

Hex code	Description
01	NMI disabled
02	CPU register test complete
03	ROM checksum tests OK
04	8259 PIC initialization OK
05	CMOS interrupt disabled
06	System timer (PIT) OK
07	PIC channel 0 test OK
08	Delta count channel (DMA) 2 test OK
09	Delta count channel (DMA) 1 test OK
0A	Delta count channel (DMA) 0 test OK
0B	Parity status cleared (DMA/PIT)
0C	Refresh and system time check OK (DMA/PIT)
0D	Refresh link toggling OK (DMA/PIT)
0E	Refresh period on/off 50% OK (RAM IC or address line)
10	Ready to start 64 kbytes base memory test
11	Address line test OK
12	64 kbytes base memory test OK
13	Interrupt vectors initialized
14	8042 keyboard controller test
15	CMOS read/write test OK
16	CMOS checksum and battery test
17	Monochrome mode set OK (6845 IC)
18	CGA mode set OK (6845 IC)
19	Checking video ROM
1A	Optional video ROM checks OK
1B	Display memory R/W test OK
1C	Alternative display memory checks OK
1D	Video retrace check OK
1E	Global byte set for video OK (video adapter)
1F	Mode set for mono/color OK (video adapter)
20	Video test OK
21	Video display OK
22	Power-on message display OK
30	Ready for virtual-mode memory test
31	Starting virtual-mode memory test
32	CPU now in virtual mode
33	Memory address line test
34	Memory address line test
35	Memory below 1 Mbyte calculated
36	Memory size computation OK
37	Memory test in progress
38	Memory initialization below 1 Mbyte complete
39	Memory initialization above 1 Mbyte complete
3A	Display memory size
3B	Ready to start memory below 1 Mbyte
3C	Memory test below 1 Mbyte OK

TABLE 5.19   POST Codes for AMI Plus BIOS (*Continued*)

Hex code	Description
3D	Memory test above 1 Mbyte OK
3E	Ready to switch to real mode
3F	Shutdown successful
40	Ready to disable A20 gate (8042 IC)
41	A20 gate disabled (8042 IC)
42	Ready to test DMA controller (8237 DMA IC)
4E	Address line test OK
4F	CPU now in real mode
50	DMA page register test OK
51	DMA unit 1 base register OK
52	DMA unit 1 channel OK
53	DMA unit 2 base register OK
54	DMA unit 2 channel OK
55	Latch test for both DMA units OK
56	DMA units 1 and 2 initialized OK
57	8259 PIC initialization complete
58	8259 PIC mask register OK
59	Master 8259 PIC mask register OK
5A	Check timer and keyboard interrupt
5B	PIT timer interrupt OK
5C	Ready to test keyboard interrupt
5D	Error—timer/keyboard interrupt
5E	8259 PIC error
5F	8259 PIC test OK
70	Start the keyboard test
71	Keyboard test OK
72	Keyboard test OK
73	Keyboard global data initialized (8042 IC)
74	Ready to start floppy controller setup
75	Floppy controller setup OK
76	Ready to start hard drive controller setup
77	Hard drive controller setup OK
79	Ready to initialize timer data
7A	Verifying CMOS battery power
7B	CMOS battery verification complete
7D	Analyze test results for memory
7E	CMOS memory size update OK
7F	Check for optional ROM at C0000h
80	Keyboard checked for SETUP keystroke
81	Optional ROM control OK
82	Printer ports initialized OK
83	Serial ports initialized OK
84	80×87 test OK
85	Ready to display any soft errors
86	Send control to system ROM E0000h
87	System ROM E0000h check complete
00	Call Int. 19 boot loader

TABLE 5.20   POST Codes for AMI Color BIOS

Hex code	Description
01	CPU flag test
02	Power-on delay
03	Chipset initialization
04	Hard/soft reset
05	ROM enable
06	ROM BIOS checksum
07	8042 KBC test
08	8042 KBC test
09	8042 KBC test
0A	8042 KBC test
0B	8042 protected-mode test
0C	8042 KBC test
0D	8042 KBC test
0E	CMOS checksum test
0F	CMOS initialization
10	CMOS/RTC status OK
11	DMA/PIC disable
12	DMA/PIC initialization
13	Chipset and memory initialization
14	8254 PIT test
15	PIT channel 2 test
16	PIT channel 1 test
17	PIT channel 0 test
18	Memory refresh test (PIT IC)
19	Memory refresh test (PIT IC)
1A	Check 15-μs refresh (PIT IC)
1B	Check 30-μs refresh (PIT IC)
20	Base 64 kbytes memory test
21	Base 64 kbytes memory parity test
22	Memory read/write test
23	BIOS vector table initialization
24	BIOS vector table initialization
25	Check of 8042 KBC
26	Global data for KBC set
27	Video mode test
28	Monochrome mode test
29	CGA mode test
2A	Parity enable test
2B	Check for optional ROMs in the system
2C	Check video ROM
2D	Reinitialize the main chipset
2E	Test video memory
2F	Test video memory
30	Test video adapter
31	Test alternative video memory

TABLE 5.20   POST Codes for AMI Color BIOS
(*Continued*)

Hex code	Description
32	Test alternative video adapter
33	Video mode test
34	Video mode set
35	Initialize the BIOS ROM data area
36	Power-on message display
37	Power-on message display
38	Read cursor position
39	Display cursor reference
3A	Display SETUP start message
40	Start protected-mode test
41	Build descriptor tables
42	CPU enters protected mode
43	Protected-mode interrupt enable
44	Check descriptor tables
45	Check memory size
46	Memory read/write test
47	Base 640 kbytes memory test
48	Check 640 kbytes memory size
49	Check extended memory size
4A	Verify CMOS extended memory
4B	Check for soft/hard reset
4C	Clear extended memory locations
4D	Update CMOS memory size
4E	Display base RAM size
4F	Perform memory test on base 640 kbytes
50	Update CMOS RAM size
51	Perform extended memory test
52	Resize extended memory
53	Return CPU to real mode
54	Restore CPU registers for real mode
55	Disable the A20 gate
56	Recheck the BIOS vectors
57	BIOS vector check complete
58	Display the SETUP start message
59	Perform DMA and PIT test
60	Perform DMA page register test
61	Perform DMA 1 test
62	Perform DMA 2 test
63	Check BIOS data area
64	BIOS data area checked
65	Initialize DMA ICs
66	Perform 8259 PIC initialization
67	Perform keyboard test
80	Keyboard reset

TABLE 5.20   POST Codes for AMI Color BIOS
(*Continued*)

Hex code	Description
81	Perform stuck key and batch test (keyboard)
82	Run 8042 KBC test
83	Perform lock key check
84	Compare memory size with CMOS
85	Perform password/soft-error check
86	Run CMOS equipment check
87	CMOS setup test
88	Reinitialize the main chipset
89	Display the power-on message
8A	Display the wait and mouse check
8B	Attempt to shadow any option ROMs
8C	Initialize XCMOS settings
8D	Reset hard/floppy disks
8E	Compare floppy setup to CMOS
8F	Initialize the floppy disk controller
90	Compare hard disk setup to CMOS
91	Initialize the hard disk controller
92	Check the BIOS data table
93	BIOS data table check complete
94	Set memory size
95	Verify the display memory
96	Clear all interrupts
97	Check any optional ROMs
98	Clear all interrupts
99	Set up timer data
9A	Locate and check serial ports
9B	Clear all interrupts
9C	Perform the math coprocessor test
9D	Clear all interrupts
9E	Perform an extended keyboard check
9F	Set the NumLock on the keyboard
A0	Keyboard reset
A1	Cache memory test
A2	Display any soft errors
A3	Set typematic rate
A4	Set memory wait states
A5	Clear the display
A6	Enable parity and NMI
A7	Clear all interrupts
A8	Turn over system control to the ROM at E0000
A9	Clear all interrupts
AA	Display configuration
00	Call Int. 19 boot loader

TABLE 5.21   POST Codes for AMI EZ-Flex BIOS

Hex code	Description
01	NMI disabled—starting CPU flag test
02	Power-on delay
03	Chipset initialization
04	Check keyboard for hard/soft reset
05	ROM enable
06	ROM BIOS checksum
07	8042 KBC test
08	8042 KBC test
09	8042 KBC test
0A	8042 KBC test
0B	8042 protected-mode test
0C	8042 KBC test
0D	Test CMOS RAM shutdown register
0E	CMOS checksum test
0F	CMOS initialization
10	CMOS/RTC status OK
11	DMA/PIC disable
12	Disable video display
13	Chipset and memory initialization
14	8254 PIT test
15	PIT channel 2 test
16	PIT channel 1 test
17	PIT channel 0 test
18	Memory refresh test (PIT IC)
19	Memory refresh test (PIT IC)
1A	Check 15-μs refresh (PIT IC)
1B	Test 64 kbytes base memory
20	Test address lines
21	Base 64 kbytes memory parity test
22	Memory read/write test
23	Perform any setups needed prior to vector table initialization
24	BIOS vector table initialization in lower 1 kbyte of system RAM
25	Check of 8042 KBC
26	Global data for KBC set
27	Perform any setups needed after vector table initialization
28	Monochrome mode test
29	CGA mode test
2A	Parity enable test
2B	Check for optional ROMs in the system
2C	Check video ROM
2D	Determine if EGA/VGA is installed
2E	Test video memory (EGA/VGA not installed)

TABLE 5.21   POST Codes for AMI EZ-Flex BIOS (*Continued*)

Hex code	Description
2F	Test video memory
30	Test video adapter
31	Test alternative video memory
32	Test alternative video adapter
33	Video mode test
34	Video mode set
35	Initialize the BIOS ROM data area
36	Set cursor for power-on message display
37	Display power-on message
38	Read cursor position
39	Display cursor reference
3A	Display SETUP start message
40	Start protected-mode test
41	Build descriptor tables
42	CPU enters protected mode
43	Protected-mode interrupt enable
44	Check descriptor tables
45	Check memory size
46	Memory read/write test
47	Base 640 kbytes memory test
48	Find amount of memory below 1 Mbyte
49	Find amount of memory above 1 Mbyte
4A	Check ROM BIOS data area
4B	Clear memory below 1 Mbyte for soft reset
4C	Clear memory above 1 Mbyte for soft reset
4D	Update CMOS memory size
4E	Display base 64 kbytes memory test
4F	Perform memory test on base 640 kbytes
50	Update RAM size for shadow operation
51	Perform extended memory test
52	Ready to return to real mode
53	Return CPU to real mode
54	Restore CPU registers for real mode
55	Disable the A20 gate
56	Recheck the BIOS data area
57	BIOS data area check complete
58	Display the SETUP start message
59	Perform DMA page register test
60	Verify display memory
61	Perform DMA 1 test
62	Perform DMA 2 test
63	Check BIOS data area
64	BIOS data area checked
65	Initialize DMA ICs

TABLE 5.21   **POST Codes for AMI EZ-Flex BIOS (*Continued*)**

Hex code	Description
66	Perform 8259 PIC initialization
67	Perform keyboard test
80	Keyboard reset
81	Perform stuck key and batch test (keyboard)
82	Run 8042 KBC test
83	Perform lock key check
84	Compare memory size with CMOS
85	Perform password/soft-error check
86	Run CMOS equipment check
87	Run CMOS setup if selected
88	Reinitialize the main chipset after setup
89	Display the power-on message
8A	Display the wait and mouse check
8B	Attempt to shadow any option ROMs
8C	Initialize system per CMOS settings
8D	Reset hard/floppy disks
8E	Compare floppy setup to CMOS
8F	Initialize the floppy disk controller
90	Compare hard disk setup to CMOS
91	Initialize the hard disk controller
92	Check the BIOS data table
93	BIOS data table check complete
94	Set memory size
95	Verify the display memory
96	Clear all interrupts
97	Check any optional ROMs
98	Clear all interrupts
99	Set up timer data
9A	Locate and check serial ports
9B	Clear all interrupts
9C	Perform the math coprocessor test
9D	Clear all interrupts
9E	Perform an extended keyboard check
9F	Set the NumLock on the keyboard
A0	Keyboard reset
A1	Cache memory test
A2	Display any soft errors
A3	Set typematic rate
A4	Set memory wait states
A5	Clear the display
A6	Enable parity and NMI
A7	Clear all interrupts
A8	Turn over system control to the ROM at E0000
A9	Clear all interrupts
AA	Display configuration
00	Call Int. 19 boot loader

Arche Legacy

The Arche Technologies Legacy BIOS is a close cousin of AMI products, although there are a significant number of different POST codes near the end of the diagnostic process. If the POST code is displayed, the corresponding test did *not* execute properly. All codes are written to port 80h. Table 5.22 lists the known POST codes for the Arche Legacy BIOS.

TABLE 5.22   POST Codes for Arche Legacy BIOS

Hex code	Description
01	Disable the NMI and test CPU registers
02	Verify the BIOS ROM checksum (32 kbytes at F8000h)
03	Initialize the KBC and CMOS RAM
04	Disable the DMA and PIC; test the CMOS RAM interrupt
05	Reset the video controller
06	Test the 8254 PIT
07	Test delta count timer channel 2
08	Test delta count timer channel 1
09	Test delta count timer channel 0
0A	Test parity circuit and turn on refresh
0B	Enable parity check and test system timer
0C	Test refresh trace link toggle
0D	Test refresh timing synchronization
10	Disable cache and shadow memory; test the 64 kbytes base memory
11	Perform 64 kbytes memory R/W test
12	Initialize interrupt vector table in lower 1 kbyte of RAM
14	Test CMOS RAM shutdown register; disable DMA and interrupt controllers
15	Test CMOS RAM battery and checksum
16	Test for floppy drive based on CMOS setup; initialize monochrome video
17	Initialize CGA video
18	Clear the parity status (if any)
19	Test for EGA/VGA video BIOS at C0000h and pass control
1A	Return from video ROM
1B	Test primary video adapter; test video memory
1C	Test secondary video adapter; test video memory
1D	Compare CMOS settings to video adapter
1E	Set video mode according to CMOS settings
20	Display CMOS RAM R/W errors and halt
21	Set cursor and call Int. 10 to display status message
22	Display power-on message
23	Read new cursor position
24	Display AMI copyright message at the bottom of the screen
25	Test shadow RAM

TABLE 5.22   **POST Codes for Arche Legacy BIOS (*Continued*)**

Hex code	Description
F0	Shadow RAM test failed
30	Ready to enter protected mode
31	Enter protected mode (A20 gate) and enable timer interrupt (IRQ0)
32	Get memory size above 1 Mbyte
33	Get memory size below 640 kbytes
34	Test memory above 1 Mbyte
35	Test memory below 1 Mbyte
37	Clear memory below 1 Mbyte
38	Clear memory above 1 Mbtye
39	Use CMOS shutdown byte and return to real mode
3A	Test 64 kbytes R/W
3B	Test RAM below 1 Mbyte and show the area being tested
3C	Test RAM above 1 Mbyte and show the area being tested
3D	RAM test completed OK
3E	Ready to return to real mode
3F	Back in real mode
40	Disable A20 gate
41	Check for AMI copyright message in ROM
42	Display the AMI copyright message if found
43	Test cache memory
4E	Process shutdown 1
4F	Restore interrupt vectors and data in BIOS RAM area
50	Test DMA controller
51	Initialize DMA controller
52	Test DMA controller with patterns
54	Test DMA controller latches
55	Initialize and enable DMA controllers 1 and 2
56	Initialize 8259 PICs
57	Test 8259 PICs and set up interrupt mask registers
61	Check DDNIL status bit and display message
70	Perform keyboard basic assurance test
71	Program keyboard to AT type
72	Disable keyboard and initialize keyboard circular buffer
73	Display message and initialize floppy controller and drive
74	Attempt to access the floppy drive
75	If CMOS RAM good, check and initialize hard disk controller and drive
76	Attempt to access the hard disk drive
77	Shuffle any internal error codes
79	Check CMOS RAM battery and checksum; clear parity status
7A	Compare size of base/extended memory to CMOS info
7C	Display AMI copyright
7D	Set AT memory expansion bit

TABLE 5.22   POST Codes for Arche Legacy BIOS (*Continued*)

Hex code	Description
7E	Verify that the ROM contains an AMI copyright
7F	Clear the <Del> message from the display; check if <Del> was pressed
80	Locate option ROM at C800h to DE00h and pass control to any found
81	Return from option ROM and initialize timer and data area
82	Set up parallel and serial ports
83	Test for math coprocessor
84	Check if keyboard locked
85	Display any soft error messages
86	Test for option ROM at E0000h
A0	Error found in 256-kbyte or 1-Mbyte RAM IC in lower 640 kbytes
A1	Base 64 kbytes random access and data pattern test
A9	Initialize on-board VGA controller
B0	Error in 256-kbyte RAM IC in lower 640 kbytes
B1	Base 64 kbytes random access and data pattern test
E0	Return to real mode and initialize base 64 kbytes RAM
E1	Initialize 640 kbytes RAM
EF	Configuration memory error—can't find memory
F0	Test shadow RAM from 04000h
00	Call the Int. 19 boot loader

AST

With the exception of two major i286-based machines, which employ a Phoenix-based BIOS, most AST systems are fitted with an Award-based BIOS version. All codes are written to port 80h and port 1080h. An interesting characteristic of the AST BIOS is that errors below 20h will be accompanied by a corresponding long-short beep sequence. For example, the code 13h will issue one long beep and three short beeps. Errors below 20h will invariably halt the system, while errors of 20h and higher will not halt the system. Table 5.23 lists the AST POST codes.

AT&T BIOS

AT&T made a short and unsuccessful effort to compete in the PC industry. The POST codes used for its BIOS are listed in Table 5.24.

Award family

The Award family includes a broad range of products that cover XT and AT systems. For the most part, Award products use standard IBM beep codes, and post codes are written to ports 80h and 300h.

TABLE 5.23   **POST Codes for AST BIOS**

Hex code	Description
01	Test CPU registers
02	Test the 8042 KBC buffer
03	Test the 8042 KBC reset
04	Verify presence of keyboard and check communication
05	Read keyboard input port
06	Initialize system board support chipset
09	Test BIOS ROM checksum
0D	Test 8254 PIT registers
0E	Test ASIC registers
0F	Test CMOS RAM shutdown byte
10	Test DMA controller 0 registers
11	Test DMA controller 1 registers
12	Test DMA page registers (EGA/VGA vertical retrace failed)
13	EGA/VGA RAM test failed
14	Test memory refresh toggle (EGA/VGA CRT registers failed)
15	Test base 64 kbytes memory
16	Set interrupt vectors in base memory
17	Initialize video
18	Test display memory
20	EISA bus board power on
30	Test PIC 1 mask register
31	Test PIC 2 mask register
32	Test PICs for stuck interrupts
33	Test for stuck NMI
34	Test for stuck DDINIL status
40	Test CMOS RAM backup battery
41	Calculate and verify CMOS checksum
42	Set up CMOS RAM options
50	Test the protected mode
51	Test protected-mode exceptions
60	Calculate RAM size
61	Test RAM
62	Test shadow RAM
63	Test cache memory
64	Copy system BIOS to shadow RAM
65	Copy video BIOS to shadow RAM
66	Test 8254 PIT channel 2
67	Initialize memory

TABLE 5.24   AT&T BIOS

Hex code	Description
01	CPU test
02	System I/O port test
03	ROM checksum test
05	DMA page register test
06	Timer 1 test
07	Timer 2 test
08	RAM refresh test
09	8/19-bit bus conversion check
0A	Interrupt controller 1 test
0B	Interrupt controller 2 test
0C	Keyboard controller test
0D	CMOS RAM/RTC test
0E	Battery power lost
0F	CMOS RAM checksum test
10	CPU protected-mode test
11	Display configuration test
12	Display controller test
13	Primary display error
14	Extended CMOS test
15	AT bus reset
16	Initialize chipset registers
17	Check for extension ROMs
18	Internal memory address test
19	Remap memory
1A	Memory interleave mode test
1B	Remap shadow memory
1C	Set up MRAM
1D	Expanded memory test
1E	AT memory error
1F	Internal memory error
20	Minimum POST tests complete
21	DMA controller 1 test
22	DMA controller 2 test
23	Timer 0 test
24	Initialize internal controllers
25	Unexpected interrupt
26	Expected interrupt
30	Switch to protected mode
31	Size AT bus memory or size external memory
32	Address lines A16 to A23 test
33	Internal memory test or conventional memory test
34	AT bus memory test or external memory test
38	Shadow ROM BIOS to RAM
39	Shadow extension BIOS to RAM

TABLE 5.24 AT&T BIOS (*Continued*)

Hex code	Description
40	Enable/disable keyboard
41	Keyboard clock and data test
42	Keyboard reset
43	Keyboard controller test
44	A20 gate test
50	Initialize interrupt table
51	Enable timer interrupt
60	Floppy controller/drive test
61	Hard disk controller test
62	Initialize floppy drives
63	Initialize hard drives
70	Real-time clock (RTC) test
71	Set real-time clock
72	Test parallel interfaces
73	Test serial interfaces
74	Check external ROMs
75	Numeric coprocessor test
76	Enable keyboard and RTC interrupts (IRQ9)
F0	Display system startup message
F1	Check for ROM at E000H
F2	Boot from floppy or hard disk
F3	Run setup program
F4	Run password program
FC	DRAM type detection
FD	CPU register test

Table 5.25 outlines the Award XT BIOS. A later XT BIOS (version 3.1) is covered in Table 5.26. Tables 5.27, 5.28, and 5.29 give the Award POST codes for three versions of AT BIOS (3.0, 3.1, and 3.3, respectively). Table 5.30 provides a listing of codes for an AT/EISA version of BIOS (4.0), while Table 5.31 presents the codes for an Award EISA BIOS. Table 5.32 lists the more recent Award PnP BIOS, and Table 5.33 shows the new Award BIOS 4.5.

Chips & Technologies

Chips & Technologies produces a single version of its BIOS which supports its NEAT, PEAK, 8291, and ELEAT chipsets. The BIOS covers both AT- and PS/2-compatible systems. While codes are passed to port 80h, some of the codes are also passed to the video system as decimal codes. Table 5.34 shows the C&T POST codes.

Compaq family

Compaq has largely gone its own way in the development of POST codes. The immediate difference for technicians is that POST codes

TABLE 5.25   POST Codes for Award XT BIOS

Hex code	Description
03	Test CPU flag registers
06	Test CPU registers
09	System chipset initialization
0C	Test BIOS checksum
0F	DMA page register initialization
12	Test DMA address and count registers
15	DMA initialization
18	8253 PIT test
1B	8253 PIT initialization
1E	Start RAM refresh
21	Test base 64 kbytes RAM
24	Set up interrupt vectors and stack
27	Initialize the 8259 PIC
2A	Test PIT interrupt mask register
2D	Test PIC hot interrupt test
30	Run V40 DMA test if present
33	Initialize the system clock
36	Run the keyboard test
39	Set up interrupt vector table
3C	Read system configuration switches
3F	Run video test
42	Locate and initialize serial ports
45	Locate and initialize parallel ports
48	Locate game port
4B	Display copyright message
4E	Calculation of CPU speed
54	Test of system memory
55	Test floppy drive
57	Finish system initialization before boot
5A	Call Int. 19 boot loader

TABLE 5.26   POST Codes for Award XT BIOS Version 3.1

Hex code	Description
01	Test CPU flag registers
02	Determine type of POST and check keyboard buffer
06	Initialize the PIT, PIC, DMA, and 6845
07	Check processor registers
09	ROM checksum
0A	Initialize the video system
15	Test the first 64 kbytes RAM
16	Set up interrupt tables
17	Set up video system
18	Test video memory
19	Test 8259 PIC mask bits channel 1
1A	Test 8259 PIC mask bits channel 2
1E	Check memory size
1F	Test base memory above 64 kbytes
20	Test stuck interrupts
21	Test stuck NMI
22	Initialize the floppy drive controller
2C	Locate and initialize COM ports
2D	Locate and initialize LPT ports
2F	Initialize the math coprocessor
31	Locate and initialize option ROMs
FF	Call the Int. 19 boot loader

TABLE 5.27   POST Codes for Award AT BIOS Version 3.0

Hex code	Description
01	Test CPU flag registers
02	Power-up check—initialize motherboard chipset
03	Clear the 8042 KBC
04	Reset the 8042 KBC
05	Test the keyboard
06	Disable video system, parity, and DMA controller
07	Test CPU registers
08	Initialize CMOS/RTC IC
09	Perform BIOS ROM checksum
0A	Initialize the video interface
0B	Test the 8254 timer channel 0
0C	Test the 8254 timer channel 1
0D	Test the 8254 timer channel 2
0E	Test CMOS RAM shutdown byte
0F	Test extended CMOS RAM (if present)
10	Test the 8237 DMA controller channel 0
11	Test the 8237 DMA controller channel 1

TABLE 5.27   POST Codes for Award AT BIOS Version 3.0 (*Continued*)

Hex code	Description
12	Test the 8237 DMA controller page registers
13	Test the 8741 KBC interface
14	Test the memory refresh and toggle circuits
15	Test the first 64 kbytes of system memory
16	Set up the interrupt vector tables in low memory
17	Set up video I/O operations
18	Test MDA/CGA video memory unless an EGA/VGA adapter is found
19	Test the 8259 PIC mask bits channel 1
1A	Test the 8259 PIC mask bits channel 2
1B	Test the CMOS RAM battery level
1C	Test the CMOS RAM checksum
1D	Set system memory size from CMOS information
1E	Check base memory size 64 kbytes at a time
1F	Test base memory from 64 kbytes to 640 kbytes
20	Test stuck interrupt lines
21	Test for stuck NMI
22	Test the 8259 PIC
23	Test the protected mode and A20 gate
24	Check the size of extended memory above 1 Mbyte
25	Test all base and extended memory found up to 16 Mbytes
26	Test protected-mode exceptions
27	Initialize shadow RAM and move system BIOS (and video BIOS) into shadow RAM
28	Detect and initialize 8242 or 8248 IC
2A	Initialize the keyboard
2B	Detect and initialize the floppy drive
2C	Detect and initialize serial ports
2D	Detect and initialize parallel ports
2E	Detect and initialize the hard drive
2F	Detect and initialize the math coprocessor
31	Detect and initialize any adapter ROMs
BD	Initialize the cache controller, if present
CA	Initialize cache memory
CC	Shut down the NMI handler
EE	Test for unexpected processor exception
FF	Call the Int. 19 boot loader

TABLE 5.28 **POST Codes for Award AT BIOS Version 3.1**

Hex code	Description
01	Test CPU flag registers
02	Power-up check—initialize motherboard chipset
03	Clear the 8042 KBC
04	Reset the 8042 KBC
05	Test the keyboard
06	Disable video system, parity, and DMA controller
07	Test CPU registers
08	Initialize CMOS/RTC IC
09	Perform BIOS ROM checksum
0A	Initialize the video interface
0B	Test the 8254 timer channel 0
0C	Test the 8254 timer channel 1
0D	Test the 8254 timer channel 2
0E	Test CMOS RAM shutdown byte
0F	Test extended CMOS RAM (if present)
10	Test the 8237 DMA controller channel 0
11	Test the 8237 DMA controller channel 1
12	Test the 8237 DMA controller page registers
13	Test the 8741 KBC interface
14	Test the memory refresh and toggle circuits
15	Test the first 64 kbytes of system memory
16	Set up the interrupt vector tables in low memory
17	Set up video I/O operations
18	Test MDA/CGA video memory unless an EGA/VGA adapter is found
19	Test the 8259 PIC mask bits channel 1
1A	Test the 8259 PIC mask bits channel 2
1B	Test the CMOS RAM battery level
1C	Test the CMOS RAM checksum
1D	Set system memory size from CMOS information
1E	Check base memory size 64 kbytes at a time
1F	Test base memory
20	Test stuck interrupt lines
21	Test for stuck NMI
22	Test the 8259 PIC
23	Test the protected mode and A20 gate
24	Check the size of extended memory above 1 Mbyte
25	Test all base and extended memory found up to 16 Mbytes
26	Test protected-mode exceptions
27	Initialize shadow RAM and move system BIOS (and video BIOS) into shadow RAM

**TABLE 5.28   POST Codes for Award AT BIOS Version 3.1
(*Continued*)**

Hex code	Description
28	Detect and initialize 8242 or 8248 IC
2A	Initialize the keyboard
2B	Detect and initialize the floppy drive
2C	Detect and initialize serial ports
2D	Detect and initialize parallel ports
2E	Detect and initialize the hard drive
2F	Detect and initialize the math coprocessor
31	Detect and initialize any adapter ROMs at C8000h to EFFFFh (and F0000h to F7FFFh)
39	Initialize the cache controller, if present
3B	Initialize cache memory
CA	Detect and initialize alternative cache controller
CC	Shut down the NMI handler
EE	Test for unexpected processor exception
FF	Call the Int. 19 boot loader

TABLE 5.29   POST Codes for Award AT BIOS Version 3.3

Hex code	Description
01	Test 8042 KBC
02	Test 8042 KBC
03	Test 8042 KBC
04	Test 8042 KBC
05	Test 8042 KBC
06	Initialize any system chipsets
07	Test the CPU flags
08	Calculate the CMOS checksum
09	Initialize the 8254 PIT
0A	Test the 8254 PIT
0B	Test the DMA controller
0C	Initialize the 8259 PIC
0D	Test the 8259 PIC
0E	Test ROM BIOS checksum
0F	Test extended CMOS
10	Test the 8259 PIT IC
11	Test the 8259 PIT IC
12	Test the 8259 PIT IC
13	Test the 8259 PIT IC
14	Test the 8259 PIT IC
15	Test the first 64 kbytes of RAM
16	Initialize the BIOS interrupt vector tables
17	Initialize the video system

TABLE 5.29   POST Codes for Award AT BIOS Version 3.3 (*Continued*)

Hex code	Description
18	Check video memory
19	Test 8259 PIC 1 mask
1A	Test 8259 PIC 2 mask
1B	Check CMOS battery level
1C	Verify the CMOS checksum
1D	Verify the CMOS/RTC IC
1E	Check memory size
1F	Verify memory in the system
20	Initialize DMA ICs
21	Initialize PIC ICs
22	Initialize PIT ICs
24	Check extended memory size
25	Test all extended memory detected
26	Enter the protected mode
27	Initialize the shadow RAM and cache controller
28	Test the shadow RAM and cache controller
2A	Initialize the keyboard
2B	Initialize the floppy drive controller
2C	Check and initialize serial ports
2D	Check and initialize parallel ports
2E	Initialize the hard drive controller
2F	Initialize the math coprocessor
31	Check for any option ROMs in the system
FF	Call the Int. 19 boot loader

TABLE 5.30   POST Codes for Award AT/EISA BIOS Version 4.0

Hex code	Description
01	Test the CPU flags
02	Test the CPU registers
03	Check the BIOS ROM checksum
04	Test the CMOS battery level
05	Initialize all system chipsets
06	Test the memory refresh toggle
07	Set up low memory
08	Set up interrupt vector table
09	Test CMOS RAM checksum
0A	Initialize the keyboard
0B	Initialize the video controller
0C	Test video memory
0D	Initialize any specialized chipsets
0F	Test DMA controller 0
10	Test DMA controller 1
11	Test DMA page registers
14	Test 8254 timer
15	Verify 8259 PIC channel 1
16	Verify 8259 PIC channel 2
17	Test for stuck interrupts
18	Test 8259 functions

TABLE 5.30   **POST Codes for Award AT/EISA BIOS Version 4.0** (*Continued*)

Hex code	Description
19	Test for stuck NMI
1F	Initialize EISA mode (for EISA systems)
20	Initialize and enable EISA slot 0
21–2F	Initialize and enable EISA slots 1 to 15
30	Check base memory size
31	Check extended memory size
32	Test any EISA memory found during slot initialization
3C	Enter protected mode
3D	Detect and initialize mouse
3E	Initialize the cache controller
3F	Enable and test shadow RAM
41	Initialize floppy disk drive controller
42	Initialize hard disk drive controller
43	Detect and initialize serial ports
44	Detect and initialize parallel ports
45	Detect and initialize math coprocessor
46	Display SETUP message
47	Set speed for boot
4E	Display any soft errors
4F	Ask for password (if feature is enabled)
50	Check all CMOS RAM values and clear the display
51	Enable parity, NMI, and cache memory
52	Initialize any option ROMs present from C8000h to EFFFFh or F7FFFh
53	Initialize time value at address 40 of BIOS RAM area
55	Initialize DDNIL counter to NULL
63	Call Int. 19 for boot loader

TABLE 5.31   **POST Codes for Award EISA BIOS**

Hex code	Description
01	Test the CPU flags
02	Test the CPU registers
03	Initialize the DMA controller, PIC, and PIT
04	Initialize memory refresh
05	Initialize the keyboard
06	Test BIOS ROM checksum
07	Check CMOS battery level
08	Test lower 256 kbytes of RAM
09	Test cache memory
0A	Configure the BIOS interrupt table
0B	Test the CMOS RAM checksum
0C	Initialize the keyboard
0D	Initialize the video adapter
0E	Test video memory

TABLE 5.31   POST Codes for Award EISA BIOS (*Continued*)

Hex code	Description
0F	Test DMA controller 0
10	Test DMA controller 1
11	Test page registers
14	Test the 8254 PIT IC
15	Verify 8259 PIC channel 1
16	Verify 8259 PIC channel 2
17	Test for stuck interrupts
18	Test 8259 functions
19	Test for stuck NMI
1F	Check extended CMOS RAM (if available)
20	Initialize and enable EISA slot 0
21–2F	Initialize and enable EISA slots 1 to 15
30	Check memory size below 256 kbytes
31	Check memory size above 256 kbytes
32	Test any EISA memory found during slot initialization
3C	Enter protected mode
3D	Detect and initialize mouse
3E	Initialize the cache controller
3F	Enable and test shadow RAM
41	Initialize floppy disk drive controller
42	Initialize hard disk drive controller
43	Detect and initialize serial ports
45	Detect and initialize math coprocessor
47	Set speed for boot
4E	Display any soft errors
4F	Ask for password (if feature is enabled)
50	Check all CMOS RAM values and clear the display
51	Enable parity, NMI, and cache memory
52	Initialize any option ROMs present from C8000h to EFFFFh or F7FFFh
53	Initialize time value at address 40 of BIOS RAM area
63	Call Int. 19 for boot loader
B0	NMI still in protected mode (protected mode failed)
B1	Disable NMI
BF	Initialize any system-specific chipsets
C0	Cache memory on/off
C1	Check memory size
C2	Test base 256 kbytes RAM
C3	Test DRAM page select
C4	Check video modes
C5	Test shadow RAM
C6	Configure cache memory
C8	Check system speed switch
C9	Test shadow RAM
CA	Initialize OEM chipset
FF	Call Int. 19 boot loader

TABLE 5.32   **Award Plug-and-Play BIOS**

Hex code	Description
C0	Turn off OEM specific cache, shadow RAM. Initialize all the standard devices with default values.
C1	Auto detection of onboard DRAM and cache.
C3	Test the first 256 kbytes DRAM. Expand the compressed codes into temporary DRAM area, including the compressed system BIOS and option ROMs.
C5	Copy the BIOS from ROM into E000–FFFF shadow RAM so that POST will go faster.
01–02	Reserved.
03	Initialize EISA registers (EISA BIOS only).
04	Reserved.
05	Keyboard controller self-test. Enable keyboard interface.
06	Reserved.
07	Verifies CMOS's basic R/W functionality.
BE	Program defaults values into chipset.
09	Program the configuration register of Cyrix CPU. OEM specific cache initialization.
0A	Initialize the first 32 interrupt vectors. Initialize INTs 33 to 120. Issue CPUID instruction to identify CPU type. Early power management initialization.
0B	Verify if the RTC time is valid or not. Detect bad battery. Read CMOS data into BIOS stack area. Perform PnP initializations (PnP BIOS only). Assign IO and memory for PCI devices (PCI BIOS only).
0C	Initialization of the BIOS data area (40:00–40:FF).
0D	Program some of the chipset's value. Measure CPU speed for display. Video initialization including MDA, CGA, EGA/VGA.
0E	Initialize the APIC (multiprocessor BIOS only). Test video RAM (if monochrome display device found). Show startup screen message.
0F	DMA channel 0 test.
10	DMA channel 1 test.
11	DMA page registers test.
12–13	Reserved.
14	Test 8254 timer 0 counter 2.
15	Test 8259 interrupt mask bits for channel 1.
16	Test 8259 interrupt mask bits for channel 2.
17	Reserved.
19	Test 8259 functionality.
1A–1D	Reserved.
1E	If EISA NVM checksum is good, execute EISA initialization (EISA BIOS only).
1F–29	Reserved.
30	Get base memory and extended memory size.

TABLE 5.32   Award Plug-and-Play BIOS (*Continued*)

Hex code	Description
31	Test base memory from 256 to 640 kbytes. Test extended memory from 1 Mbyte to the top of memory.
32	Display the Award plug-and-play BIOS extension message (PnP BIOS only). Program all onboard super I/O chips (if any), including COM ports, LPT ports, FDD port, and so on.
33–3B	Reserved.
3C	Set flag to allow users to enter CMOS Setup utility.
3D	Initialize keyboard. Install PS/2 mouse.
3E	Try to turn on level 2 cache.
3F–40	Reserved.
BF	Program the rest of the chipset.
41	Initialize floppy disk drive controller.
42	Initialize hard drive controller.
43	If it is a PnP BIOS, initialize serial and parallel ports.
44	Reserved.
45	Initialize math coprocessor.
46–4D	Reserved.
4E	If there is any error, show all the error messages on the screen and wait for user to press <F1> key.
4F	If password is needed, ask for password. Clear the Energy Star logo (green BIOS only).
50	Write all the CMOS values currently in the BIOS stack areas back into the CMOS.
51	Reserved.
52	Initialize all ISA ROMs. Later PCI initializations (PCI BIOS only). PnP initializations (PnP BIOS only). Program shadow RAM according to setup settings. Program parity according to setup setting. Power management initialization.
53	If it is not a PnP BIOS, initialize serial and parallel ports. Initialize time value in BIOS data area.
54–5F	Reserved.
60	Set up virus protection (boot-sector protection).
61	Try to turn on level 2 cache. Set the boot-up speed according to setup setting. Last chance for chipset initialization. Last chance for power management initialization. Show the system configuration table.
62	Set up daylight savings according to setup values. Program the NUM lock, type rate, and type speed according to setup setting.
63	If there is any changes in the hardware configuration, update the ESCD information (PnP BIOS only). Clear memory that has been used. Boot system via Int. 19h.
FF	System booting. This means that the BIOS already passed control to the operating system.

TABLE 5.33   Award BIOS Version 4.5

Hex code	Description
C0	Turn off chipset cache.
01	Processor test 1.
02	Processor test 2.
03	Initialize chips. Reset math coprocessor. Clear all page registers and CMOS shutdown byte. Initialize timers 0, 1, and 2, then set EISA timer to a known state. Initialize DMA controllers 0 and 1. Initialize interrupt controllers 0 and 1. Initialize EISA extended registers.
04	Test memory refresh toggle.
05	Blank video and initialize keyboard.
06	Reserved.
07	Test CMOS interface and battery status.
BE	Chipset default initialization.
C1	Memory presence test.
C5	Early shadow ROM enable for fast boot.
C6	Cache presence test.
08	Set up low memory. Memory presence test. OEM chipset routines. Clear low 64 kbytes of memory. Test first 64 kbytes memory.
09	Early cache initialization. Cache initialization.
0A	Set up interrupt vector table.
0B	Test CMOS RAM checksum.
0C	Initialize keyboard. Set NUM_LOCK status.
0D	Initialize video interface. Detect and initialize video adapter.
0E	Test video memory. Set up shadow RAM.
0F	Test DMA controller 0. Keyboard detect and initialization.
10	Test DMA controller 1.
11	Test DMA page registers.
12–13	Reserved.
14	Test timer counter 2.
15	Test 8259-1 mask bits.
16	Test 8259-2 mask bits.
17	Test stuck 8259's interrupt bits.
18	Test 8259 interrupt functionality.
19	Test stuck NMI bits.
1A	Display CPU clock.
1B–1E	Reserved.
1F	Set EISA mode. Test EISA configuration memory integrity.
20	Enable slot 0.
21–2F	Enable slots 1–15.
30	Size base and extended memory.
31	Test base and extended memory.
32	Test EISA extended memory.

TABLE 5.33   Award BIOS Version 4.5 (*Continued*)

Hex code	Description
33–3B	Reserved.
3C	Setup enabled.
3D	Initialize and install mouse.
3E	Set up cache controller.
3F	Reserved.
BF	Chipset initialization.
40	Display virus protect status (disable or enable).
41	Initialize floppy drive(s) and controller.
42	Initialize hard drive(s) and controller.
43	Detect and initialize serial/parallel/game ports.
44	Reserved.
45	Detect and initialize math coprocessor.
46	Reserved.
47	Reserved.
48–4D	Reserved.
4E	Manufacturing POST loop or display messages.
4F	Password check (if active).
50	Write CMOS values to RAM.
51	Enable parity checker. Enable NMI. Enable cache before boot.
52	Initialize ROMs present from C8000h to EFFFFh.
53	Initialize time value.
60	Set up virus protect.
61	Set boot speed.
62	Set up NumLock.
63	Boot attempt via Int. 19h.
B0	Spurious interrupt error.
B1	Unclaimed NMI error.
E1–EF	Set up pages.
FF	Boot under way.

TABLE 5.34   POST Codes for Chips & Technologies BIOS

Hex code	Description
01	CPU flag test failed
02	CPU register test failed
03	BIOS ROM checksum test failed
04	DMA controller test failed
05	System timer IC failed
06	Base 64 kbytes address line test failure
07	Base 64 kbytes memory test failure
08	Interrupt controller test failed
09	Hot interrupt occurred
0A	System timer interrupt test failed

TABLE 5.34   POST Codes for Chips & Technologies BIOS (*Continued*)

Hex code	Description
0B	CPU won't leave protected mode
0C	DMA page register test failed
0D	Memory refresh fault
0E	Keyboard controller not responding
0F	CPU could not enter protected mode
10	KBC protected-mode test failed
1	KBC protected-mode test failed
12	KBC protected-mode test failed
13	KBC protected-mode test failed
14	KBC protected-mode test failed
15	KBC protected-mode test failed
16	KBC A20 gate failed
17	Exception or unexpected exception test failed
18	Shutdown during memory size check
19	BIOS ROM checksum error
1A	BMS checksum error (BIOS, shadow memory, or memory controller fault)
50	Initialize system chipsets
51	Initialize system time IC
52	Initialize DMA controller
53	Initialize the 8259 PIC
54	Initialize system chipsets
56	Entering protected mode
57	Check memory ICs
58	Configure memory interleave
59	Exit protected mode
5A	Determine system board memory size
5B	Relocate shadow RAM
5C	Configure possible EMS
5D	Set up wait state configuration
5E	Retest base 64 kbytes
5F	Test shadow RAM
60	Test CMOS RAM
61	Test the video controller
63	Protected-mode interrupt test
64	Test the A20 line
65	Test the memory address lines
66	Base 64 kbytes memory test
67	Run extended memory test
68	Run system timer interrupt test
69	RTC clock test
6A	Keyboard test
6B	Identify and test math coprocessor
6C	Locate and initialize serial ports

TABLE 5.34   POST Codes for Chips & Technologies BIOS
(*Continued*)

Hex code	Description
6D	Locate and initialize parallel ports
6F	Initialize floppy disk controller
70	Initialize hard disk controller
71	Check for key lock
72	Mouse test
90	System RAM setup
91	Calculate CPU speed
92	Check system configuration against CMOS data
93	BIOS initialized
94	Power-on diagnostic bootstrap (call Int. 19)
95	Reset ICs
96	Set up cache controller
97	VGA power-on diagnostics

are sent to port 84h rather than port 80h. Also, port 85h is used to indicate the category of the error (i.e., 00 = system BIOS, 01 = error after boot, and 05 = video POST). Table 5.35 illustrates the extensive array of general Compaq POST codes. Tables 5.36, 5.37, and 5.38 list the POST codes for Compaq i286, i386, and i486 Deskpro systems, respectively. The POST codes for Compaq's video BIOS are listed in Table 5.39.

TABLE 5.35   POST Codes for General Compaq BIOS

Hex code	Description
00	Initialize and test CPU flags
01	Check manufacturing jumper
02	8042 KBC test
03	No response from 8042 KBC
04	Look for ROM at E000h
05	Look for ROM at C800h
06	Normal CMOS reset code
08	Initialize the PIT and math coprocessor
09	Jump indexed by CMOS reset code (KBC)
0A	Vector 40:67 reset function (KBC)
0B	Vector 40:67 with E01 function (KBC)
0C	Boot reset function
0D	Test 8254 PIT counter 0
0E	Test 8254 PIT counter 2
0F	Warm boot

TABLE 5.35   POST Codes for General Compaq BIOS (*Continued*)

Hex code	Description
10	PPI disabled, test 8254 PIT 0 and 1
11	Initialize video controller
12	Clear display and turn video on
13	Set test time 0
14	Disable RTC interrupts
15	Check battery power levels
16	Battery has lost power
17	Clear CMOS diagnostics
18	Test base memory (first 128 kbytes)
19	Initialize base memory
1A	Initialize video adapter
1B	Check BIOS ROM checksum
1C	Check CMOS checksum
1D	Test DMA controller page registers
1E	Test the keyboard controller
1F	Test the protected mode
20	Test real and extended memory
21	Initialize the time of day
22	Initialize the math coprocessor
23	Test the keyboard and KBC
24	Reset the A20 line and set default CPU speed
25	Test the floppy disk controller
26	Test the fixed disk controller
27	Initialize all printer ports
28	Search for optional ROMs
29	Test system configuration against CMOS setup
2A	Clear the screen
2B	Check for invalid time and date
2C	Search for optional ROMs
2D	Test PIT 2
2F	Write to diagnostic byte
30	Clear the first 128 kbytes of RAM
31	Load interrupt vectors 70–77
32	Load interrupt vectors 00–1F
33	Initialize MEMSIZE and RESETWD
34	Verify CMOS checksum
35	CMOS checksum is not valid
36	Check CMOS battery power
37	Check for game adapters
38	Initialize all serial ports
39	Initialize all parallel ports
3A	Initialize Port and Comm timeouts
3B	Flush the keyboard buffer
40	Save the RESETWD value
41	Check RAM refresh

TABLE 5.35   POST Codes for General Compaq BIOS (*Continued*)

Hex code	Description
42	Start write of 128 kbytes RAM
43	Reset parity checks
44	Start verify of 128 kbytes RAM test
45	Check for parity errors
46	No RAM errors
47	RAM error detected
50	Check for dual frequency in CMOS
51	Check CMOS video configuration
52	Search for video ROM
53	Send control to video option ROM
54	Initialize the first video adapter
55	Initialize the secondary video adapter
56	No display adapters installed
57	Initialize primary video mode
58	Start of video test
59	Check for the presence of a video adapter
5A	Check video registers
5B	Start screen memory test
5C	Stop video test and clear memory
5D	Error detected on adapter
5E	Test the next detected adapter
5F	All found adapters successfully tested
60	Start of memory tests
61	Enter the protected mode
62	Find memory size
63	Get CMOS size
64	Start test of real memory
65	Start test of extended memory
66	Save memory size in CMOS
67	128-kbyte option installed
68	Ready to return to real mode
69	Successful return to real mode
6A	Protected-mode error during test
6B	Display error message
6C	End of memory test
6D	Initialize kilobyte OK string
6E	Determine memory size to test
6F	Start of MEMTEST
70	Display XXXXX kbytes OK
71	Test each RAM segment
72	High-order address test
73	Exit MEMTEST
74	Parity error on the bus
75	Start protected-mode test
76	Ready to enter protected mode
77	Test software exceptions

TABLE 5.35   POST Codes for General Compaq BIOS (*Continued*)

Hex code	Description
78	Prepare to return to real mode
79	Successful return to real mode
7A	Back in real mode (error has been detected)
7B	Exit protected-mode testing
7C	High-order address test failure
7D	Start cache controller test
7E	Configuring cache memory
7F	Copy system ROM to shadow RAM
80	Start of 8042 KBC test
81	Run 8042 KBC self-test
82	KBC check result received
83	Error returned
84	8042 checks OK
86	Start 8042 test and reset the keyboard
87	Got acknowledge and read the result
88	Got the result and checking it
89	Testing for stuck keys
8A	Key seems to be stuck
8B	Test keyboard interface
8C	Got the result and checking it
8D	End of KBC test—no errors detected
90	Start of CMOS test
91	CMOS checks OK
92	Error in CMOS R/W test
93	Start of DMA controller test
94	DMA page registers test OK
95	DMA controller tests OK
96	8237 DMA initialization is OK
97	Start of RAM test
A0	Start of diskette tests
A1	FDC reset active
A2	FDC reset inactive
A3	FDC motor on
A4	FDC time-out error
A5	FDC failed reset
A6	FDC passed reset
A8	Determine drive type
A9	Start seek operation
AA	Waiting for FDC seek status
AF	Diskette tests complete
B0	Start of hard drive tests
B1	Controller board not found
B2	Controller test failed
B3	Testing drive 1
B4	Testing drive 2
B5	Drive error

TABLE 5.35   POST Codes for General Compaq BIOS (*Continued*)

Hex code	Description
B6	Drive failed
B7	No hard disks detected
B8	Hard drive tests complete
B9	Attempt to boot diskette
BA	Attempt to boot hard drive
BB	Boot attempt has failed
BC	Jump to boot record
BD	Drive error—retry boot
BE	Testing Weitek coprocessor
D0	Starting clear memory routine
D1	Ready to switch to protected mode
D2	Ready to clear extended memory
D3	Ready to return to real mode
D4	Successful return to real mode
D5	Clearing base memory
DD	KBC self-test failed
E0	Ready to shadow E000h ROM
E1	Finished shadowing ROM at E000h
E2	Ready to shadow EGA/VGA ROM
E3	Finished shadowing video ROM

TABLE 5.36   POST Codes for Compaq i286
Deskpro BIOS

Hex code	Description
01	Test the CPU
02	Test the math coprocessor
03	Testing 8237 DMA controller
04	Testing 8259 PIC
05	Testing KBC port 61h
06	Testing 8042 KBC
07	CMOS test
08	CMOS test
09	CMOS test
10	Testing 8254 PIT
11	Testing 8254 PIT refresh detect
12	System speed test
14	Speaker test
21	Memory R/W test
24	Memory address test

**TABLE 5.36   POST Codes for Compaq i286
Deskpro BIOS (*Continued*)**

Hex code	Description
25	Memory walking I/O test
31	Keyboard short test
32	Keyboard long test
33	Keyboard LED test
35	Keyboard lock test
41	Printer test failed
42	Testing printer port
43	Testing printer port
48	Parallel-port failure
51	Video controller test
52	Video controller test
53	Video attribute test
54	Video character set test
55	Video 80×25 mode test
56	Video 80×25 mode test
57	Video 40×25 mode test
60	Floppy disk ID test
61	Floppy disk format test
62	Floppy disk read test
63	Floppy disk R/W compare test
64	Floppy disk random seek test
65	Floppy disk media ID test
66	Floppy disk speed test
67	Floppy disk wrap test
68	Floppy disk write-protect test
69	Floppy disk reset controller test

TABLE 5.37 **POST Codes for Compaq i386 Deskpro BIOS**

Hex code	Description
01	I/O ROM checksum error
02	System memory board failure
12	System option error
13	Time and date not set (not expected from CMOS)
14	Memory size error (not what was expected from CMOS settings)
21	System memory error
23	Memory address line error
25	Memory test error
26	Keyboard error
33	Keyboard controller error
34	Keyboard or KBC error
41	Parallel-port error
42	Monochrome video adapter failure
51	Display adapter failure
61	Floppy disk controller error
62	Floppy disk boot error
65	Floppy drive error
67	Floppy disk controller failed
6A	Floppy port address conflict
6B	Floppy port address conflict
72	Math coprocessor detected

TABLE 5.38 **POST Codes for Compaq i486 Deskpro BIOS**

Hex code	Description
01	CPU test failed
02	Math coprocessor test failed
03	Testing 8237 DMA page registers
04	Testing 8259 PIC
05	8042 KBC port 61 error
06	8042 KBC self-test error
07	CMOS RAM test failed
08	CMOS interrupt test failed
09	CMOS clock load data test failed
10	8254 PIT test failed
11	8254 PIT refresh detect test failed
12	System speed test mode too slow
13	Protected-mode test failed
14	Speaker test failed
16	Cache memory configuration failed

TABLE 5.38   POST Codes for Compaq i486 Deskpro BIOS (*Continued*)

Hex code	Description
19	Testing installed devices
21	Memory configuration test failed
22	BIOS ROM checksum failed
23	Memory R/W test failed
26	Memory increment pattern test failed
24	Memory address line test failed
25	Walking I/O test failed
26	Memory increment batten test failed
31	Keyboard short test
32	Keyboard long test
33	Keyboard LED test
34	Keyboard typematic test failed
41	Printer test failed or not connected (parallel-port circuits)
42	Printer data register failed (parallel-port circuits)
43	Printer pattern test (parallel-port circuits)
48	Printer not connected (parallel-port circuits)
51	Video controller test failed
52	Video memory test failed
53	Video attribute test failed
54	Video character set test failed
55	Video 80×25 mode test failed
56	Video 80×25 mode test failed
57	Video 40×25 mode test failed
58	Video 320×200 mode color set 1 test
59	Video 320×200 mode color set 1 test
60	Floppy disk ID drive types test failed
61	Floppy disk format failed
62	Floppy disk read test failed
63	Floppy disk write, read, seek test failed
65	Floppy disk ID media failed
66	Floppy disk speed test failed
67	Floppy disk wrap test failed
68	Floppy disk write-protect failed
69	Floppy disk reset controller test failed
82	Video memory test failed
84	Video adapter test failed

TABLE 5.39   POST Codes for Compaq Video BIOS

Hex code	Description
00	Entry into video ROM
01	Test alternative adapters
02	Perform vertical sync tests
03	Perform horizontal sync tests
04	Perform static system tests
05	Perform bug tests
06	Perform configuration tests
07	Perform alternative ROM tests
08	Run color gun off tests
09	Run color gun on tests
0A	Test video memory
0B	Check that adapter board present
10	Error—illegal configuration
20	Error—no vertical sync present
21	Error—vertical sync out of range
30	Error—no horizontal sync present
40	Error—color register failure
50	Error—slot type conflict error
51	Error—video memory conflict error
52	Error—ROM conflict error
60	Error—red DAC stuck low
61	Error—green DAC stuck low
62	Error—blue DAC stuck low
63	Error—DAC stuck high
64	Error—red DAC fault
65	Error—green DAC fault
66	Error—blue DAC fault
70	Error—bad alternative ROM version
80	Error—color gun stuck on
90	Error—color gun stuck off
A0	Error—video memory failure
F0	Error—equipment failure
00	Video POST complete

Dell

The Dell systems use a close OEM derivative of Phoenix BIOS. As a result, the Dell beep codes are virtually identical to the Phoenix beep codes. Table 5.40 lists the Dell POST codes.

DTK

The DTK BIOS (evolved from ERSO BIOS) does not issue many POST codes, but Table 5.41 provides a listing of the codes that are available.

TABLE 5.40   POST Codes for Dell BIOS

Hex code	Description
01	CPU register test in progress
02	CMOS R/W test failed
03	BIOS ROM checksum bad
04	8254 PIT test failed
05	DMA controller initialization failed
06	DMA page register test failed
08	RAM refresh verification failed
09	Starting first 64 kbytes RAM test
0A	First 64 kbytes RAM IC or data line bad
0B	First 64 kbytes RAM odd/even logic bad
0C	First 64 kbytes address line bad
0D	First 64 kbytes parity error
10	Bit 0 bad in first 64 kbytes
11	Bit 1 bad in first 64 kbytes
12	Bit 2 bad in first 64 kbytes
13	Bit 3 bad in first 64 kbytes
14	Bit 4 bad in first 64 kbytes
15	Bit 5 bad in first 64 kbytes
16	Bit 6 bad in first 64 kbytes
17	Bit 7 bad in first 64 kbytes
18	Bit 8 bad in first 64 kbytes
19	Bit 9 bad in first 64 kbytes
1A	Bit 10 bad in first 64 kbytes
1B	Bit 11 bad in first 64 kbytes
1C	Bit 12 bad in first 64 kbytes
1D	Bit 13 bad in first 64 kbytes
1E	Bit 14 bad in first 64 kbytes
1F	Bit 15 bad in first 64 kbytes
20	Slave DMA register bad
21	Master DMA register bad
22	Master interrupt mask register bad
23	Slave interrupt mask register bad
25	Loading interrupt vectors
27	Keyboard controller test failed
28	CMOS RAM battery bad
29	CMOS configuration validation in progress
2B	Video memory test failed
2C	Video initialization failed
2D	Video retrace failure
2E	Searching for a video ROM
30	Switching to video ROM
31	Monochrome operation OK
32	Color (CGA) operation OK
33	Color operation OK

TABLE 5.40   POST Codes for Dell BIOS (*Continued*)

Hex code	Description
34	Timer tick interrupt in progress (or bad)
35	CMOS shutdown test in progress (or bad)
36	Gate A20 bad
37	Unexpected interrupt in protected mode
38	RAM test in progress or high address line bad
3A	Interval timer channel 2 bad
3B	Time-of-day test bad
3C	Serial-port test bad
3D	Parallel-port test bad
3E	Math coprocessor test bad
3F	Cache memory test bad

TABLE 5.41   POST Codes for DTK BIOS

Hex code	Description
01	Testing the CPU
03	Initialize the 8258 interrupt controller
05	Initialize the video board
0D	Initialize the DMA controller
0E	Initialize the DMA page register
12	Test the 8042 keyboard controller
16	Test the DMA controller and timer
22	Testing DRAM refresh circuitry
25	Base 64 kbytes memory test
30	Set up system stack
33	Read system configuration through KBC
37	Test keyboard clock and data line
40	Determine video type
44	Locating and testing MDA and CGA video
48	Initialize video 80×25 mode
4D	Display DTK BIOS copyright message
4F	Check serial and parallel ports
50	Check floppy disk controller
55	Check shadow RAM
58	Display total memory and switch to real mode
5A	Successful switch back to real mode
60	Check hard disk drive controller
62	Initialize floppy drive
65	Initialize hard drive
67	Initialize the drives
6A	Disable gate A20 and test math coprocessor
70	Set system date and time
77	Call Int. 19 boot loader

Eurosoft/Mylex family

The general-purpose Eurosoft/Mylex BIOS was developed by both of those companies to serve on the Mylex EISA motherboard, but it may be found in a few other systems. The Eurosoft/Mylex BIOS generates both beep codes and POST codes at port 80h, but the conventional Eurosoft BIOS issues only POST codes. Table 5.42 lists the POST codes for the Eurosoft/Mylex BIOS, and the Eurosoft version 4.71 BIOS POST codes are listed in Table 5.43.

TABLE 5.42   POST Codes for Eurosoft/Mylex BIOS

Hex code	Description
01	CPU test failed
02	DMA page register test failed
03	Keyboard controller test failed
04	BIOS ROM checksum error
05	Keyboard command test failed
06	CMOS RAM test failed
07	RAM refresh test failed
08	First 64 kbytes memory test failed
09	DMA controller test failed
0A	Initialize DMA controller
0B	Interrupt test failed
0C	Checking RAM size
0D	Initializing video system
0E	Video BIOS checksum failed
10	Search for monochrome video adapter
11	Search for color video adapter
12	Word splitter and byte shift test failed (KBC)
13	Keyboard test failed
14	RAM test failed
15	System timer test failed
16	Initialize keyboard controller output port
17	Keyboard interrupt test failed
18	Initialize keyboard
19	Real-time clock test failed
1A	Math coprocessor test failed
1B	Reset floppy and hard drive controllers
1C	Initialize the floppy drive
1D	Initialize the hard drive
1E	Locate adapter ROMs from C800h to DFFFh
1F	Locate and initialize serial and parallel ports
20	Initialize time of day in RTC
21	Locate adapter ROMs from E000h to EFFFh
22	Search for boot device
23	Boot from floppy disk
24	Boot from hard disk
25	Gate A20 enable/disable failure
26	Parity error
30	DDNIL bit scan failure
FF	Fatal error—system halted

TABLE 5.43   POST Codes for Eurosoft 4.71 BIOS

Pass	Fail	Description
03	04	DMA page register test
05	06	Keyboard test
07	08	Keyboard self-test
09	0A	8042 KBC checking links
0B	—	RATMOD/DIAG link
0C	0D	Keyboard port 60h test
0E	0F	Keyboard parameter test
10	11	Keyboard command byte
12	13	Keyboard command byte return
14	15	RAM refresh toggle test
16	17	RAM bit test
18	19	RAM parity test
1A	1B	CMOS RAM test
1C	1D	CMOS RAM battery test
1E	1F	CMOS RAM checksum test
—	20	CMOS RAM battery fault bit set
21	22	Master DMA controller 1 test
21	23	Slave DMA controller 2 test
24	—	Protected mode entered successfully
25	—	RAM test completed
26	27	BIOS RAM checksum test
28	—	Exiting protected mode
29	2A	Keyboard power-up reply received test
2B	2C	Keyboard disable command test
—	2D	Checking for video system
—	2E	POST errors have been reported
—	2F	About to halt
30	—	Protected mode entered safely
31	—	RAM test complete
32	33	Master interrupt controller test
34	35	Slave interrupt controller test
36	37	Chipset initialization
38	39	Shadowing system BIOS
3A	3B	Shadowing video BIOS

Faraday A-Tease

The Faraday BIOS is a rarely used BIOS which is owned by Western Digital. Table 5.44 lists the POST codes generated by Faraday A-Tease.

TABLE 5.44   POST Codes for Faraday A-Tease BIOS

Hex code	Description
01	CPU test failed
02	BIOS ROM checksum test failed
03	CMOS shutdown byte failed
04	Testing DMA page register
05	Testing system timer (PIT)
06	Testing system refresh
07	Testing 8042 keyboard controller
08	Testing lower 128 kbytes of RAM
09	Testing video controller
0A	Testing RAM 128 to 640 kbytes
0B	Testing DMA controller 1
0C	Testing DMA controller 2
0D	Testing interrupt controller 1
0E	Testing interrupt controller 2
0F	Testing control port
10	Testing parity
11	Testing CMOS RAM checksum
12	Testing for manufacturing-mode jumper
13	Configuring interrupt vectors
14	Testing the keyboard
15	Configuring parallel ports
16	Configuring serial ports
17	Configuring lower 640 kbytes RAM
18	Configuring RAM above 1 Mbyte
19	Configuring keyboard
1A	Configuring floppy drive
1B	Configuring hard disk drive
1C	Configuring game port adapter
1D	Testing and initializing math coprocessor
1E	Checking CMOS real-time clock
1F	Calculate and verify CMOS RAM checksum
21	Initialize PROM drivers
22	Test parallel-port loopback
23	Test serial-port loopback
24	Test CMOS RTC
25	Test the CMOS shutdown
26	Test memory over 1 Mbyte
80	Error—divide overflow
81	Error—single-step fault
82	Error—NMI stuck or error
83	Error—breakpoint fault
84	Error—Int. 0 detect fault
85	Error—bound error
86	Error—invalid opcode (BIOS or CPU fault)

TABLE 5.44 POST Codes for Faraday A-Tease BIOS (*Continued*)

Hex code	Description
87	Error—processor extension not available
88	Error—double exception error
89	Error—processor extended segment error
8A	Error—invalid task state segment
8B	Error—needed segment not present
8C	Error—stack segment not present
8D	Error—general protection error
8E	Error—general protection error
8F	Error—general protection error
90	Error—processor extension error
91–FF	Error—spurious interrupts
F3	Error—CPU protected-mode fault
F9	Error—virtual block move error

TABLE 5.45 POST Codes for IBM XT BIOS

Hex code	Description
00 or FF	CPU register test failed
01	BIOS ROM checksum failed
02	System timer 1 failed
03	8237 DMA register R/W failed
04	Base 32 kbytes RAM failed

IBM family

The IBM POST codes represent the classical codes used by the original IBM PC products. Table 5.45 lists the POST codes for for an IBM PC/XT. It is important to note that IBM XT POST codes are sent to port 60h. Your POST board may not be able to check this location. However, there are only about five codes generated by the IBM XT. The codes for an IBM PC/AT are listed in Table 5.46. Finally, the POST codes for an IBM PS/2 are listed in Table 5.47.

Landmark family

Landmark Research International (now called Quarterdeck Select, a subsidiary of Quarterback Corporation) does not offer BIOS commercially, but it includes a custom BIOS as part of its KickStart series of diagnosis cards. The POST codes generated by the JumpStart ROMs are sent to port 80h and port 280h. The diagnostics in Landmark's SuperSoft BIOS product act as a replacement for system ROMs. Tables 5.48 and 5.49 present the Xt and AT JumpStart ROM POST codes, while Table 5.50 illustrates the SuperSoft BIOS POST codes.

TABLE 5.46 POST Codes for IBM AT BIOS

Hex code	Description
01	CPU flag and register test
02	BIOS ROM checksum test
03	CMOS shutdown byte test
04	8254 PIT test—bits on
05	8254 PIT test—bits on
06	8237 DMA initialize registers test 0
07	8237 DMA initialize registers test 1
08	DMA page register test
09	Memory refresh test
0A	Soft reset test
0B	Reset 8042 KBC
0C	KBC reset OK
0D	Initialize the 8042 KBC
0E	Test memory
0F	Get I/P buffer switch settings
DD	RAM error
11	Initialize protected mode
12	Test protected-mode registers
13	Initialize 8259 PIC 2
14	Set up temporary interrupt vectors
15	Establish BIOS interrupt vectors
16	Verify CMOS checksum and battery OK
17	Set the defective CMOS battery flag
18	Ensure CMOS set
19	Set return address byte in CMOS
1A	Set temporary stack
1B	Test segment address 01-0000 (second 64 kbytes)
1C	Decide if 512 or 640 kbytes installed
1D	Test segment address 10-0000 (over 640 kbytes)
1E	Set expansion memory as contained in CMOS
1F	Test address lines 19–23
20	Ready to return from protected mode
21	Successful return from protected mode
22	Test video controller
23	Check for EGA/VGA BIOS
24	Test 8259 PIC R/W mask register
25	Test interrupt mask registers
26	Check for hot (unexpected) interrupts
05	Display 101 error (system board error)
27	Check the POST logic (system board error)

TABLE 5.46 POST Codes for IBM AT BIOS (*Continued*)

Hex code	Description
28	Check unexpected NMI interrupts (system board error)
29	Test timer 2 (system board error)
2A	Test 8254 timer
2B	System board error
2C	System board error
2D	Check 8042 KBC for last command
2F	Go to next area during a warm boot
30	Set shutdown return 2
31	Switch to protected mode
33	Test next block of 64 kbytes
34	Switch back to real mode
F0	Set data segment
F1	Test interrupts
F2	Test exception interrupts
F3	Verify protected-mode instructions
F4	Verify protected-mode instructions
F5	Verify protected-mode instructions
F6	Verify protected-mode instructions
F7	Verify protected-mode instructions
F8	Verify protected-mode instructions
F9	Verify protected-mode instructions
FA	Verify protected-mode instructions
34	Test keyboard
35	Test keyboard type
36	Check for "AA" scan code
38	Check for stuck key
39	8042 KBC error
3A	Initialize the 8042
3B	Check for expansion ROM in 2-kbyte blocks
40	Enable hardware interrupts
41	Check system code at segment E0000h
42	Exit to system code
43	Call boot loader
3C	Check for initial program load
3D	Initialize floppy for drive type
3E	Initialize hard drive
81	Build descriptor table
82	Switch to virtual mode
90–B6	Memory and bootstrap tests
32	Test address lines 0–15
44	Attempt to boot from fixed disk
45	Unable to boot—go to BASIC

TABLE 5.47   **POST Codes for IBM PS/2 BIOS**

Hex code	Description
00	CPU flag test
01	32-bit CPU register test
02	Test BIOS ROM checksum
03	Test system enable
04	Test system POS register
05	Test adapter setup port
06	Test RTC/CMOS RAM shutdown byte
07	Test extended CMOS RAM
08	Test DMA and page register channels
09	Initialize DMA command and mode registers
0A	Test memory refresh toggle
0B	Test keyboard controller buffers
0C	Keyboard controller self-test
0D	Continue keyboard controller self-test
0E	Keyboard self-test error
0F	Set up system memory configuration
10	Test first 512 kbytes RAM
11	Halt system if memory test occurs
12	Test protected-mode instructions
13	Initialize interrupt controller 1
14	Initialize interrupt controller 2
15	Initialize 120 interrupt vectors
16	Initialize 16 interrupt vectors
17	Check CMOS/RTC battery
18	Check CMOS/RTC checksum
19	CMOS/RTC battery bad
1A	Skip memory test in protected mode
1B	Prepare for CMOS shutdown
1C	Set up stack pointer to end of first 64 kbytes
1D	Calculate low memory size in protected mode
1E	Save the memory size detected
1F	Set up system memory split address
20	Check for extended memory beyond 64 Mbytes
21	Test memory address bus lines
22	Clear parity error and channel lock
23	Initialize interrupt 0
24	Check CMOS RAM validity
25	Write keyboard controller command byte
40	Check valid CMOS RAM and video system
41	Display error code 160
42	Test registers in both interrupt controllers
43	Test interrupt controller registers
44	Test interrupt mask registers

TABLE 5.47   POST Codes for IBM PS/2 BIOS (*Continued*)

Hex code	Description
45	Test NMI
46	NMI error has been detected
47	Test system timer 0
48	Check stuck speaker clock
49	Test system timer 0 count
4A	Test system timer 2 count
4B	Check if timer interrupt occurred
4C	Test timer 0 for improper operation (too fast or too slow)
4D	Verify timer interrupt 0
4E	Check 8042 keyboard controller
4F	Check for soft reset
50	Prepare for shutdown
51	Start protected-mode test
52	Test memory in 64-kbyte increments
53	Check if memory test done
54	Return to real mode
55	Test for regular or manufacturing mode
56	Disable the keyboard
57	Check for keyboard self-test
58	Keyboard test passed
59	Test the keyboard controller
5A	Configure the mouse
5B	Disable the mouse
5C	Initialize interrupt vectors
5D	Initialize interrupt vectors
5E	Initialize interrupt vectors
60	Save DDNIL status
61	Reset floppy drive
62	Test floppy drive
63	Turn floppy drive motor off
64	Set up serial ports
65	Enable real-time clock interrupt
66	Configure floppy drives
67	Configure hard drives
68	Enable system CPU arbitration
69	Scan for adapter ROMs
6A	Verify serial and parallel ports
6B	Set up equipment byte
6C	Set up configuration
6D	Set keyboard typematic rate
6E	Call Int. 19 boot loader

TABLE 5.48   POST Codes for Landmark JumpStart XT BIOS

Hex code	Description
01	Jump to reset area in BIOS ROM
02	Initialize DMA page register
03	Initialize DMA refresh register
04	Clear all RAM
05	Perform RAM test on first 64 kbytes
06	Clear first 64 kbytes
07	Initialize BIOS stack to 0FC0h
08	Set the equipment flag based on XT switches
09	Initialize default interrupt vectors
0A	Initialize the 8255 if it exists
0B	Initialize the 8259 PIT and enable interrupts
0C	Set up adapters and peripherals
0D	Set up video system
0E	Initialize the video system
0F	Initialize the equipment
10	Initialize memory configuration
11	Set up system timer function
12	Initialize system timer
13	Set up time-of-day function
14	Initialize time of day from RTC data
15	Set up and initialize "print screen" function
16	Set up and initialize cassette interface if available
17	Set up and initialize bootstrap function
18	Set up and initialize keyboard function
19	Enable speaker
1A	Set up system timer
1B	Enable the RTC
1C	Set up timer 2
1D	Determine memory size
1E	Read first and last word of segment
1F	Compare first and last words
20	Report found memory size to display
21	Perform BIOS ROM checksum test
22	Perform complete RAM testing on cold boot
23	Move system stack to bottom of memory and save pointer
24	Reset parity after RAM sizing
25	Enable timer and keyboard interrupts
26	Set up the serial and parallel ports
27	Set up the game port
28	Set up the floppy disk controller
29	Scan for optional ROMs in 2-kbyte chunks from C8000h
2A	Call the boot loader

TABLE 5.49   POST Codes for Landmark JumpStart AT BIOS

Hex code	Description
03	Sound one short beep
04	Initialize the bell tone
05	Enable CMOS RAM
06	Reset video controller
07	Disable parity checking
08	Start memory refresh
09	Clear the reset flag in RAM
0A	Test DMA page registers
10	Use CMOS to determine if a soft reset has occurred
11	Check BIOS ROM checksum
12	Test system timer A
13	Test DMA channel 0
14	Test DMA channel 1
15	Test memory refresh
16	Flush 8042 KBC input buffer
17	Reset the 8042
18	Get keyboard type
19	Initialize the keyboard
1A	Clear any existing parity
1B	Enable on-board parity
1C	Test base 64 kbytes memory
1D	Test base 64 kbytes parity
1E	Initialize POST stack
20	Check keyboard type
65	Set video speed
21	Test protected-mode CPU registers
22	Initialize 8259 PIC
23	Initialize all interrupts
24	Test all interrupts
25	Perform DRAM checksum
26	Adjust configuration based on hardware found and CMOS settings
27	Check for presence of manufacturing switch
28	Initialize video controller
2A	Test video memory
2B	Test video sync
2C	Check for auxiliary video controller
2D	Change video configuration
2F	Initialize the video system
30	Change video interrupt
31	Display any POST messages

TABLE 5.49   POST Codes for Landmark JumpStart AT BIOS (*Continued*)

Hex code	Description
32	Test memory and calculate size
33	Adjust memory configuration
34	Enable I/O parity
35	Test 8259 PIC
36	Perform byte swap test
37	Test NMI
38	Perform timer test
39	Initialize system timer A
3A	Protected-mode memory test
3B	Test keyboard
3C	Test keyboard interrupt
3D	Enable A20
3E	Reset hard disk controller
3F	Set up floppy disk controller
40	Test floppy drive system
41	Set up keyboard
42	Enable interrupt timer
43	Check for dual floppy disk/hard drive controller
44	Locate floppy drive A
45	Locate floppy drive B
46	Reset hard disk controller
47	Enable slave DMA
48	Locate any external ROMs
49	Initialize the parallel port(s)
4A	Initialize the serial port(s)
4B	Initialize the math coprocessor
4C	Read CMOS RAM status
4D	Check CMOS configuration against detected hardware
4E	Initialize timer ticks
4F	Enable IRQ9
50	Enable on-board parity
51	Run any add-on ROMs
52	Enable keyboard interrupt
53	Reset the parallel port
60	Check for any errors
61	Sound one short beep
62	Print sign-on message
64	Call Int. 19 boot loader

TABLE 5.50 **POST Codes for Landmark SuperSoft AT BIOS**

Hex code	Description
11	CPU register or logic error
12	ROMPOST A checksum error
13	ROMPOST B checksum error
14	8253 timer channel 0
15	8253 timer channel 1
16	8253 timer channel 2
17	8237 DMA controller 1 error
18	8237 DMA controller 2 error
19	DMA page register error
1A	8042 KBC parity error
21	Scan 16 kbytes critical RAM error
22	Memory refresh error
23	CPU protected-mode error
24	8259 interrupt controller 1 error
25	8259 interrupt controller 2 error
26	Unexpected interrupt detected
27	Interrupt 0 (system timer) error
28	CMOS RTC error
29	NMI error
2A	Locate and test math coprocessor
31	Keyboard controller error
32	Stuck key detected or CMOS RAM error
33	Floppy controller error
34	Floppy disk read error
35	MDA video memory error
36	Color video memory error
37	EGA/VGA RAM error
38	BIOS ROM checksum error
41	Memory error
42	Refresh fault
43–45	Display problem
59	No monitor detected

Microid Research

The Microid Research BIOS (Mr. BIOS 1.0A) POST codes are listed in Table 5.51. Note that all codes are delivered to port 80h. Table 5.52 lists both beep codes and POST codes for the more recent release of Mr. BIOS.

NCR family

The National Cash Register (NCR) Corporation (now a subsidiary of AT&T) has been providing motherboards for AT&T PCs. Older motherboards used an OEM version of an AMI design (with POST codes

TABLE 5.51 POST Codes for Microid Research BIOS

Hex code	Description
01	Chipset problem
02	Disable NMI and DMA
03	Check BIOS ROM checksum
04	Test DMA page register
05	Keyboard controller test
06	Initialize the RTC, 8237, 8254, and 8259
07	Check memory refresh
08	DMA master test
09	OEM-specific test
0A	Test memory bank 0
0B	Test PIC units
0C	Test PIC controllers
0D	Initialize PIT channel 0
0E	Initialize PIT channel 2
0F	Test CMOS RAM battery
10	Check video ROM
11	Test RTC
12	Test keyboard controller
13	OEM-specific test
14	Run memory test
15	Keyboard controller
16	OEM-specific test
17	Test keyboard controller
18	Run memory test
19	Execute OEM memory test
1A	Update RTC contents
1B	Initialize serial ports
1C	Initialize parallel ports
1D	Test math coprocessor
1E	Test floppy disk
1F	Test hard disk
20	Validate CMOS contents
21	Check keyboard lock
22	Set number lock on keyboard
23	OEM-specific test
29	Test adapter ROMs
2F	Call Int. 19 boot loader

TABLE 5.52   Mr. BIOS POST and Beep Codes

Beep*	POST	Description
LH-LLL	03	ROM-BIOS checksum failure
LH-HLL	04	DMA page register failure
LH-LHL	05	Keyboard controller self-test failure
LH-HHL	08	Memory refresh circuitry failure
LH-LLH	09	Master (16-bit) DMA controller failure
LH-HLH	09	Slave (8-bit) DMA controller failure
LH-LLLL	0A	Base 64 kbytes pattern test failure
LH-HLLL	0A	Base 64 kbytes parity circuitry failure
LH-LHLL	0A	Base 64 kbytes parity error
LH-HHLL	0A	Base 64 kbytes data bus failure
LH-LLHL	0A	Base 64 kbytes address bus failure
LH-HLHL	0A	Base 64 kbytes block access read failure
LH-LHHL	0A	Base 64 kbytes block access write failure
LH-HHHL	0B	Master 8259 failure
LH-LLLH	0B	Slave 8259 failure
LH-HLLH	0C	Master 8259 interrupt address failure
LH-LHLH	0C	Slave 8259 interrupt address failure
LH-HHLH	0C	8259 interrupt address error
LH-LLHH	0C	Master 8259 stuck interrupt error
LH-HLHH	0C	Slave 8259 stuck interrupt error
LH-LHHH	0C	System timer 8254 CH0/IRQ0 failure
LH-HHHH	0D	8254 channel 0 (system timer) failure
LH-LLLLH	0E	8254 channel 2 (speaker) failure
LH-HLLLH	0E	8254 OUT2 (speaker detect) failure
LH-LHLLH	0F	CMOS RAM read/write test failure
LH-HHLLH	0F	RTC periodic interrupt/IRQ8 failure
LH-LLHLH	10	Video ROM checksum failure
None	11	RTC battery discharged or CMOS contents corrupt
LH-HLHLH	12	Keyboard controller failure
None	12	Keyboard error—stuck key
LH-LHHLH	14	Memory parity error
LH-HHHLH	14	I/O channel error
None	14	RAM pattern test failed
None	15	Keyboard failure or no keyboard present
LH-LLLHH	17	A20 test failure due to 8042 timeout
LH-HLLHH	17	A20 gate stuck in disabled state
None	17	A20 gate stuck in asserted state
None	18	Parity circuit failure
None	19	Data bus test failed or address line test failed or block access read failure or block access read/write failure or banks decode to same location
LH-LHLHH	1A	Real-time clock (RTC) is not updating
None	1A	RTC settings are invalid

TABLE 5.52   **Mr. BIOS POST and Beep Codes** (*Continued*)

Beep*	POST	Description
None	1E	Diskette CMOS configuration invalid or diskette controller failure or diskette drive A: failure or diskette drive B: failure
None	1F	FDD CMOS configuration invalid or fixed disk C: failure or fixed disk D: failure
None	20	Fixed disk configuration change or diskette configuration change or serial-port configuration change or parallel-port configuration change or video configuration change or memory configuration change or coprocessor configuration change
None	21	System key is in locked position
None	29	Adapter ROM checksum failure

*L = low tone and H = high tone.

matching pre-1990 AMI codes). NCR-designed AT and MCA motherboards round out the selection. You should note that NCR XT systems send POST codes to LPT1 at port 378h or 3BCh, while the AT systems provide POST codes to port 80h and LPT1. MicroChannel systems supply POST codes to port 680h and LPT1. Before testing an NCR system, make sure that your POST card can read the proper port. Table 5.53 lists the codes for an NCR PC6 (XT-compatible), and Table 5.54 outlines the codes for NCR AT-compatible systems (3302, 3304, and 3728). The PC916 AT system codes are shown in Table 5.55.

TABLE 5.53   **POST Codes for NCR PC6 (XT) BIOS**

Hex code	Description
AA	8088 CPU failure
B1	2764 EPROM checksum failure
B2	8237 DMA controller failure
B3	8253 PIT failure
B4	RAM failure
B5	8259 PIC failure
B6	RAM parity error
BB	All tests passed; ready to boot

TABLE 5.54   **POST Codes for NCR AT BIOS**

Hex code	Description
01	Test the CPU registers
02	Test system support I/O
03	Test BIOS ROM checksum
04	Test DMA page registers
05	Test timer channel 1
06	Test timer channel 2
07	Test RAM refresh logic
08	Test base 64 kbytes
09	Test 8/16-bit bus conversion
0A	Test interrupt controller 1
0B	Test interrupt controller 2
0C	Test I/O controller
0D	Test CMOS RAM R/W operation
0E	Test battery power
0F	Test CMOS RAM checksum
10	Test CPU protected mode
11	Test video configuration
12	Test primary video controller
13	Test secondary video controller
20	Display results of tests to this point
21	Test DMA controller 1
22	Test DMA controller 2
23	Test system timer channel 0
24	Initialize interrupt controllers
25	Test interrupts
26	Test interrupts
30	Check base 640 kbytes memory
31	Check extended memory size
32	Test higher 8 address lines
33	Test base memory
34	Test extended memory
40	Test keyboard
41	Test keyboard
42	Test keyboard
43	Test keyboard
44	Test A20 gate
50	Set up hardware interrupt vectors
51	Enable interrupt timer channel 0
52	Check BIOS ROM
60	Test floppy disk controller and drive
61	Test hard drive controller
62	Initialize floppy drives
63	Initialize hard drives
70	Test real-time clock

TABLE 5.54   POST Codes for NCR AT BIOS
(*Continued*)

Hex code	Description
71	Set time of day in RTC
72	Check parallel interface port(s)
73	Check serial interface port(s)
74	Check for any option ROMs
75	Check math coprocessors
76	Enable keyboard and RTC interrupts
F0	System not configured properly (or hardware defect)
F1	Scan and execute any option ROMs
F2	Call Int. 19 boot loader

TABLE 5.55   POST Codes for NCR PC916 BIOS

Hex code	Description
01	Test CPU registers
03	Test BIOS ROM checksum
04	Test DMA page registers
05	Test timer channel 1
06	Test timer channel 2
0C	Test 8042 keyboard controller
14	Test disabling speed stretch at port 69h
15	Start refresh timer 1
16	Enable speed stretch at port 69h
17	Clear write-protect bit
1B	Test 64 kbytes shadow RAM
18	Write and test interrupt descriptor table
19	Verify RAM
02	Verify port 61h
07	Test refresh logic
08	Test base 64 kbytes RAM
09	Test 8/16-bit bus conversion logic
0A	Test interrupt mask register A
0B	Test interrupt mask register B
1A	Check 8042 keyboard controller
0D	Test CMOS RAM shutdown byte
0E	Test CMOS RAM battery power
0F	Test CMOS RAM checksum
10	Test CPU protected mode
11	Test video configuration
12	Initialize and test primary video controller
13	Primary video error

TABLE 5.55 **POST Codes for NCR PC916 BIOS**
(*Continued*)

Hex code	Description
20	Display results of tests to this point
21	Test DMA controller 1
22	Test DMA controller 2
23	Test timer 1 counter 0 840-ns clock timer
27	Test timer 2 counter 0 for NMI
28	Test timer 2 counter 1
24	Initialize both interrupt controllers
25	Check for unexpected interrupts
26	Wait for interrupt
30	Check base 640 kbytes memory
31	Check extended memory size
32	Test higher 8 address lines
33	Test base memory
34	Test extended memory (up to 256 Mbytes)
35	Test RAM in segment E000h
40	Test keyboard enable/disable
41	Test keyboard reset command
42	Test keyboard
43	Test keyboard
F4	Display speed setting
45	Initialize the mouse and enable IRQ1
44	Test address overrun capability
50	Set up hardware interrupt vectors
51	Enable IRQ0 interval interrupt from timer 0
60	Test for floppy and hard disk controllers and drives
61	Test disk controller
62	Initialize floppy drives
63	Initialize hard drives
74	Check and execute option ROMs from C8000h to DFFFFh
70	Test RTC
71	Set interval timer
72	Configure and test parallel interface
73	Configure and test serial interface
75	Test math coprocessor if installed
76	Enable keyboard and RTC
F0	Display any logged errors
F6	Test base memory
F7	Run comprehensive base memory test
F3	Go to setup if F1 was pressed

TABLE 5.55 POST Codes for NCR PC916 BIOS (*Continued*)

Hex code	Description
F4	Display speed setting
F5	Initialize counter 2 for speed testing
F1	Test system code at E0000h and copy video ROM to shadow memory
F2	Call Int. 19 boot loader
F6	Test base memory
F7	Test extended memory

Olivetti family

Olivetti has created a wide selection of BIOS versions to support its PCs since the early 1980s. Most Olivetti BIOS versions provide POST codes to a parallel port (278h or 378h). The Olivetti 1076/AT&T 6312WGS sends the POST codes shown in Table 5.56. The M24 (imported as an AT&T 6300) was Olivetti's first true PC clone, and its POST codes are shown in Table 5.57. A more recent BIOS is the Olivetti EISA BIOS 2.01, and its codes are presented in Table 5.58. Finally, Table 5.59 covers the POST codes for an Olivetti PS/2 BIOS.

TABLE 5.56 POST Codes for Olivetti 1076/AT&T BIOS

Pass	Fail	Description
41	7F	CPU flag and register test
42	7E	Check and verify CMOS shutdown code
43	7D	BIOS ROM checksum test
44	7C	Test the 8253 timer
45	7B	Start memory refresh
46	7A	Test the 8041 keyboard controller
47	79	Test the first 8 kbytes of RAM
48	78	Test protected-mode operation
49	77	Test CMOS RAM shutdown byte
4A	76	Test protected-mode operation
4B	75	Test RAM from 8 to 640 kbytes
4C	74	Test all RAM above 1 Mbyte
4D	73	Test NMI
4E	72	Test RAM parity system
50	71	Test 8259 PIC 1
51	6F	Test 8259 PIC 2
52	6E	Test DMA page register
53	6D	Test the 8237 DMA controller 1
54	6C	Test the 8237 DMA controller 2
55	6B	Test PIO port 61h

TABLE 5.56 POST Codes for Olivetti 1076/AT&T BIOS (*Continued*)

Pass	Fail	Description
56	6A	Test the keyboard controller
57	69	Test the CMOS clock/calendar IC
59	68	Test the CPU protected mode
5A	66	Test CMOS RAM battery
5B	65	Test CMOS RAM
5C	64	Verify CMOS RAM checksum
5D	63	Test parallel-port configuration
5E	62	Test serial-port configuration
5F	61	Test memory configuration below 640 kbytes
60	60	Test memory configuration above 1 Mbyte
61	5F	Detect and test math coprocessor
62	5E	Test configuration of game port adapter
62	5D	Test key lock switch
63	5D	Test hard drive configuration
64	5C	Configure floppy drives
66	5B	Test option ROMs
—	—	Call Int. 19 boot loader

TABLE 5.57 POST Codes for Olivetti M24 BIOS

Hex code	Description
Triangle	Test CPU registers and instructions
Triangle	Test system RAM
4 vertical lines	Test CPU call and trap instructions
Diamond	Initialize screen and printer drivers
EC0	8255 parallel interface IC test failed
EC1	6845 CRT controller IC test failed
EC2	1797 floppy disk controller chip failed
EC3	8253 timer IC failed
EC4	8251 keyboard interface failed
EC5	8251 keyboard test failed
EC6	8259 PIC IC test failed
EK0	Keyboard did not respond
EK1	Keyboard responds, but self-test failed
ED1	Disk drive 1 test failed
ED0	Disk drive 0 test failed
EI0	Nonvectored interrupt error
E11	Vectored interrupt error

NOTE: M24 codes are displayed on the monitor and sent to the printer port

TABLE 5.58   EISA BIOS 2.01

Hex code	Description
40	CPU flags and register test failed
41	BIOS ROM checksum test failed
42	Disable 8253 timer channel 1
43	8237 DMA controller test failed
44	8259 PIC test failed
45	Install the real interrupt vectors
48	Send beep and initialize all basic hardware

TABLE 5.59   POST Codes for Olivetti PS/2 BIOS

Hex code	Description
01	Test CPU
02	Check CMOS shutdown byte
03	Initialize the PIC
04	Test refresh
05	Test CMOS/RTC periodic interrupt
06	Test timer ratio
07	Test first 64 kbytes of RAM
08	Test 8042 keyboard controller
09	Test NMI
0A	Test 8254 PIT
0B	Test port 94h
0C	Test port 103h
0D	Test port 102h
0E	Test port 96h
0F	Test port 107h
10	Blank the display
11	Check the keyboard
12	Test CMOS RAM battery
13	Verify CMOS RAM checksum
14	Verify extended CMOS RAM checksum
15	Initialize system board and adapter
16	Initialize and test RAM
17	Test protected-mode registers
18	Test CMOS RAM shutdown byte
19	Test CMOS protected mode
1A	Initiate video adapter ROM scan
1B	Test BIOS ROM checksum
1C	Test PIC 1

TABLE 5.59   POST Codes for Olivetti PS/2 BIOS
(*Continued*)

Hex code	Description
1D	Test PIC 2
1E	Initialize interrupt vectors
1F	Test CMOS RAM
20	Test extended CMOS RAM
21	Test CMOS real-time clock
22	Test clock calendar
23	Dummy checkpoint
24	Test watchdog timer
25	Test 64 to 640 kbytes RAM
26	Configure lower 640 kbytes RAM
27	Test extended memory
28	Initialize extended BIOS data segment and log POST errors
29	Configure memory above 1 Mbyte
2A	Dummy checkpoint
2B	Test RAM parity
2C	Test DMA page registers
2D	Test DMA controller registers
2E	Test DMA transfer count register
2F	Initialize DMA controller
30	Test PIO 61
31	Test the keyboard
32	Initialize keyboard typematic rate and delay
33	Test auxiliary device
34	Test advanced protected mode
35	Configure parallel ports
36	Configure 8250 serial ports
37	Test and configure game math co-processor
38	Test and configure game port adapter
39	Configure and initialize hard disk
40	Initialize math coprocessor
42	Initiate adapter ROM scan
CC	Unexpected processor exception occurred
DD	Save DDNL status
EE	NMI handler shutdown
FF	Call Int. 19 boot loader

Phillips

Designed by Phillips Home Electronics in Canada, Phillips motherboards make use of a proprietary BIOS which sends POST codes to port 80h. An interesting aspect of Phillips BIOS is that the beep codes use the binary-coded decimal representations of the POST code (where a 1 causes a long beep and a 0 causes a short beep). As an example, a POST code of 17 has a BCD equivalent of (1 0111). This means that the corresponding beep code is (long, short, long, long, long). Table 5.60 shows the codes for a Phillips BIOS.

TABLE 5.60   POST Codes for Phillips BIOS

Hex code	Description
0A	DMA page register R/W bad
10	CMOS RAM R/W error
11	System BIOS ROM checksum error
12	Timer A error
13	DMA controller A error
14	DMA controller B error
15	Memory refresh error
16	Keyboard controller error
17	Keyboard controller error
19	Keyboard controller error
1C	Base 64 kbytes RAM error
1D	Base 64 kbytes RAM parity error
1F	LSI sync missing
21	PVAM register error
25	System options error
2B	Video sync error
2C	Video BIOS ROM error
2D	Monochrome/color configuration error
2E	No video memory detected
35	Interrupt controller error

TABLE 5.60   POST Codes for Phillips BIOS (*Continued*)

Hex code	Description
36	Byte swapper error
37	NMI error
38	Timer interrupt fault
39	LSI timer halted
3A	Main memory test error
3B	Keyboard error
3C	Keyboard interrupt error
3D	DDNIL scan halted and cache disabled
40	Diskette error
48	Adapter card error
4C	CMOS battery/checksum error
4D	System options error
52	Keyboard controller error
6A	Failure shadowing BIOS ROM
70	Memory size configuration error

Phoenix family

Phoenix Technologies Ltd. created one of the first IBM BIOS clones, and now has a very large share of the BIOS market. Part of its great appeal is that Phoenix makes its BIOS available to the OEM market, allowing its BIOS to be optimized by other PC makers. The classical Phoenix XT BIOS produces only a few POST codes (shown in Table 5.61). On the other hand, the Phoenix AT BIOS listed in Table 5.62 (for ISA/EISA/MCA systems) offers a proliferation of POST codes (as well as beep codes). POST codes for the Phoenix BIOS 4.0 are listed in Table 5.63.

TABLE 5.61   POST Codes for Phoenix Technologies XT 2.52 BIOS

Hex code	Description
01	Test 8253 system timer
02	First 64 kbytes RAM failure
03	First 1 kbyte parity check failed
04	Initialize the 8259 PIC IC
05	Second 1 kbyte RAM (BIOS data area) failed
—	Initialize the display

TABLE 5.62   POST Codes for Phoenix Technologies ISA/EISA/MCA BIOS

Hex code	Description
01	CPU register test
02	CMOS R/W test
03	Testing BIOS ROM checksum
04	Testing 8253 PIT IC
05	Initializing the 8237 DMA controller
06	Testing the 8237 DMA page register
08	RAM refresh circuit test
09	Test first 64 kbytes of RAM
0A	Test first 64 kbytes RAM data lines
0B	Test first 64 kbytes RAM parity
0C	Test first 64 kbytes RAM address lines
0D	Parity failure detected for first 64 kbytes RAM
10–1F	Data bit (0–15) bad in first 64 kbytes RAM
20	Slave DMA register faulty
21	Master DMA register faulty
22	Master PIC register faulty
23	Slave PIC register faulty
25	Initializing interrupt vectors
27	Keyboard controller test
28	Testing CMOS checksum and battery power
29	Validate CMOS contents
2B	Video initialization faulty
2C	Video retrace test failed
2D	Search for video ROM
2E	Test video ROM
30	Video system checks OK
31	Monochrome video mode detected
32	Color (40-column) mode detected
33	Color (80-column) mode detected
34	Timer tick interrupt test
35	CMOS shutdown byte test
36	Gate A20 failure (8042 KBC)
37	Unexpected interrupt
38	Extended RAM test
3A	Interval timer channel 2
3B	Test time-of-day clock
3C	Locate and test serial ports
3D	Locate and test parallel ports
3E	Locate and test math coprocessor
41	System board select bad
42	Extended CMOS RAM bad

TABLE 5.63 **POST Codes for Phoenix BIOS 4.0**

Beep	POST	Meaning
1-1-1-3	02	Verify real-mode operation
1-1-2-1	04	Get the CPU type
1-1-2-3	06	Initialize system hardware
1-1-3-1	08	Initialize chipset registers with POST values
1-1-3-2	09	Set POST flag
1-1-3-3	0A	Initialize CPU registers
1-1-4-1	0C	Initialize cache to initial POST values
1-1-4-3	0E	Initialize I/O
1-2-1-1	10	Initialize power management
1-2-1-2	11	Load alternative registers with POST values
1-2-1-3	12	Jump to UserPatch0
1-2-2-1	14	Initialize keyboard controller
1-2-2-3	16	BIOS ROM checksum
1-2-3-1	18	8254 timer initialization
1-2-3-3	1A	8237 DMA controller initialization
1-2-4-1	1C	Reset programmable interrupt controller
1-3-1-1	20	Test DRAM refresh
1-3-1-3	22	Test 8742 keyboard controller
1-3-2-1	24	Set ES segment to register to 4 Gbytes
1-3-3-1	28	Auto-size DRAM
1-3-3-3	2A	Clear 512 kbytes base RAM
1-3-4-1	2C	Test 512 base address lines
1-3-4-3	2E	Test 512 kbytes base memory
1-4-1-3	32	Test CPU bus-clock frequency
1-4-2-4	37	Reinitialize the motherboard chipset
1-4-3-1	38	Shadow system BIOS ROM
1-4-3-2	39	Reinitialize the cache
1-4-3-3	3A	Auto-size cache
1-4-4-1	3C	Configure advanced chipset registers
1-4-4-2	3D	Load alternative registers with CMOS values
2-1-1-1	40	Set initial CPU speed
2-1-1-3	42	Initialize interrupt vectors
2-1-2-1	44	Initialize BIOS interrupts
2-1-2-3	46	Check ROM copyright notice
2-1-2-4	47	Initialize manager for PCI options ROMs
2-1-3-1	48	Check video configuration against CMOS
2-1-3-2	49	Initialize PCI bus and devices
2-1-3-3	4A	Initialize all video adapters in system
2-1-4-1	4C	Shadow video BIOS ROM
2-1-4-3	4E	Display copyright notice
2-2-1-1	50	Display CPU type and speed
2-2-1-3	52	Test keyboard
2-2-2-1	54	Set key click if enabled
2-2-2-3	56	Enable keyboard
2-2-3-1	58	Test for unexpected interrupts

TABLE 5.63   POST Codes for Phoenix BIOS 4.0 (*Continued*)

Beep	POST	Meaning
2-2-3-3	5A	Display prompt "Press F2 to enter SETUP"
2-2-4-1	5C	Test RAM between 512 and 640 kbytes
2-3-1-1	60	Test expanded memory
2-3-1-3	62	Test extended memory address lines
2-3-2-1	64	Jump to UserPatch1
2-3-2-3	66	Configure advanced cache registers
2-3-3-1	68	Enable external and CPU caches
2-3-3-3	6A	Display external cache size
2-3-4-1	6C	Display shadow message
2-3-4-3	6E	Display nondisposable segments
2-4-1-1	70	Display error messages
2-4-1-3	72	Check for configuration errors
2-4-2-1	74	Test real-time clock
2-4-2-3	76	Check for keyboard errors
2-4-4-1	7C	Set up hardware interrupts vectors
2-4-4-3	7E	Test coprocessor if present
3-1-1-1	80	Disable onboard I/O ports
3-1-1-3	82	Detect and install external RS-232 ports
3-1-2-1	84	Detect and install external parallel ports
3-1-2-3	86	Reinitialize onboard I/O ports
3-1-3-1	88	Initialize BIOS data area
3-1-3-3	8A	Initialize extended BIOS data area
3-1-4-1	8C	Initialize floppy controller
3-2-1-1	90	Initialize hard disk controller
3-2-1-2	91	Initialize local bus hard disk controller
3-2-1-3	92	Jump to UserPatch2
3-2-2-1	94	Disable A20 address line
3-2-2-3	96	Clear huge ES segment register
3-2-3-1	98	Search for option ROMs
3-2-3-3	9A	Shadow option ROMs
3-2-4-1	9C	Set up power management
3-2-4-3	9E	Enable hardware interrupts
3-3-1-1	A0	Set time of day
3-3-1-3	A2	Check key lock
3-3-3-1	A8	Erase F2 prompt
3-3-3-3	AA	Scan for F2 key stroke
3-3-4-1	AC	Enter SETUP
3-3-4-3	AE	Clear in-POST flag
3-4-1-1	B0	Check for errors
3-4-1-3	B2	POST done—prepare to boot operating system
3-4-2-1	B4	One beep
3-4-2-3	B6	Check password (optional)
3-4-3-1	B8	Clear global descriptor table
3-4-4-1	BC	Clear parity checkers
3-4-4-3	BE	Clear screen (optional)

TABLE 5.63   POST Codes for Phoenix BIOS 4.0 (*Continued*)

Beep	POST	Meaning
3-4-4-4	BF	Check virus and backup reminders
4-1-1-1	C0	Try to boot with Int. 19
4-2-1-1	D0	Interrupt handler error
4-2-1-3	D2	Unknown interrupt error
4-2-2-1	D4	Pending interrupt error
4-2-2-3	D6	Initialize option ROM error
4-2-3-1	D8	Shutdown error
4-2-3-3	DA	Extended block move
4-2-4-1	DC	Shutdown 10 error
4-3-1-3	E2	Initialize the motherboard chipset
4-3-1-4	E3	Initialize refresh counter
4-3-2-1	E4	Check for forced flash
4-3-2-2	E5	Check HW status of ROM
4-3-2-3	E6	BIOS ROM is OK
4-3-2-4	E7	Do a complete RAM test
4-3-3-1	E8	Do OEM initialization
4-3-3-2	E9	Initialize interrupt controller
4-3-3-3	EA	Read in bootstrap code
4-3-3-4	EB	Initialize all vectors
4-3-4-1	EC	Boot the flash program
4-3-4-2	ED	Initialize the boot device
4-3-4-3	EE	Boot code was read OK

Quadtel family

The Quadtel Corporation provides BIOS versions for XT and AT systems. The POST codes for a Quadtel 16-kbyte XT BIOS are listed in Table 5.64. Table 5.65 illustrates the POST codes for a Quadtel AT 3.0 BIOS.

Tandon family

Tandon has been producing PC clones for many years. Its Type A BIOS (in Table 5.66) dates back to 1988, and its Type B BIOS (in Table 5.67) was introduced in 1992. Tandon also introduced a BIOS to support i486 EISA systems, which is listed in Table 5.68. All Tandon BIOS versions send codes to port 80h.

Zenith Orion

Although a few Zenith systems use Phoenix BIOS, the majority of Zenith systems use proprietary BIOS products. POST codes for the Zenith Orion 4.1E BIOS are shown in Table 5.69.

TABLE 5.64   POST Codes for Quadtel XT BIOS

Hex code	Description
03	Test CPU flags
06	Test CPU registers
09	Initialize any system-specific chipsets
0C	Test BIOS ROM checksum
0F	Initialize 8237 DMA page registers
12	Test 8237 DMA address and count registers
15	Initialize 8237 DMA
18	Test 8253 system timer IC (PIT)
1B	Initialize the 8253 PIT
1E	Start memory refresh test
21	Test the base 64 kbytes RAM
24	Set up interrupt vectors
27	Initialize 8259 PIC
2A	Test interrupt mask register
2D	Test for unexpected interrupt
30	Test V40 DMA if present
31	Test for DDNIL bits
33	Verify system clock interrupt
36	Test the keyboard
39	Set up interrupt table
3C	Read system configuration switches
3F	Test and initialize video
42	Locate and test COM ports
45	Locate and test LPT ports
48	Locate and test game adapter port
4B	Display BIOS copyright message on screen
4E	Calculate CPU speed
54	Test system memory
55	Test floppy drive
57	Initialize system before boot
5A	Call Int. 19 boot loader

TABLE 5.65   POST Codes for Quadtel AT 3.0 BIOS

Hex code	Description
02	Test CPU flags
04	Test CPU registers
06	Perform system hardware initialization
08	Initialize specific chipset registers
0A	Test BIOS ROM checksum
0C	Test 8237 DMA page registers
0E	Test 8254 PIT
10	Initialize the 8254 PIT
12	Test 8237 DMA controller
14	Initialize 8237 DMA controller
16	Initialize 8259 PIC
18	Test and set the 8259 PIC
1A	Test memory refresh
1C	Test base 64 kbytes memory
1E	Test base 64 kbytes memory
20	Test base 64 kbytes memory
22	Test keyboard and keyboard controller
24	Test CMOS checksum and battery
26	Start first protected-mode test
28	Check memory size
2A	Auto-size memory
2C	Set memory IC interleave
2E	Exit first protected-mode test
30	Unexpected shutdown
32	System board memory size
34	Relocate shadow RAM if available
36	Configure extended memory
38	Configure wait states
3A	Retest 64 kbytes base RAM
3C	Calculate CPU speed
3E	Get configuration from 8042 KBC
40	Configure CPU speed
42	Initialize interrupt vectors
44	Verify video configuration
46	Initialize the video system
48	Test unexpected interrupts
4A	Start second protected-mode test

TABLE 5.65   POST Codes for Quadtel AT 3.0 BIOS (*Continued*)

Hex code	Description
4B	Verify protected-mode instruction
4D	Verify protected-mode instruction
50	Verify protected-mode instruction
52	Verify protected-mode instruction
54	Verify protected-mode instruction
56	Unexpected exception
58	Test address line A20
5A	Test keyboard
5C	Determine AT or XT keyboard
5E	Start third protected-mode test
60	Test base memory
62	Test base memory address
64	Test shadow memory
66	Test extended memory
68	Test extended memory addresses
6A	Determine memory size
6C	Display error messages
6E	Copy BIOS to shadow memory
70	Test 8254 PIT
73	Test RTC
74	Test keyboard for stuck keys
76	Initialize system hardware
78	Locate and test the math coprocessor
7A	Determine COM ports
7C	Determine LPT ports
7E	Initialize the BIOS data area
80	Check for a floppy/hard drive controller
82	Test floppy disk
84	Test fixed disk
86	Check for option ROMs
88	Check for keyboard lock
8A	Wait for <F1> key pressed
8C	Final system initialization
8E	Call Int. 19 boot loader

TABLE 5.66   POST Codes for Tandon Type A BIOS

Hex code	Description
01	Test CPU flags and registers
02	Test BIOS ROM checksum
03	Test CMOS RAM battery
04	Test 8254 timer
05	8254 timer test failed
06	Test RAM refresh
07	Test first 16 kbytes RAM
08	Initialize interrupt vectors
09	Test 8259 PIC
0A	Configure temporary interrupt vectors
0B	Initialize interrupt vector table 1
0C	Initialize interrupt vector table 2
0D	Initialize fixed disk vector
0E	Interrupt vector test failed
0F	Clear keyboard controller
10	Keyboard controller test failed
11	Run keyboard controller self-test
12	Initialize equipment check data area
13	Check and initialize math coprocessor
14	Test CMOS RAM contents
15	Test and configure parallel ports
16	Test and configure serial ports
17	Call Int. 19 boot loader

TABLE 5.67   POST Codes for Tandon Type B BIOS

Hex code	Description
01	Cold boot initialization started
06	Initialize any specialized chipsets
07	Warm reboot starts here
08	Keyboard initialization passed
09	Keyboard self-test finished
0A	Test CMOS RAM battery
0B	Save CMOS RAM battery level in CMOS diagnostic register
0C	Finished saving CMOS battery condition
0D	Test 8254 PIT and disable RAM parity check
0E	8254 PIT test failed
0F	Initialize 8254 PIT channels and start memory refresh test
10	Refresh test failed
11	Test base 64 kbytes RAM
12	Base 64 kbytes RAM test failed

TABLE 5.67   POST Codes for Tandon Type B BIOS
(*Continued*)

Hex code	Description
13	Base 64 kbytes RAM test passed
14	Perform R/W test of CMOS RAM
15	CMOS RAM R/W test complete
16	Calculating CPU speed
18	Test and initialize 8259 PICs
1A	8259 PIC initialization complete
1B	Spurious interrupt detected
1C	Spurious interrupt did not occur
1D	Error—timer 0 interrupt failed
1E	8259 PIC tests passed
20	Set up interrupt vectors 02 to 1F
21	Set up interrupt vectors 70 to 77
22	Clear interrupt vectors 41 to 46
23	Read 8042 self-test result
24	Test for proper 8042 KBC self-test
25	Error—KBC self-test failed
26	8042 KBC self-test passed
27	Confirm DMA working
28	Initialize video system
29	Set video with cursor off
2A	Video parameters are initialized
2B	Enable NMI and I/O channel check
2C	Run RAM test to check RAM size
2D	RAM sizing complete
2E	Reset keyboard controller
2F	Initialize the CMOS RTC
30	Initialize floppy drive controller
31	Initialize hard disk controller
32	Disk controller has been initialized
33	Perform equipment check and initialize math coprocessor
34	Initialize serial and parallel ports
35	Test CMOS RAM battery level
36	Check for keystroke
37	Enable 8254 PIT channel 0
38	Configure cache memory
39	Enable keyboard interface and interrupts
3A	Setup finished—clear display
3B	Test the floppy and hard disk drives
3C	Scan and run any option BIOS ROMs between C800h and E000h
3D	Disable gate A20
3E	Gate A20 is disabled
3F	Call Int. 19 boot loader

TABLE 5.68   POST Codes for Tandon i486 EISA BIOS

Hex code	Description
01	Disable cache and EISA NMIs, enable BIOS ROM
05	Initialize address decoder and 640 kbytes RAM
06	Clear CMOS RAM shutdown flag
07	Test 8042 KBC
08	Run 8042 KBC self-test
AA	8042 KBC self-test result
09	Test BIOS ROM checksum
0A	Read CMOS registers 3 times
0B	Bad CMOS RAM battery
0C	Send command to port 61 to disable speaker
0D	Test 8254 PIT
0E	8254 PIT is faulty
0F	Enable and test memory refresh
10	Memory refresh failed
11	Check and clear first 64 kbytes of RAM
12	First 64 kbytes RAM failed
13	First 64 kbytes memory test passed
14	Test CMOS RAM
15	Shadow BIOS and set system speed high
16	Check CMOS shutdown flag
17	Reset was cold boot
18	Prepare 8259 PICs
19	8259 PIC initialization failed
1A	Test 8259 PIC
1B	Check for spurious interrupts
1C	Check system timer IC
1D	PIT failure
1E	Initialize interrupt vectors
1F	Initialize interrupt vectors 00 to 6F
20	Set vectors for interrupt 02-1F
21	Set interrupt vectors for 70–77
22	Clear interrupt vectors for 41 and 46
23	Read 8042 self-test results from DMA page register
24	Test for proper 8042 self-test result
25	8042 self-test failed
26	Initialize the 8042 keyboard controller
27	Check shutdown flag
28	Install video ROM and initialize video
29	Install video ROM, set for mono/color operation, and initialize video
2A	Check for bad CMOS RAM
2B	Check shutdown flag
2C	Test memory for proper size
2D	Display any error messages
2E	Initialize 8042 KBC

TABLE 5.68   POST Codes for Tandon i486 EISA BIOS (*Continued*)

Hex code	Description
2F	Initialize time of day in the RTC
30	Test for and initialize floppy disk controller
31	Enable C&T IDE interface and test for hard drive
32	Test and initialize 8259 DMA registers
33	Test and initialize math coprocessor
34	Test and initialize parallel and serial ports
35	Check CMOS RAM
36	Check for keyboard lock
37	Enable system clock tick, keyboard, and interrupt controller interrupts
38	Initialize RAM variables
39	Enter CMOS Setup mode if proper keystroke pressed
3A	Clear display
3B	Initialize floppy and fixed disk drives
3C	Scan and run option ROMs
3D	Clear CMOS shutdown flag and turn off gate A20
3E	Set interrupt vectors
3F	Call Int. 19 boot loader

TABLE 5.69   POST Codes for Zenith Orion 4.1E BIOS

Hex code	Description
02	Enter protected mode
03	Perform main board initialization
F0	Start basic hardware initialization
F1	Clear CMOS status locations
F2	Starting CLIO initialization
F3	Initialize SYSCFG register
F4	DXPI initialization for boot block
F5	Turning cache off
F6	Configure CPU socket
F7	Checking for math coprocessor
F8	82C206 default initialization
F9	Chipset default initialization
FF	End of machine-specific boot block
04	Check the flash ROM checksum
05	Flash ROM OK
3D	Save CPU ID
06	Reset or power-up
07	CLIO default initialization
08	SYSCFG registers initialized
09	CMOS RAM initialization
10	SCP initialized
11	DRAM autosize detection complete

TABLE 5.69   POST Codes for Zenith Orion 4.1E BIOS
(*Continued*)

Hex code	Description
12	Parity checking enabled
18	Video ROM test at C0000h
19	Internal video ROM checked
1A	Returning to real mode
1B	Internal video hardware enabled
1D	CPU clock frequency detected
1E	BIOS data area cleared
20	Reset
21	Continue after setting memory size
22	Continue after memory test
23	Continue after memory error
24	Continue with boot loader request
25	Jump to user code
26	Continue after protected mode passed
27	Continue after protected mode failed
28	Continue after extended protected-mode test
29	Continue after block move
2A	Jump to user code
30	Exit from protected mode
31	Test/reset passed
32	Check the ROM checksum
33	Clear the video screen
34	Check system DRAM configuration
35	Check CMOS contents
36	Turn off the UMB RAM
37	Test parity generation
38	Initialize system variables
39	Check for power errors
3A	Initialize SCP mode
3B	Test CMOS diagnostic power reset
3C	Test CPU reset
3D	Save CPU ID
3E	Initialize the video system
3F	Initialize the DMA controllers
40	System speed error detected
41	Test EEPROM checksum
42	Configure parallel ports, floppy disks, and hard disks
43	Test extended video BIOS
44	Turn cache off
45	Test extended RAM
46	Test base RAM
47	Determine the amount of memory in the system
48	Set warm boot flag
49	Clear 16 kbytes of base RAM

TABLE 5.69   POST Codes for Zenith Orion 4.1E BIOS
(*Continued*)

Hex code	Description
4A	Install BIOS interrupt vector
4B	Test system timer
4C	Initialize interrupt
4D	Enable default hardware initialization
4E	Determine global I/O configuration
4F	Initialize video
50	Initialize WD90C30 scratchpad
51	Check for errors before boot
53	Test system and initialize
55	Initialize the keyboard processor
56	Initialize the PS/2 mouse
57	Configure CLIO for mouse
58	Configure CLIO for LAN
59	Configure CLIO for SCSI
5A	Configure CLIO for WAM
5B	Wait for user to enter password
5C	Initialize and enable system clock
5D	Test and initialize the floppy drive
5E	Check for Z150-type disk
5F	Initialize hard drive subsystem
60	Set default I/O device parameters
61	Get LAN ID from LAN
62	Install option ROM(s) at C8000h
63	Install option ROM(s) at E0000h
64	Initialize the SCSI interface
65	Run with A20 line off
66	Turn off the SCP
67	Set machine speed based on CMOS contents
68	Turn on cache
69	Calibrate 1-ms constants
6A	Enable NMI
6C	Clear warm boot flag
6D	Check for errors before boot
6E	Call Int. 19 boot loader

POST board troubleshooting

Generally speaking, POST boards are among the best all-around PC hardware troubleshooting tools available. They are quick and easy to use; they are compatible across ISA, EISA, and MCA platforms; and even the simplest POST board can provide you with remarkable insight into a system's operation. The trouble with POST boards is that every BIOS, although testing virtually the same functions, uses different codes, and these are often cryptic and poorly documented (this chapter takes great pains to provide you with a fairly compre-hensive index of POST codes). Armed with the proper code list, a POST board can often pinpoint a fault to the exact IC, and if not to the exact IC, then certainly to the major subassembly.

Symptom 1: *The power and cooling fan(s) are on, but nothing else happens.*   In virtually all cases, you have a power problem.

■ *Check your ac.*   Start by using a multimeter to check the ac power available at the wall outlet. *Use extreme caution to protect yourself from accidental electrocution.* If the ac level is unusually low, try the PC in an outlet with an adequate voltage level.

■ *Check the power supply outputs.*   Check the power connector at the motherboard. Observe the power LEDs on the POST board. If one or more of the power LEDs are dim or absent, there may be a fault in the power supply. Replace the power supply.

Symptom 2: *After power-up, you hear the fan change pitch notice-ably (there may also be a chirping sound coming from the supply).* First, be aware that some PCs use a variable-speed fan to optimize cooling. If you hear the fan pitch vary, you should make sure that this is abnormal for your particular system before pursuing a repair.

■ *Check your ac.*   Start by using a multimeter to check the ac power available at the wall outlet. *Use extreme caution to protect yourself from accidental electrocution.* If the ac level is unusually low, try the PC in an outlet with an adequate voltage level.

■ *Check the power supply outputs.*   Check the power connector at the motherboard. Observe the power LEDs on the POST board. If one or more of the power LEDs are dim or absent, there may be a fault in the power supply. Replace the power supply.

Symptom 3: *You see one or more POST board power LEDs off, very dim, or flickering.*   In virtually all cases, the power supply has failed.

■ *Check the expansion bus.*   Before assuming that the problem is in the supply, try the POST board in a different socket—the expansion bus connector at that location may be bad.

■ *Replace the power supply.*   Try a known-good working power sup-ply in the system.

Symptom 4: *The Reset LED remains on (the POST display will probably remain blank).*   There is probably a problem with the "Power Good" signal.

■ *Check the power supply outputs.*   Check the power connector at the motherboard. Observe the power LEDs on the POST board. If one or more of the power LEDs are dim or absent, there may be a fault in the power supply. Replace the power supply.

■ *Replace the motherboard.* If the "Power Good" signal is correct, but Reset is still locked up, there is probably a defect on the motherboard. Replace the motherboard.

Symptom 5: *One or more activity LEDs are out (the POST display will probably remain blank).* Most POST boards provide several LEDs that are used to indicate signal activity on major bus lines. If one or more of these LEDs are out, there is probably a motherboard fault in the corresponding circuit.

■ *ALE*—the clock generator, CPU, DMA controller, or bus controller may have failed. Try replacing the motherboard.

■ *OSC*—the clock generator IC or time-base crystal may have failed. Replace those components, or replace the motherboard.

■ *CLK*—check for excessive ripple in the ac source. Try a clean ac source. There may also be a problem with the clock generator or time-base crystal. Replace those components or replace the motherboard.

■ *I/OR, I/OW*—check for excessive ripple or inadequate ground in the system power lines. Try a new power supply if necessary. There may also be a fault in the DMA controller, CPU, PIT, or PIC devices. Try another motherboard.

■ *MR/W*—there may be a fault in the DMA controller, bus controller, BIOS ROM, PIT, or PIC devices. Try another motherboard.

Symptom 6: *You hear a beep code pattern from the system speaker, but no POST codes are displayed.* Any beep pattern other than a single short beep indicates a serious system problem; however, there may be several reasons why the POST board is not displaying POST codes.

■ *Check your BIOS.* Make sure that the BIOS for your system actually generates POST codes—most do, but a few do not.

■ *Check your POST board.* Make sure that your POST board is set to read the I/O address to which the codes are being written. Many systems send codes to port 80h, but other ports such as 1080h, 680h, and 378h may be used. Configure the POST board to use the proper address.

■ *Try a different expansion slot.* Try the POST board in a different slot—the bus slot may be loose or defective.

■ *Try a new BIOS.* Replace the BIOS with an updated version.

Diagnostic Codes

Diagnostic codes are split into two sections: the test code and the fault code. The *test code* is simply the number that corresponds to the particular test being run. The *fault code* is a two-digit decimal number which corresponds to the specific type of error that is identified. A fault code of 00 indicates that *no* problem was found. For example, the message "100" means that the motherboard was tested (01), and that no errors were detected (00)—thus "0100," or just "100." If a fault code other than 00 appears, a problem has been detected which a technician will have to address. System initialization may or may not continue, depending on the location and severity of the error. Table 5.70 provides a relatively comprehensive list of diagnostic codes for XT, AT, and PS/2 systems.

TABLE 5.70   IBM Diagnostic Codes

System Board (01xx)	
101	Interrupt failure (unexpected interrupt)
102	BIOS ROM checksum error (PC, XT); timer error (AT, MCA)
103	BASIC ROM checksum error (PC, XT); timer interrupt error (AT, MCA)
104	Interrupt controller error (PC, XT); protected-mode error (AT, MCA)
105	Timer failure (PC, XT); keyboard controller failure (MCA)
106	System board converting logic test failure
107	System board adapter card or math coprocessor fault; hot NMI test failed (MCA)
108	System board timer bus failure
109	DMA test memory select failure
110	PS/2 system board memory problem (ISA); system board parity check error (MCA)
111	PS/2 adapter memory problem (ISA); memory adapter parity check error (MCA)
112	PS/2 watchdog time-out error
113	PS/2 DMA arbitration time-out error
114	PS/2 external ROM checksum error
115	Cache parity error, BIOS ROM checksum error, or DMA error
116	System board port R/W error
118	System board L2 cache error
119	2.88-Mbyte floppy drive installed but not supported by floppy disk controller
120	CPU self-test error
121	Unexpected hardware interrupt occurred
131	Cassette wrap test (PC)
132	DMA extended registers error
133	DMA verify logic error
134	DMA arbitration logic error
151	Battery, real-time clock, or CMOS RAM failure
152	Real-time clock or CMOS RAM failure
160	PS/2 system board ID not recognized
161	CMOS chip lost power—battery dead
162	CMOS checksum or CRC error
163	CMOS error—time and date not set (the clock not updating)

TABLE 5.70   IBM Diagnostic Codes (*Continued*)

System Board (01xx) (*Continued*)	
164	Memory size error—CMOS data does not match system memory found
165	PS/2 adapter ID mismatch
166	PS/2 adapter time-out—card busy
167	PS/2 system clock not updating
168	Math coprocessor error in the CMOS configuration
169	System board and processor card configuration mismatch
170	ASCII setup conflict error
171	Rolling bit test failure on CMOS shutdown byte
172	Rolling bit test failure on NVRAM diagnostic byte
173	Bad CMOS/NVRAM checksum
174	Bad system configuration
175	Bad EEPROM CRC
177	Bad password CRC
178	Bad EEPROM
179	NVRAM error log full
180x	Subaddress data error in slot x
181	Unsupported configuration
182	Password switch is not in the writing position
183	System halted—password required
184	Bad power-on password
185	Bad startup sequence
186	Password protection hardware error
187	Serial number error
188	Bad EEPROM checksum
189	Too many incorrect password attempts
191	Cache controller test failure (82385)
194	System board memory error
199	User-indicated device list not correct

System Memory (02xx)	
201	Memory error (physical location will probably be displayed)
202	Memory address line 0–15 error
203	Memory address line 16–23 error; line 16–31 error (MCA)
204	Memory remapped to compensate for error (PS/2)
205	Error in first 128 kbytes (PS/2 ISA) of RAM
207	BIOS ROM failure
210	System board memory parity error
211	Error in first 64 kbytes of RAM (MCA)
212	Watchdog timer error
213	DMA bus arbitration time-out
215	Memory address error; 64 kbytes on daughter/SIP 2 failed (70)
216	Memory address error; 64 kbytes on daughter/SIP 1 failed (70)

TABLE 5.70 **IBM Diagnostic Codes (*Continued*)**

	System Memory (02xx) (*Continued*)
221	ROM to RAM copy (shadowing) failed (MCA)
225	Wrong speed memory on system board (MCA)
230	Memory on motherboard and adapter board overlaps
231	Noncontiguous adapter memory installed
235	Stuck data line on memory module
241	Memory module 2 failed
251	Memory module 3 failed

	Keyboard (03xx)
301	Keyboard did not respond correctly (stuck key detected)
302	Keyboard locked (AT, models 25, 30)
303	Keyboard/system board interface error—keyboard controller fault
304	Keyboard or system unit error (keyboard clock stuck high)
305	Keyboard fuse failed on system board (PS/2 50, 60, 80) or +5-volt error (PS/2 70)
306	Unsupported keyboard attached
341	Keyboard error
342	Keyboard cable error
343	Enhancement card or cable error
365	Keyboard failure
366	Interface cable failure
367	Enhancement card or cable failure

	Monochrome Display Adapter (04xx)
401	Memory, horizontal sync frequency, or vertical sync test failure
408	User-indicated display attribute failure
416	User-indicated character set failure
424	User-indicated 80×25 mode failure
432	MDA card parallel-port test failure

	Color Graphics Adapter (05xx)
501	Memory, horizontal sync frequency, or vertical sync test failure
503	CGA adapter controller failure
508	User-indicated display attribute failure
516	User-indicated character set failure
524	User-indicated 80×25 mode failure
532	User-indicated 40×25 mode failure
540	User-indicated 320×200 graphics mode failure
548	User-indicated 640×200 graphics mode failure
556	Light pen test failed
564	User-indicated screen paging test failed

TABLE 5.70   IBM Diagnostic Codes (*Continued*)

Floppy Drives and Adapters (06xx)

601	General diskette or adapter test failure
602	Diskette boot sector is not valid
603	Diskette size error
604	Media sense error
605	Diskette drive locked
606	Diskette verify test failure
607	Write-protect error
608	Drive command error
610	Diskette initialization failure
611	Drive time-out error
612	NEC drive controller IC error
613	Floppy system DMA error
614	Floppy system DMA boundary overrun error
615	Drive index timing error
616	Drive speed error
621	Drive seek error
622	Drive CRC error
623	Sector not found error
624	Disk address mark error
625	NEC drive controller IC seek error
626	Diskette data compare error
627	Diskette change line error
628	Diskette removed from drive
630	Drive A: index stuck high
631	Drive A: index stuck low
632	Drive A: track 0 stuck off
633	Drive A: track 0 stuck on
640	Drive B: index stuck high
641	Drive B: index stuck low
642	Drive B: track 0 stuck off
643	Drive B: track 0 stuck on
645	No index pulse
646	Drive track 00 detection failed
647	No transitions on Read Data line
648	Format test failed
649	Incorrect media type in drive
650	Drive speed incorrect
651	Format failure
652	Verify failure
653	Read failure
654	Write failure
655	Drive controller error
656	Drive mechanism failure
657	Write-protect stuck in "protected" state

TABLE 5.70   IBM Diagnostic Codes (*Continued*)

	Floppy Drives and Adapters (06xx) (*Continued*)
658	Change line stuck in "changed" state
659	Write-protect stuck in "unprotected" state
660	Change line stuck in "unchanged" state

	Math Coprocessor (07xx)
701	MCP presence or initialization error
702	Exception errors test failure
703	Rounding test failure
704	Arithmetic test 1 failure
705	Arithmetic test 2 failure
706	Arithmetic test 3 (80387 only)
707	Combination test failure
708	Integer load/store test failure
709	Equivalent expressions errors
710	Exception (interrupt) errors
711	Save state errors
712	Protected-mode test failure
713	Voltage/temperature sensitivity test failure

	Parallel Printer Adapter (09xx)
901	Data register latch error
902	Control register latch error
903	Register address decode error
904	Address decode error
910	Status line wrap connector error
911	Status line bit 8 wrap error
912	Status line bit 7 wrap error
913	Status line bit 6 wrap error
914	Status line bit 5 wrap error
915	Status line bit 4 wrap error
916	Printer adapter interrupt wrap error
917	Unexpected printer adapter interrupt
92x	Feature register error

	Alternative Printer Adapter (10xx)
1001	Data register latch error
1002	Control register latch error
1003	Register address decode error
1004	Address decode error
1010	Status line wrap connector error
1011	Status line bit 8 wrap error
1012	Status line bit 7 wrap error
1013	Status line bit 6 wrap error
1014	Status line bit 5 wrap error
1015	Status line bit 4 wrap error

TABLE 5.70   IBM Diagnostic Codes (*Continued*)

Alternative Printer Adapter (10xx) (*Continued*)	
1016	Printer adapter interrupt wrap error
1017	Unexpected printer adapter interrupt
102x	Feature register error

Communication Devices (11xx)	
1101	16450/16550 UART error
1102	Card-selected feedback error
1103	Port 102h register test failure
1106	Serial option cannot be shut down
1107	Communications cable or system board error
1108	IRQ3 error
1109	IRQ4 error
1110	16450/16550 chip register failure
1111	UART control line internal wrap test failure
1112	UART control line external wrap test failure
1113	UART transmit error
1114	UART receive error
1115	UART transmit and receive data unequal—receive error
1116	UART interrupt function error
1117	UART baud rate test failure
1118	UART interrupt-driven receive external data wrap test error
1119	UART FIFO buffer failure
1120	UART interrupt enable register failure: all bits cannot be set
1121	UART interrupt enable register failure: all bits cannot be reset
1122	Interrupt pending—stuck on
1123	Interrupt ID register stuck on
1124	Modem control register failure: all bits cannot be set
1125	Modem control register failure: all bits cannot be reset
1126	Modem status register failure: all bits cannot be set
1127	Modem status register failure: all bits cannot be reset
1128	Interrupt ID error
1129	Cannot force overrun error
1130	No modem status interrupt
1131	Invalid interrupt pending
1132	No data ready
1133	No data available at interrupt
1134	No transmit holding at interrupt
1135	No interrupts
1136	No received line status interrupt
1137	No receive data available
1138	Transmit holding register not empty
1139	No modem status interrupt
1140	Transmit holding register not empty
1141	No interrupts

TABLE 5.70 **IBM Diagnostic Codes** (*Continued*)

Communication Devices (11xx) (*Continued*)

1142	No IRQ4 interrupt
1143	No IRQ3 interrupt
1144	No data transferred
1145	Maximum baud rate error
1146	Minimum baud rate error
1148	Time-out error
1149	Invalid data returned
1150	Modem status register error
1151	No DSR and delta DSR
1152	No DSR
1153	No delta DSR
1154	Modem status register not clear
1155	No CTS and delta CTS
1156	No CTS
1157	No delta CTS

Alternative Communications Devices (12xx)

1201	16450/16550 UART error
1202	Card-selected feedback error
1203	Port 102h register test failure
1206	Serial option cannot be shut down
1207	Communications cable or system board error
1208	IRQ3 error
1209	IRQ4 error
1210	16450/16550 chip register failure
1211	UART control line internal wrap test failure
1212	UART control line external wrap test failure
1213	UART transmit error
1214	UART receive error
1215	UART transmit and receive data unequal—receive error
1216	UART interrupt function error
1217	UART baud rate test failure
1218	UART interrupt-driven receive external data wrap test error
1219	UART FIFO buffer failure
1220	UART interrupt enable register failure: all bits cannot be set
1221	UART interrupt enable register failure: all bits cannot be reset
1222	Interrupt pending—stuck on
1223	Interrupt ID register stuck on
1224	Modem control register failure: all bits cannot be reset
1225	Modem control register failure: all bits cannot be reset
1226	Modem status register failure: all bits cannot be set
1227	Modem status register failure: all bits cannot be reset
1228	Interrupt ID error

TABLE 5.70 IBM Diagnostic Codes (*Continued*)

	Alternative Communications Devices (12xx) (*Continued*)
1229	Cannot force overrun error
1230	No modem status interrupt
1231	Invalid interrupt pending
1232	No data ready
1233	No data available at interrupt
1234	No transmit holding at interrupt
1235	No interrupts
1236	No received line status interrupt
1237	No receive data available
1238	Transmit holding register not empty
1239	No modem status interrupt
1240	Transmit holding register not empty
1241	No interrupts
1242	No IRQ4 interrupt
1243	No IRQ3 interrupt
1244	No data transferred
1245	Maximum baud rate error
1246	Minimum baud rate error
1248	Time-out error
1249	Invalid data returned
1250	Modem status register error
1251	No DSR and delta DSR
1252	No DSR
1253	No delta DSR
1254	Modem status register not clear
1255	No CTS and delta CTS
1256	No CTS
1257	No delta CTS

	Game Port Adapters (13xx)
1301	Game port adapter test failure
1302	Joystick test failure

	Matrix Printers (14xx)
1401	Printer test failure
1402	Printer not ready, not on-line, or out of paper
1403	Printer "no paper" error
1404	Matrix printer test failure; system board time-out
1405	Parallel adapter failure
1406	Printer presence test failed
1501	SDLC adapter test failure

	SDLC Communications Adapter (15xx)
1510	8255 port B failure
1511	8255 port A failure

TABLE 5.70 IBM Diagnostic Codes (*Continued*)

SDLC Communications Adapter (15xx) (*Continued*)	
1512	8255 port C failure
1513	8253 timer 1 did not reach terminal count
1514	8253 timer 1 output stuck on
1515	8253 timer 0 did not reach terminal count
1516	8253 timer 0 output stuck on
1517	8253 timer 2 did not reach terminal count
1518	8253 timer 2 output stuck on
1519	8273 port B error
1520	8273 port A error
1521	8273 command/read time-out error
1522	Interrupt level 4 error
1523	Ring Indicate stuck on
1524	Receive clock stuck on
1525	Transmit clock stuck on
1526	Test Indicate stuck on
1527	Ring Indicate not on
1528	Receive clock not on
1529	Transmit clock not on
1530	Test Indicate not on
1531	Data Set Ready not on
1532	Carrier Detect not on
1533	Clear-to-Send not on
1534	Data Set Ready stuck on
1535	Carrier Detect stuck on
1536	Clear-to-Send stuck on
1537	Interrupt level 3 failure
1538	Receive interrupt results error
1539	Wrap data compare error
1540	DMA channel 1 transmit error
1541	DMA channel 1 receive error
1542	8273 error-checking or status-reporting error
1547	Stray interrupt level 4 error
1548	Stray interrupt level 3 error
1549	Interrupt presentation sequence time-out
DSEA Units (16xx)	
1604	DSEA or twinaxial network adapter
1608	DSEA or twinaxial network adapter
1624 through 1658	DSEA system error
1662	DSEA interrupt level error
1664	DSEA system error
1668	DSEA interrupt level error
1669	DSEA diagnostics error
1674	DSEA diagnostics error
1684	DSEA device address error
1688	DSEA device address error

TABLE 5.70   IBM Diagnostic Codes (*Continued*)

Hard Drives and Adapters (17xx)	
1701	Fixed disk or adapter general error
1702	Drive and controller time-out error
1703	Drive seek error
1704	Drive controller failed
1705	Drive sector not found error
1706	Write fault error
1707	Drive track 00 error
1708	Head select error
1709	Bad ECC returned
1710	Sector buffer overrun
1711	Bad address mark
1712	Internal controller diagnostics failure
1713	Data compare error
1714	Drive not ready
1715	Track 00 indicator failure
1716	Diagnostics cylinder errors
1717	Surface read errors
1718	Hard drive type error
1720	Bad diagnostics cylinder
1726	Data compare error
1730	Drive controller error
1731	Drive controller error
1732	Drive controller error
1733	BIOS undefined error return
1735	Bad command error
1736	Data corrected error
1737	Bad drive track error
1738	Bad sector error
1739	Bad initialization error
1740	Bad sense error
1750	Drive verify error
1751	Drive read error
1752	Drive write error
1753	Drive random read test failure
1754	Drive seek test failure
1755	Drive controller failure
1756	Controller ECC test failure
1757	Controller head select failure
1780	Drive seek failure (drive 0)
1781	Drive seek failure (drive 1)
1782	Hard disk controller failure
1790	Diagnostic cylinder read error (drive 0)
1791	Diagnostic cylinder read error (drive 1)
I/O Expansion Unit (18xx)	
1801	Expansion unit POST error

TABLE 5.70   IBM Diagnostic Codes (*Continued*)

	I/O Expansion Unit (18xx) (*Continued*)
1810	Enable/disable failure
1811	Extender card wrap test failure while disabled
1812	High-order address lines failure while disabled
1813	Wait state failure while disabled
1814	Enable/disable could not be set on
1815	Wait state failure while enabled
1816	Extender card wrap test failure while enabled
1817	High-order address lines failure while enabled
1818	Disable not functioning
1819	Wait request switch not set correctly
1820	Receiver card wrap test failed
1821	Receiver high-order address lines failure

	Bisynchronous Communications Adapters (20xx)
2001	BSC adapter test failure
2010	8255 port A failure
2011	8255 port B failure
2012	8255 port C failure
2013	8253 timer 1 did not reach terminal count
2014	8253 timer 1 output stuck on
2015	8253 timer 2 did not reach terminal count
2016	8253 timer 2 output stuck on
2017	8251 Data-Set-Ready failed to come on
2018	8251 Clear-to-Send not sensed
2019	8251 Data-Set-Ready stuck on
2020	8251 Clear-to-Send stuck on
2021	8251 hardware reset failure
2022	8251 software reset command failure
2023	8251 software error-reset command failure
2024	8251 Transmit-Ready did not come on
2025	8251 Receive-Ready did not come on
2026	8251 could not force overrun error status
2027	Interrupt failure—no timer interrupt
2028	Interrupt failure—replace card or planar board
2029	Interrupt failure—replace card only
2030	Interrupt failure—replace card or planar board
2031	Interrupt failure—replace card only
2033	Ring Indicate signal stuck on
2034	Receive clock stuck on
2035	Transmit clock stuck on
2036	Test Indicate stuck on
2037	Ring Indicate not on
2038	Receive clock not on
2039	Transmit clock not on
2040	Test Indicate not on

TABLE 5.70 IBM Diagnostic Codes (*Continued*)

Bisynchronous Communications Adapters (20xx) (*Continued*)	
2041	Data-Set-Ready stuck on
2042	Carrier Detect not on
2043	Clear-to-Send not on
2044	Data-Set-Ready stuck on
2045	Carrier Detect stuck on
2046	Clear-to-Send stuck on
2047	Unexpected transmit interrupt
2048	Unexpected receive interrupt
2049	Transmit data did not equal receive data
2050	8251 detected overrun error
2051	Lost Data-Set-Ready signal during data wrap
2052	Receive time-out during data wrap

Alternative Bisynchronous Communications Adapters (21xx)	
2101	BSC adapter test failure
2110	8255 port A failure
2111	8255 port B failure
2112	8255 port C failure
2113	8253 timer 1 did not reach terminal count
2114	8253 timer 1 output stuck on
2115	8253 timer 2 did not reach terminal count
2116	8253 timer 2 output stuck on
2117	8251 Data-Set-Ready failed to come on
2118	8251 Clear-to-Send not sensed
2119	8251 Data-Set-Ready stuck on
2120	8251 Clear-to-Send stuck on
2121	8251 hardware reset failure
2122	8251 software reset command failure
2123	8251 software error-reset command failure
2124	8251 Transmit-Ready did not come on
2125	8251 Receive-Ready did not come on
2126	8251 could not force overrun error status
2127	Interrupt failure—no timer interrupt
2128	Interrupt failure—replace card or planar board
2129	Interrupt failure—replace card only
2130	Interrupt failure—replace card or planar board
2131	Interrupt failure—replace card only
2133	Ring Indicate signal stuck on
2134	Receive clock stuck on
2135	Transmit clock stuck on
2136	Test Indicate stuck on
2137	Ring Indicate not on
2138	Receive clock not on
2139	Transmit clock not on
2140	Test Indicate not on

TABLE 5.70   IBM Diagnostic Codes (*Continued*)

Alternative Bisynchronous Communications Adapters (21xx) (*Continued*)	
2141	Data-Set-Ready stuck on
2142	Carrier Detect not on
2143	Clear-to-Send not on
2144	Data-Set-Ready stuck on
2145	Carrier Detect stuck on
2146	Clear-to-Send stuck on
2147	Unexpected transmit interrupt
2148	Unexpected receive interrupt
2149	Transmit data did not equal receive data
2150	8251 detected overrun error
2151	Lost Data-Set-Ready signal during data wrap
2152	Receive time-out during data wrap
Cluster Adapters (22xx)	
22xx	A cluster adapter error has been encountered—replace the cluster adapter
Plasma Monitor Adapter (23xx)	
23xx	A plasma display fault has been detected—replace the plasma monitor assembly
Enhanced Graphics Adapter (24xx)	
2401	Video adapter test failure
2402	Video display (monitor) error
2408	User-indicated display attribute test failed
2409	Video display (monitor) error
2410	Video adapter error
2416	User-indicated character set test failed
2424	User-indicated 80 × 25 mode failure
2432	User-indicated 40 × 25 mode failure
2440	User-indicated 320 × 200 graphics mode failure
2448	User-indicated 640 × 200 graphics mode failure
2456	User-indicated light pen test failure
2464	User-indicated screen paging test failure
Alternative Enhanced Graphics Adapter (25xx)	
2501	Video adapter test failure
2502	Video display (monitor) error
2508	User-indicated display attribute test failed
2509	Video display (monitor) error
2510	Video adapter error
2516	User-indicated character set test failed
2524	User-indicated 80 × 25 mode failure
2532	User-indicated 40 × 25 mode failure

TABLE 5.70   IBM Diagnostic Codes (Continued)

Alternative Enhanced Graphics Adapter (25xx) (Continued)	
2540	User-indicated 320 × 200 graphics mode failure
2548	User-indicated 640 × 200 graphics mode failure
2556	User-indicated light pen test failure
2564	User-indicated screen paging test failure

PC/370-M Adapter (26xx)	
2601 through 2672	370-M (memory) adapter error
2673 through 2680	370-P (processor) adapter error
2681	370-M (memory) adapter error
2682 through 2697	370-P (processor) adapter error
2698	XT or AT/370 diagnostic diskette error

PC3277 Emulation Adapter (27xx)	
2701	3277-EM adapter error
2702	3277-EM adapter error
2703	3277-EM adapter error

3278/3279 Emulation Adapter (28xx)	
28xx	An emulation adapter fault has been detected—replace the adapter

Color/Graphics Printers (29xx)	
29xx	A general fault has been detected with the printer or its printer port—replace the printer or adapter port

Primary PC Network Adapter (30xx)	
3001	Network adapter test failure
3002	ROM checksum test failure
3003	Unit ID PROM test failure
3004	RAM test failure
3005	Host interface controller (HIC) test failure
3006	+/−12-volt dc test failure
3007	Digital loopback test failure
3008	Host-detected HIC failure
3009	Sync signal failure and no-go bit
3010	HIC test OK and no-go bit
3011	Go bit OK but no command 41
3012	Card not present
3013	Digital failure—fall-through
3015	Analog failure
3041	Hot carrier—on other card
3042	Hot carrier—on this card

Secondary PC Network Adapter (31xx)	
3101	Network adapter test failure
3102	ROM checksum test failure

TABLE 5.70 **IBM Diagnostic Codes (*Continued*)**

	Secondary PC Network Adapter (31xx) (*Continued*)
3103	Unit ID PROM test failure
3104	RAM test failure
3105	Host interface controller (HIC) test failure
3106	+/−12-volt dc test failure
3107	Digital loopback test failure
3108	Host-detected HIC failure
3109	Sync signal failure and no-go bit
3110	HIC test OK and no-go bit
3111	Go bit OK but no command 41
3112	Card not present
3113	Digital failure—fall-through
3115	Analog failure
3141	Hot carrier—on other card
3142	Hot carrier—on this card

	3270 PC/AT Display (32xx)
32xx	A fault has been detected in the display system—replace the display system

	Compact Printer Errors (33xx)
33xx	A fault has been detected in the printer or printer adapter—replace the printer or adapter

	Enhanced DSEA Units (35xx)
3504	Adapter connected to twinaxial cable during off-line test
3508	Workstation address error
3509	Diagnostic program failure; retry on new diskette
3540	Workstation address invalid
3588	Adapter address switch error
3599	Diagnostic program failure; retry on new diskette

	IEEE 488 (GPIB) Adapter (36xx)
3601	Adapter test failure
3602	Write error at serial poll mode register (SPMR)
3603	Adapter addressing problems
3610	Adapter cannot be programmed to listen
3611	Adapter cannot be programmed to talk
3612	Adapter control error
3613	Adapter cannot switch to standby mode
3614	Adapter cannot take control asynchronously
3615	Adapter cannot take control asynchronously
3616	Adapter cannot pass control
3617	Adapter cannot be addressed to listen
3618	Adapter cannot be unaddressed to listen
3619	Adapter cannot be addressed to talk

TABLE 5.70   **IBM Diagnostic Codes** (*Continued*)

IEEE 488 (GPIB) Adapter (36xx) (*Continued*)	
3620	Adapter cannot be unaddressed to talk
3621	Adapter cannot be addressed to listen with extended addressing
3622	Adapter cannot be unaddressed to listen with extended addressing
3623	Adapter cannot be addressed to talk with extended addressing
3624	Adapter cannot be unaddressed to talk with extended addressing
3625	Adapter cannot write to self
3626	Adapter error—cannot generate handshake signal
3627	Adapter error—cannot detect Device Clear (DCL) message
3628	Adapter error—cannot detect Selected Device Clear (SDC) message
3629	Adapter error—cannot detect end of transfer with EOI signal
3630	Adapter error—cannot detect end of transmission with EOI signal
3631	Adapter cannot detect END with 0-bit EOS
3632	Adapter cannot detect END with 7-bit EOS
3633	Adapter cannot detect Group Execute Trigger (GET)
3634	Mode 3 addressing not functioning
3635	Adapter cannot recognize undefined command
3636	Adapter error—cannot detect REM, REMC, LOK, or LOKC signals
3637	Adapter error—cannot clear REM or LOK signals
3638	Adapter cannot detect service request (SRQ)
3639	Adapter cannot conduct serial poll
3640	Adapter cannot conduct parallel poll
3650	Adapter error—cannot DMA to 7210
3651	Data error on DMA to 7210
3652	Adapter error—cannot DMA from 7210
3653	Data error on DMA from 7210
3658	Uninvoked interrupt received
3659	Adapter cannot interrupt on ADSC signal
3660	Adapter cannot interrupt on ADSC signal
3661	Adapter cannot interrupt on CO
3662	Adapter cannot interrupt on DO
3663	Adapter cannot interrupt on DI
3664	Adapter cannot interrupt on ERR
3665	Adapter cannot interrupt on DEC
3666	Adapter cannot interrupt on END
3667	Adapter cannot interrupt on DET
3668	Adapter cannot interrupt on APT
3669	Adapter cannot interrupt on CPT
3670	Adapter cannot interrupt on REMC
3671	Adapter cannot interrupt on LOKC
3672	Adapter cannot interrupt on SRQI

TABLE 5.70   IBM Diagnostic Codes (*Continued*)

IEEE 488 (GPIB) Adapter (36xx) (*Continued*)	
3673	Adapter cannot interrupt on terminal count on DMA to 7210
3674	Adapter cannot interrupt on terminal count on DMA from 7210
3675	Spurious DMA terminal count interrupt
3697	Illegal DMA configuration setting detected
3698	Illegal interrupt-level configuration setting detected
System Board SCSI Controller (37xx)	
37xx	The system board SCSI controller has failed—replace the motherboard
Data Acquisition Adapter (38xx)	
3801	Adapter test failure
3810	Timer read test failure
3811	Timer interrupt test failure
3812	Binary input 13 test failure
3813	Binary input 13 test failure
3814	Binary output 14—interrupt request test failure
3815	Binary output 0, count-in test failure
3816	Binary input strobe (STB), count-out test failure
3817	Binary output 0, Clear-to-Send (CTS) test failure
3818	Binary output 1, binary input 0 test failure
3819	Binary output 2, binary input 1 test failure
3820	Binary output 3, binary input 2 test failure
3821	Binary output 4, binary input 3 test failure
3822	Binary output 5, binary input 4 test failure
3823	Binary output 6, binary input 5 test failure
3824	Binary output 7, binary input 6 test failure
3825	Binary output 8, binary input 7 test failure
3826	Binary output 9, binary input 8 test failure
3827	Binary output 10, binary input 9 test failure
3828	Binary output 11, binary input 10 test failure
3829	Binary output 12, binary input 11 test failure
3830	Binary output 13, binary input 12 test failure
3831	Binary output 15, analog input CE test failure
3832	Binary output strobe (STB), binary output GATE test failure
3833	Binary input Clear-to-Send (CTS), binary input HOLD test failure
3834	Analog input Command Output (CO), binary input 15 test failure
3835	Counter interrupt test failure
3836	Counter read test failure
3837	Analog output 0 ranges test failure
3838	Analog output 1 ranges test failure
3839	Analog input 0 values test failure

TABLE 5.70 **IBM Diagnostic Codes (*Continued*)**

Data Acquisition Adapter (38xx) (*Continued*)	
3840	Analog input 1 values test failure
3841	Analog input 2 values test failure
3842	Analog input 3 values test failure
3843	Analog input interrupt test failure
3844	Analog input 23 address or value test failure

Professional Graphics Adapter (PGA) (39xx)	
3901	PGA test failure
3902	ROM1 self-test failure
3903	ROM2 self-test failure
3904	RAM self-test failure
3905	Cold start cycle power error
3906	Data error in communications RAM
3907	Address error in communications RAM
3908	Bad data detected while read/write to 6845 register
3909	Bad data detected in lower E0h bytes while read/writing 6845 registers
3910	Display bank output latch error
3911	Basic clock error
3912	Command control error
3913	Vertical sync scanner error
3914	Horizontal sync scanner error
3915	Intech error
3916	Lookup table (LUT) address error
3917	LUT "red" RAM chip error
3918	LUT "green" RAM chip error
3919	LUT "blue" RAM chip error
3920	LUT data latch error
3921	Horizontal display error
3922	Vertical display error
3923	Light pen error
3924	Unexpected error
3925	Emulator addressing error
3926	Emulator data latch error
3927 through 3930	Emulator RAM error
3931	Emulator horizontal/vertical display problem
3932	Emulator cursor position error
3933	Emulator attribute display problem
3934	Emulator cursor display error
3935	Fundamental emulation RAM problem
3936	Emulation character set problem
3937	Emulation graphics display error
3938	Emulation character display problem
3939	Emulation bank select error

TABLE 5.70   IBM Diagnostic Codes (*Continued*)

	Professional Graphics Adapter (PGA) (39xx) (*Continued*)
3940	Display RAM U2 error
3941	Display RAM U4 error
3942	Display RAM U6 error
3943	Display RAM U8 error
3944	Display RAM U10 error
3945	Display RAM U1 error
3946	Display RAM U3 error
3947	Display RAM U5 error
3948	Display RAM U7 error
3949	Display RAM U9 error
3950	Display RAM U12 error
3951	Display RAM U14 error
3952	Display RAM U16 error
3953	Display RAM U18 error
3954	Display RAM U20 error
3955	Display RAM U11 error
3956	Display RAM U13 error
3957	Display RAM U15 error
3958	Display RAM U17 error
3959	Display RAM U19 error
3960	Display RAM U22 error
3961	Display RAM U24 error
3962	Display RAM U26 error
3963	Display RAM U28 error
3964	Display RAM U30 error
3965	Display RAM U21 error
3966	Display RAM U23 error
3967	Display RAM U25 error
3968	Display RAM U27 error
3969	Display RAM U29 error
3970	Display RAM U32 error
3971	Display RAM U34 error
3972	Display RAM U36 error
3973	Display RAM U38 error
3974	Display RAM U40 error
3975	Display RAM U31 error
3976	Display RAM U33 error
3977	Display RAM U35 error
3978	Display RAM U37 error
3979	Display RAM U39 error
3980	Graphics controller RAM timing error
3981	Graphics controller read/write latch error
3982	Shift register bus output latch error
3983	Addressing error (vertical column of memory; U2 at top)

TABLE 5.70   **IBM Diagnostic Codes (Continued)**

Professional Graphics Adapter (PGA) (39xx) (Continued)	
3984	Addressing error (vertical column of memory; U4 at top)
3985	Addressing error (vertical column of memory; U6 at top)
3986	Addressing error (vertical column of memory; U8 at top)
3987	Addressing error (vertical column of memory; U10 at top)
3988 through 3991	Horizontal bank latch errors
3992	RAG/CAG graphics controller error
3993	Multiple write modes, nibble mask errors
3994	Row nibble (display RAM) error
3995	Graphics controller addressing error
5278 Display Attachment Unit and 5279 Display (44xx)	
44xx	A fault has been detected with the display system—replace the display system
IEEE 488 (GPIB) Interface Adapter (45xx)	
45xx	A fault has been detected with the GPIB—replace the adapter
ARTIC Multiport/2 Interface Adapter (46xx)	
4611	ARTIC adapter error
4612 or 4613	Memory module error
4630	ARTIC adapter error
4640 or 4641	Memory module error
4650	ARTIC interface cable error
Internal Modem (48xx)	
48xx	The internal modem has failed—replace the internal modem
Alternative Internal Modem (49xx)	
49xx	The alternative internal modem has failed—replace the alternate internal modem
PC Convertible LCD (50xx)	
5001	LCD buffer failure
5002	LCD font buffer failure
5003	LCD controller failure
5004	User-indicated PEL/drive test failed
5008	User-indicated display attribute test failed
5016	User-indicated character set test failed
5020	User-indicated alternative character set test failure

TABLE 5.70   IBM Diagnostic Codes (*Continued*)

PC Convertible LCD (50xx) (*Continued*)	
5024	User-indicated 80 × 25 mode test failure
5032	User-indicated 40 × 25 mode test failure
5040	User-indicated 320 × 200 graphics test failure
5048	User-indicated 640 × 200 graphics test failure
5064	User-indicated paging test failure

PC Convertible Portable Printer (51xx)	
5101	Portable printer interface failure
5102	Portable printer busy error
5103	Portable printer paper or ribbon error
5104	Portable printer time-out
5105	User-indicated print pattern test error

Financial Communication System (56xx)	
56xx	A fault has been detected in the financial communication system—replace the financial communication system

Phoenix BIOS/Chipset Specific Error Codes (70xx)	
7000	Chipset CMOS failure
7001	Shadow RAM failure (ROM not shadowed to RAM)
7002	Chipset CMOS configuration data error

Voice Communications Adapter (VCA) (71xx)	
7101	Adapter test failure
7102	Instruction or external data memory error
7103	PC-to-VCA interrupt error
7104	Internal data memory error
7105	DMA error
7106	Internal registers error
7107	Interactive shared memory error
7108	VCA-to-PC interrupt error
7109	DC wrap error
7111	External analog wrap and tone output error
7114	Telephone attachment test failure

3.5-in Floppy Disk Drive (73xx)	
7301	Diskette drive/adapter test failure
7306	Diskette change line error
7307	Write-protected diskette
7308	Drive command error
7310	Diskette initialization failure—track 00 error
7311	Drive time-out error
7312	NEC drive controller IC error
7313	DMA error
7314	DMA boundary overrun error

TABLE 5.70 IBM Diagnostic Codes (*Continued*)

3.5-in Floppy Disk Drive (73xx) (*Continued*)	
7315	Drive index timing error
7316	Drive speed error
7321	Drive seek error
7322	Drive CRC check error
7323	Sector not found error
7324	Address mark error
7325	NEC controller IC seek error
8514/A Display Adapter (74xx)	
7426	8514 display error
7440 through 7475	8514/A memory module error
4216 Page Printer Adapter (76xx)	
7601	Adapter test failure
7602	Adapter card error
7603	Printer error
7604	Printer cable error
PS/2 Speech Adapter (84xx)	
84xx	A fault has been detected in the speech adapter—replace the speech adapter
2-Mbyte XMA Memory Adapter (85xx)	
85xx	A fault has been detected in the memory adapter—replace the memory adapter
PS/2 Pointing Device (86xx)	
8601	Pointing device; mouse time-out error
8602	Pointing device; mouse interface error
8603	System board; mouse interrupt failure
8604	Pointing device or system board error
8611	System bus error
8612	TrackPoint II error
8613	System bus or TrackPoint II error
MIDI Interface (89xx)	
89xx	A fault has been detected in the MIDI adapter—replace the MIDI adapter
3363 Worm Optical Drive/Adapters (91xx)	
91xx	A fault has been detected in the drive or adapter—replace the adapter and the drive
SCSI Adapter (W/32-bit Cache) (96xx)	
96xx	A fault has been detected in the SCSI adapter—replace the adapter board

TABLE 5.70   IBM Diagnostic Codes (*Continued*)

Multiprotocol Adapters (100xx)	
10001	Presence test failure
10002	Card selected feedback error
10003	Port 102h register test failure
10004	Port 103h register test failure
10006	Serial option cannot be disabled
10007	Cable error
10008	IRQ3 error
10009	IRQ4 error
10010	UART register failure
10011	Internal wrap test of UART control line failed
10012	External wrap test of UART control line failed
10013	UART transmit error
10014	UART receive error
10015	UART receive error—data not equal to transmit data
10016	UART interrupt error
10017	UART baud rate test failure
10018	UART receive external wrap test failure
10019	UART FIFO buffer failure
10026	8255 Port A error
10027	8255 Port B error
10028	8255 Port C error
10029	8254 timer 0 error
10030	8254 timer 1 error
10031	8254 timer 2 error
10032	Bi-sync Data Set Ready (DSR) response error
10033	Bi-sync Clear-to-Send (CTS) error
10034	8251 hardware reset test failed
10035	8251 function generator
10036	8251 status error
10037	Bi-sync timer interrupt error
10038	Bi-sync transmit interrupt error
10039	Bi-sync receive interrupt error
10040	Stray IRQ3 error
10041	Stray IRQ4 error
10042	Bi-sync external wrap error
10044	Bi-sync data wrap error
10045	Bi-sync line status error
10046	Bi-sync time-out error during wrap test
10050	8273 command acceptance or time-out error
10051	8273 Port A error
10052	8273 Port B error
10053	SDLC modem status logic error
10054	SDLC timer IRQ4 error
10055	SDLC IRQ4 error
10056	SDLC external wrap error

TABLE 5.70 IBM Diagnostic Codes (*Continued*)

Multiprotocol Adapters (100xx) (*Continued*)	
10057	SDLC interrupt results error
10058	SDLC data wrap error
10059	SDLC transmit interrupt error
10060	SDLC receive interrupt error
10061	DMA channel 1 transmit error
10062	DMA channel 1 receive error
10063	8273 status detect failure
10064	8273 error detect failure

Internal 300/1200-bps Modem (101xx)	
10101	Presence test failure
10102	Card-selected feedback error
10103	Port 102h register test error
10106	Serial option cannot be disabled
10108	IRQ3 error
10109	IRQ4 error
10110	UART chip register failure
10111	UART control line internal wrap test failure
10113	UART transmit error
10114	UART receive error
10115	UART error—transmit and receive data not equal
10116	UART interrupt function error
10117	UART baud rate test failure
10118	UART interrupt-driven receive external data wrap test failure
10125	Modem reset result code error
10126	Modem general result code error
10127	Modem S-registers write/read error
10128	Modem echo on/off error
10129	Modem enable/disable result codes error
10130	Modem enable number/word result codes error
10133	Connect results for 300 baud not received
10134	Connect results for 1200 baud not received
10135	Modem fails local analog loopback 300-baud test
10136	Modem fails local analog loopback 1200-baud test
10137	Modem does not respond to escape/reset sequence
10138	S-register 13 shows incorrect parity or number of data bits
10139	S-register 15 shows incorrect bit data

ESDI or MCA IDE Drive/Adapters (104xx)	
10450	Write/read test failed
10451	Read verify test failed
10452	Seek test failed
10453	Wrong drive type indicated
10454	Controller failed sector buffer test
10455	Controller failed—invalid

TABLE 5.70   IBM Diagnostic Codes (*Continued*)

ESDI or MCA IDE Drive/Adapters (104xx) (*Continued*)	
10456	Controller diagnostic command failure
10461	Drive format error
10462	Controller head select error
10463	Drive write/read sector error
10464	Drive primary defect map unreadable
10465	Controller ECC 8-bit error
10466	Controller ECC 9-bit error
10467	Drive soft seek error
10468	Drive hard seek error
10469	Drive soft seek error count exceeded
10470	Controller attachment diagnostic error
10471	Controller wrap mode interface error
10472	Controller wrap mode drive select error
10473	Error during ESDI read verify test
10480	Seek failure on drive 0
10481	Seek failure on drive 1
10482	Controller transfer acknowledge error
10483	Controller reset error
10484	Controller head select 3 selected bad
10485	Controller head select 2 selected bad
10486	Controller head select 1 selected bad
10487	Controller head select 0 selected bad
10488	Read gate command error
10489	Read gate command error
10490	Diagnostic read error on drive 0
10491	Diagnostic read error on drive 1
10492	Drive 1 controller error
10493	Drive 1 reset error
10499	Controller failure

5.25-in External Disk Drive/Adapter (107xx)	
107xx	A fault has been detected in the drive or adapter—replace the adapter and drive

SCSI Adapter (16-bit W/O Cache) (112xx)	
112xx	A fault has been detected in the SCSI adapter—replace the SCSI adapter

System Board SCSI Adapter (113xx)	
113xx	A fault has been detected in the SCSI adapter—replace the motherboard

CPU Board (129xx)	
12901	Processor test failed
12902	CPU board cache test failed

TABLE 5.70   **IBM Diagnostic Codes (Continued)**

CPU Board (129xx) (Continued)	
12904	Second-level (L2) cache failure
12905	Cache enable/disable errors
12907	Cache fatal error
12908	Cache POST program error
12912	Hardware failure
12913	MCA bus time-out
12914	Software failure
12915	CPU board error
12916	CPU board error
12917	CPU board error
12918	CPU board error
12919	CPU board error
12940	CPU board error
12950	CPU board error
12990	CPU serial number mismatch

P70/P75 Plasma Display Adapter (149xx)	
14901	Plasma display adapter failure
14902	Plasma display adapter failure
14922	Plasma display failure
14932	External display device failure

XGA Display Adapter (152xx)	
152xx	A fault has been detected in the XGA adapter—replace the adapter

120-Mbyte Internal Tape Drive (164xx)	
164xx	A fault has been detected in the tape drive—replace the tape drive

6157 Streaming Tape Drive (165xx)	
16520	Streaming tape drive failure
16540	Tape attachment adapter failure

Primary Token-Ring Network Adapters (166xx)	
166xx	A fault has been detected with the network adapter—replace the network adapter

Secondary Token-Ring Network Adapters (167xx)	
167xx	A fault has been detected with the network adapter—replace the network adapter

PS/2 Wizard Adapter (180xx)	
18001	Interrupt controller failure
18002	Incorrect timer count

TABLE 5.70   IBM Diagnostic Codes (*Continued*)

	PS/2 Wizard Adapter (180xx) (*Continued*)
18003	Timer interrupt failure
18004	Sync check interrupt failure
18005	Parity check interrupt failure
18006	Access error interrupt failure
18012	Bad checksum
18013	MCA bus interface error
18021	Wizard memory compare or parity error
18022	Wizard memory address line error
18023	Dynamic RAM controller failure
18029	Wizard memory byte enable error
18031	Wizard memory expansion module compare or parity error
18032	Wizard memory expansion module address line error
18039	Wizard memory expansion module byte enable error

	DBCS Japanese Display Adapter (185xx)
185xx	A fault has been detected in the display adapter—replace the adapter

	80286 Memory Expansion Option Module (194xx)
194xx	A fault has been detected in the memory module—replace the memory module

	Image Adapter (200xx)
200xx	A fault has been detected in the image adapter—replace the image adapter

	Unknown SCSI Devices (208xx)
208xx	A fault has been detected in an unknown SCSI device—systematically isolate and replace the defective SCSI device

	SCSI Removable Disk (209xx)
209xx	A fault has been detected in the SCSI removable disk—replace the removable disk

	SCSI Fixed Disk (210xx)
210xx	A fault has been detected in the SCSI fixed disk—replace the fixed disk

CMOS/RTC Issues

CMOS RAM holds all of the PC's configuration and setup information. The RTC keeps track of the system's date and time. Both elements are backed up by a battery while system power is off. Any
problems with CMOS RAM, the RTC, or the battery can inhibit the
system's operation. Before you try diagnosing the problem, there are
several things for you to check:

- *Check the battery placement.* Make sure that the CMOS backup
  battery is fresh and installed properly (make sure your polarities
  are correct). For coin cells, the battery clips should contact the cell
  securely. For battery packs, the battery connector should be
  attached to the proper motherboard connector.

- *Check your motherboard jumpers.* Motherboards typically use a
  jumper to select between an on-board battery and a battery pack.
  Make sure the battery jumper (if present) is set correctly.

- *Check the CMOS/RTC IC.* Make sure that the CMOS/RTC IC is
  installed correctly in its socket and is in the proper orientation.

- *CMOS Setup entries.* If you add new drives to the system or
  replace the battery, you must enter new setup information into the
  CMOS. Before suspecting CMOS/RTC problems, always check to
  see that the CMOS entries are all correct.

Symptom 1: *The PC loses its system setup each time the power is
turned off.* In almost all cases, the CMOS battery has failed or has
been inserted backward.

- *Check the battery.* Make sure that the battery has been installed
  correctly.

- *Replace the battery.* Try another battery in the system.

Symptom 2: *The PC refuses to keep track of the time and/or date.*
You find that the CMOS contents are right (not being lost when
power is removed). In most cases, the RTC circuit has failed.

- *Replace the CMOS/RTC IC.* If the CMOS/RTC IC is mounted as
  a plug-in module, try a known-good CMOS/RTC IC in the system.

- *Replace the motherboard.* If the CMOS/RTC IC is soldered to the
  motherboard, you may have to replace the entire motherboard.

Symptom 3: *The newly installed battery refuses to keep CMOS contents.* Chances are very good that the battery has been installed
backward.

- *Check the battery installation.* Make sure that the battery has
  been installed correctly and completely.

- *Check the battery jumper(s).* If you are shifting from a coin cell to
  a battery pack (or vice versa), make sure that the motherboard
  battery jumper is set to the correct selection.

6

Video and Sound Troubleshooting

Video and sound are certainly two of the most exciting aspects of the PC. New video systems promise high performance, with resolutions and color depths that simply weren't practical a few years ago. Enhanced video systems even provide support for features like video-conferencing and MPEG video playback. Today's sound boards offer symphonic sound with MIDI and wave table synthesis. Taken together, video and sound supply the backbone of a computer's multimedia capability. Still, the advances in video and sound have not come without a price—namely, the demand for computing power. In addition, advanced chipsets and their drivers are sometimes incompatible with PC configurations. This chapter looks at background and troubleshooting for video and sound systems.

Video Adapters

The conventional frame buffer is the oldest and best-established type of video adapter. The term *frame buffer* refers to the adapter's operation—image data is loaded and stored in video memory one "frame" at a time. Frame buffer architecture (as shown in Fig. 6.1) has changed very little since PCs first started displaying text and graphics. A typical frame buffer video board is composed of four major sections:

- *CRTC (cathode-ray-tube controller).* A highly integrated controller which generates control signals and manages the video adapter's operation. The functions of the CRTC are now normally handled by video chipsets.

- *VRAM (video RAM).* An amount of RAM used to store image data which is processed and passed to the monitor.

- *Character ROM.* A relatively small ROM used to hold the dot patterns of text characters. The character ROM is disabled while the video adapter is in the graphics mode.

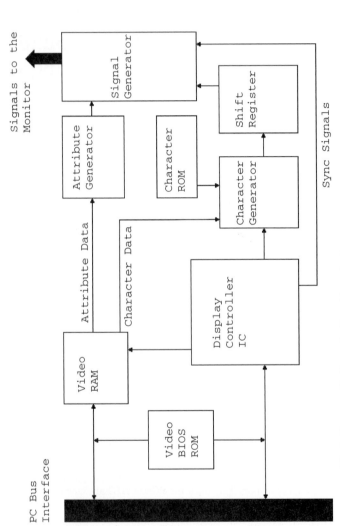

Figure 6.1 Block diagram of a frame buffer video adapter.

326

- *Video BIOS.*   A ROM used to hold the low-level instructions need-ed to operate the video board. All video adapters from EGA onward use video BIOS in one form or another.

Graphics accelerators

Video designers seek to overcome the limitations of conventional video adapters by incorporating processing power on the video board itself rather than relying on the system CPU for graphic processing. By off-loading work from the system CPU and assigning the graph-ics processing to local processing components, graphics performance can be improved by a factor of three or more. There are several means of acceleration depending on the sophistication of the board. *Fixed-function* acceleration relieves the load on the system CPU by providing adapter support for a limited number of specific functions such as BitBlt or line draws. Fixed-function accelerators were an improvement over frame buffers, but do not offer the performance of more sophisticated accelerators. A *graphics accelerator* uses an application-specific IC (ASIC) which intercepts graphics tasks and processes them without the intervention of the system CPU. Graphics accelerators are perhaps the most cost-effective type of accelerator. *Graphics coprocessors* are the most sophisticated type of accelerator. The coprocessor acts as a CPU which is dedicated to handling image data. Current graphics coprocessors such as the TMS34010 and TMS34020 represent the *Texas Instruments Graphical Architecture* (TIGA), which is broadly used for high-end accelerators. Unfortunately, not all graphics coprocessors increase performance enough to warrant the higher cost.

Figure 6.2 shows the block diagram for a typical graphics acceler-ator. The core of the accelerator is the graphics IC (or chipset). The graphics IC connects directly with the PC expansion bus. Graphics commands and data are translated into pixel data, which is stored in video RAM. High-performance video memory offers a second data bus which is routed directly to the board's RAMDAC (random-access memory digital-to-analog converter). The graphics IC directs RAM-DAC operation and ensures that VRAM data is available. The RAM-DAC then translates video data into red, green, and blue analog sig-nals along with horizontal and vertical synchronization signals. Output signals generated by the RAMDAC drive the monitor. This architecture may appear simple, but that is due to the extremely high level of integration of the ICs and chipsets being used.

Video standards

As video technology developed for the PC, there have been a number of important standards that you should be familiar with:

- *MDA* (*Monochrome Display Adapter—1981*).   The Monochrome Display Adapter is the oldest video adapter available for the PC. Text is available in 80-column × 25-row format using 9 × 14-pixel characters, as shown in Table 6.1. Being a text-only system, MDA offered no graphics capability, but it achieved popularity because

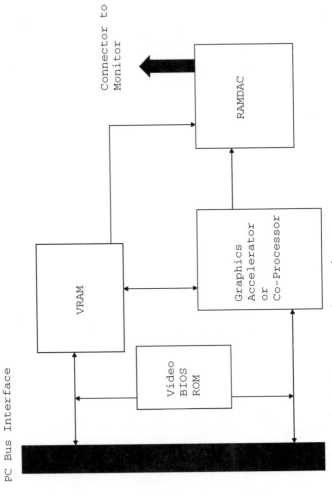

PC Bus Interface

Connector to Monitor

Figure 6.2 Block diagram of a graphics accelerator.

TABLE 6.1   Comparison of Video Modes and Standards

Standard	Resolution(s)	Colors	Mode	Text format	Vertical scan	Horizontal scan
MDA	N/A	N/A	Text	80 × 25	50 Hz	18.432 kHz
CGA	320 × 200	16	Text	40 × 25	60 Hz	15.750 kHz
	640 × 200	16	Text	80 × 25	60 Hz	15.750 kHz
	160 × 200	16	Graphics	n/a	60Hz	15.750 kHz
	320 × 200	4	Graphics	40 × 25	60 Hz	15.750 kHz
	640 × 200	2	Graphics	80 × 25	60 Hz	15.750 kHz
EGA	320 × 350	16	Text	40 × 25	60 Hz	21.850 kHz
	640 × 350	16	Text	80 × 25	60 Hz	21.850 kHz
	720 × 350	4	Text	80 × 25	50 Hz	18.432 kHz
	320 × 200	16	Graphics	40 × 25	60 Hz	15.750 kHz
	620 × 200	16	Graphics	80 × 25	60 Hz	15.750 kHz
	640 × 350	4	Graphics	80 × 25	50 Hz	18.432 kHz
	640 × 350	16	Graphics	80 × 25	60 Hz	21.850 kHz
PGA	320 × 200	16	Text	40 × 25	60 Hz	15.750 kHz
	640 × 200	16	Text	80 × 25	60 Hz	15.750 kHz
	320 × 200	4	Graphics	40 × 25	60 Hz	15.750 kHz
	640 × 200	2	Graphics	80 × 25	60 Hz	15.750 kHz
	640 × 480	256	Graphics	n/a	60 Hz	30.480 kHz
MCGA	320 × 400	16	Text	40 × 25	70 Hz	31.500 kHz
	640 × 400	16	Text	80 × 25	70 Hz	31.500 kHz
	320 × 200	4	Graphics	40 × 25	70 Hz	31.500 kHz
	640 × 200	2	Graphics	80 × 25	70 Hz	31.500 kHz
	640 × 480	2	Graphics	80 × 30	60 Hz	31.500 kHz
	320 × 200	256	Graphics	40 × 25	70 Hz	31.500 kHz
VGA	360 × 400	16	Text	40 × 25	70 Hz	31.500 kHz
	720 × 400	16	Text	80 × 25	70 Hz	31.500 kHz
	320 × 200	4	Graphics	40 × 25	70 Hz	31.500 kHz
	640 × 200	2	Graphics	80 × 25	70 Hz	31.500 kHz
	720 × 400	16	Text	80 × 25	70 Hz	31.500 kHz
	320 × 200	16	Graphics	40 × 25	70 Hz	31.500 kHz
	640 × 200	16	Graphics	80 × 25	70 Hz	31.500 kHz
	640 × 350	4	Graphics	80 × 25	70 Hz	31.500 kHz
	640 × 350	16	Graphics	80 × 25	70 Hz	31.500 kHz
	640 × 480	2	Graphics	80 × 30	60 Hz	31.500 kHz
	640 × 480	16	Graphics	80 × 30	60 Hz	31.500 kHz
	320 × 200	256	Graphics	40 × 25	70 Hz	31.500 kHz
8514	1024 × 768	256	Graphics	85 × 38	43.48 Hz	35.520 kHz
	640 × 480	256	Graphics	80 × 34	60 Hz	31.500 kHz
	1024 × 768	256	Graphics	146 × 51	43.48 Hz	35.520 kHz

TABLE 6.1 Comparison of Video Modes and Standards (*Continued*)

Standard	Resolu-tion(s)	Colors	Mode	Text format	Vertical scan	Horizontal scan
XGA	360 × 400	16	Text	40 × 25	70 Hz	31.500 kHz
	720 × 400	16	Text	80 × 25	70 Hz	31.500 kHz
	320 × 200	4	Graphics	40 × 25	70 Hz	31.500 kHz
	640 × 200	2	Graphics	80 × 25	70 Hz	31.500 kHz
	720 × 400	16	Text	80 × 25	70 Hz	31.500 kHz
	320 × 200	16	Graphics	40 × 25	70 Hz	31.500 kHz
	640 × 200	16	Graphics	80 × 25	70 Hz	31.500 kHz
	640 × 350	4	Graphics	80 × 25	70 Hz	31.500 kHz
	640 × 350	16	Graphics	80 × 25	70 Hz	31.500 kHz
	640 × 480	2	Graphics	80 × 30	60 Hz	31.500 kHz
	640 × 480	16	Graphics	80 × 30	60 Hz	31.500 kHz
	320 × 200	256	Graphics	40 × 25	70 Hz	31.500 kHz
	1056 × 400	16	Text	132 × 25	70 Hz	31.500 kHz
	1056 × 400	16	Text	132 × 43	70 Hz	31.500 kHz
	1056 × 400	16	Text	132 × 56	70 Hz	31.500 kHz
	1056 × 400	16	Text	132 × 60	70 Hz	31.500 kHz
	1024 × 768	256	Graphics	85 × 38	43.48 Hz	35.520 kHz
	640 × 480	65,536	Graphics	80 × 34	60 Hz	31.500 kHz
	1024 × 768	256	Graphics	128 × 54	43.48 Hz	35.520 kHz
	1024 × 768	256	Graphics	146 × 51	43.48 Hz	35.520 kHz

1	Ground
2	Ground
3	n/a
4	n/a
5	n/a
6	(+) Intensity
7	(+) Video
8	(+) Horizontal Sync
9	(−) Vertical Sync

MDA

Figure 6.3 MDA video pinout.

of its relatively low cost, good text display quality, and integrated printer port. Figure 6.3 shows the video connector pinout for an MDA board. The 9-pin monitor connection uses four active TTL signals; intensity, video, horizontal, and vertical. *Video* and *intensity* signals provide the on/off and high/low intensity information for each pixel. The *horizontal* and *vertical* signals control the monitor's synchronization. MDA boards have long been obsolete, and the probability of your encountering one is remote at best.

- *CGA (Color Graphics Adapter—1981).* The Color Graphics Adapter was the first to offer color text and graphics modes for the PC. A 160 × 200 low-resolution mode offered 16 colors, but such low resolution received very little attention. A 320 × 200 medium-resolution graphics mode allowed finer graphic detail, but with only 4 colors. The highest-resolution mode provided 640 × 200 with 2 colors (usually black and one other color). The relationship between resolution and colors is important, since a CGA *frame* requires 16 kbytes of video RAM. Providing 640 × 200 resolution results in 128,000 pixels. With 8 bits able to represent 8 pixels (128,000/8), 16,000 bytes are adequate. Providing 320 × 200 resolution results in 64,000 pixels, but with 2 bits needed to represent 1 pixel (4 pixels/byte) (64,000/4), 16,000 bytes are still required. Figure 6.4 shows the pinout for a typical CGA video connector. Like the earlier MDA design, CGA video signals reserve pins 1 and 2 as ground lines, while the horizontal sync signal is produced on pin 8 and the vertical sync signal is produced on pin 9. CGA is strictly a digital display system, with TTL signals used on the Red (3), Green (4), Blue (5), and Intensity (6) lines.

- *EGA (Enhanced Graphics Adapter—1984).* The demand for higher resolutions and color depths drove designers to introduce the next generation of video adapter, known as the *Enhanced Graphics Adapter.* One of the unique appeals of EGA was its backward compatibility—an EGA board would emulate CGA and MDA modes on the proper monitor, as well as providing its native resolutions and color depths when using an EGA monitor. EGA is known for its 320 × 200 × 16, 640 × 200 × 16, and 640 × 350 × 16 video modes. More memory is needed for EGA, and 128 kbytes is common for EGA boards (although many boards can be expanded to 256 kbytes). The EGA connector pinout is illustrated in Fig. 6.5. TTL signals are used to provide Primary Red (3), Primary Green (4), and Primary Blue (5) color signals. When a set of secondary color signals (or color *intensity* signals) such as Red Intensity (2), Green

1	Ground
2	Ground
3	Red
4	Green
5	Blue
6	Intensity
7	n/a
8	Horizontal Sync
9	Vertical Sync

CGA

Figure 6.4 CGA video pinout.

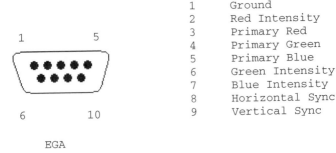

1	Ground
2	Red Intensity
3	Primary Red
4	Primary Green
5	Primary Blue
6	Green Intensity
7	Blue Intensity
8	Horizontal Sync
9	Vertical Sync

EGA

Figure 6.5 EGA video pinout.

Intensity (6), and Blue Intensity (7), is added, the total of six color control signals allows the EGA to produce up to 64 possible colors. However, although 64 colors are possible, only 16 of those colors are available in the palette at any one time. Pin 8 carries the horizontal sync signal, pin 9 carries the vertical sync signal, and pin 1 remains ground.

■ *PGA (Professional Graphics Adapter—1984).* The Professional Graphics Adapter was introduced in 1984. This system offered a then-revolutionary display capability of 640 × 480 × 256. Three-dimensional rotation and graphic clipping was included as a hardware function, and the adapter could update the display at 60 frames per second. The PGA was incredibly expensive and beyond the reach of all but the most serious business user. In actual operation, a PGA system required two or three expansion boards, so it also represented a serious commitment of limited system space. Ultimately, PGA failed to gain any significant market acceptance. It is unlikely that you will ever encounter a PGA board—most that ever saw service in PCs have since been upgraded.

■ *MCGA (Multi-Color Graphics Array—1987).* The Multi-Color Graphics Array was originally integrated into the motherboard of IBM's PS/2-25 and PS/2-30. As Table 6.1 shows, MCGA supports all of the CGA video modes, and also offers several new video modes, including a 320 × 200 × 256 mode that has become a preferred mode for game software. MCGA was one of the first graphic systems to use analog color signals rather than TTL signals. Analog signals were necessary to allow MCGA to produce its 256 colors using only three primary color lines. IBM also took the opportunity to employ a new, high-density 15-pin connector, as shown in Fig. 6.6. One of the striking differences between the "analog" connector and older TTL connectors is the use of an individual ground line for each color. Careful grounding is vital, since any signal noise on the analog lines will result in color anomalies. If you inspect a video cable closely, you will find that one or both ends are terminated with a square metal box which actually contains a noise filter. It is important to realize that although the MCGA

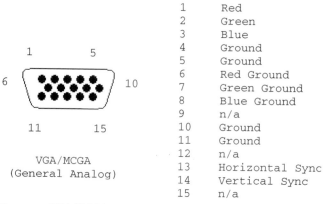

1	Red
2	Green
3	Blue
4	Ground
5	Ground
6	Red Ground
7	Green Ground
8	Blue Ground
9	n/a
10	Ground
11	Ground
12	n/a
13	Horizontal Sync
14	Vertical Sync
15	n/a

Figure 6.6   VGA/MCGA video pinout.

could *emulate* CGA modes, older TTL monitors were no longer compatible.

- *VGA (Video Graphics Array—1987).*   The Video Graphics Array was introduced along with MCGA and implemented in other members of the PS/2 line. The line between MCGA and VGA has always been a bit fuzzy, since both were introduced simultaneously (and use the same 15-pin video connector) and VGA can handle every mode that MCGA can. For all practical purposes, we can say that MCGA is a *subset* of VGA. It is VGA that provides the familiar 640×480×16 screen mode which has become the baseline for Microsoft Windows displays. The use of analog color signals allows VGA systems to produce a palette of 16 colors from 262,144 possible colors. VGA also provides backward compatibility for all older screen modes. Although the PS/2 line has been discontinued, the flexibility and backward compatibility of VGA proved so successful that VGA adapters were soon developed for the PC. For a time, VGA support was considered to be "standard equipment" for all new PCs, but SVGA boards have largely replaced VGA systems, and most SVGA adapters offer full VGA support.

- *8514 (1987).*   The 8514/A video adapter is a high-resolution system that was also developed for the PS/2. In addition to full support for MDA, CGA, EGA, and VGA modes, the 8514/A can display 256 colors at 640 × 480 and 1024 × 768 (interlaced) resolutions. Unfortunately, the 8514/A was a standard ahead of its time. The lack of available software and the demise of the PS/2 line doomed the 8514/A to extinction before it could become an accepted standard. Today, the XGA is rapidly becoming the PC standard for high-resolution/high-color display systems.

- *SVGA (Super Video Graphics Array).*   Ever since VGA became the de facto standard for PC graphics, there has been a strong demand from PC users to move beyond the 640 × 480 × 16 limit imposed by "conventional" VGA to provide higher resolutions and color depths. As a result, a new generation of extended or *super VGA* (SVGA) adapters have moved into the PC market. Unlike VGA, which adhered to strict hardware configurations, there is no generally accepted standard on which to develop an SVGA board (this is why there is no SVGA reference in Table 6.1). Each manufacturer makes an SVGA board which supports a variety of different—and not necessarily compatible—video modes. For example, one manufacturer may produce an SVGA board capable of 1024 × 768 × 65,536, while another manufacturer may produce a board that reaches 640 × 480 × 16 million (more than 16 million colors).

This mixing and matching of resolutions and color depths has resulted in a very fractured market—no two SVGA boards are necessarily capable of the same things. This proliferation of video hardware also makes it impossible for applications software to take advantage of super video modes without *video drivers*. Windows takes particular advantage of video drivers, since the Windows interface allows *all* Windows applications to use the same graphics system rather than requiring a driver for every application, as is necessary in DOS. Using an incorrect, obsolete, or corrupted video driver can be a serious source of problems for SVGA installations. The one common attribute of SVGA boards is that *most* offer full support for conventional VGA (which requires no video drivers). There are only a handful of SVGA board manufacturers that abandon conventional VGA support.

The Video Electronics Standards Association (VESA) has started the push for SVGA standards by proposing the VESA BIOS Extension—a *universal* video driver. The extension would provide a uniform set of functions that would allow application programs to detect a card's capabilities and use the optimum adapter configuration regardless of how the particular board's hardware is designed. Many of the quality SVGA boards in production today support the VESA BIOS Extensions, and it is worthwhile to recommend boards that support VESA SVGA. Some SVGA boards even incorporate the extensions into the video BIOS ROM, which saves the RAM space that would otherwise be needed by a video driver.

- *XGA (1990).* The XGA and XGA/2 are 32-bit high-performance video adapters developed by IBM to support MicroChannel-based PCs. XGA design with MicroChannel architecture allows the adapter to take control of the system for rapid data transfers. The XGA standards are shown in Table 6.1. You can see that MDA, CGA, EGA, and VGA modes are all supported for backward compatibility. In addition, several color depths are available at 1024 × 768 resolution, and a photo-realistic 65,536 colors are available at 640 × 480 resolution. To improve performance even further, fast video RAM and a graphics coprocessor are added to the XGA design. For the time being, XGA is limited to high-performance applications in MicroChannel systems. The migration to ISA-based PCs has been slow because the ISA bus is limited to 16 bits and does not support *bus mastering* as MicroChannel buses do. For PCs, SVGA adapters will likely provide extended screen modes as they continue to grow in sophistication as graphics accelerators.

Video speed factors

There is no *one* element that defines the performance of an accelerator board. Overall performance is actually a combination of five major factors: (1) the video accelerator IC, (2) the video RAM, (3) the video BIOS/drivers, (4) the RAMDAC, and (5) the bus architecture.

- *Video chipset.* The video accelerator IC itself (or the graphics chipset being used) is at the core of the accelerator board. The type of IC (fixed-function, graphics accelerator, or graphics coprocessor) loosely defines the board's capabilities. All other factors being equal, a board with a graphics accelerator will certainly perform better than a fixed-function accelerator. Companies like ATI Technologies, Advance Logic, Chips & Technologies, Headland Technology, Matrox Electronic Systems, and Primus Technology develop many of the accelerator ICs in use today. Many of the ICs provide a 32-bit data bus (even newer designs are providing a 64-bit data bus) and sustain very high data rates, but a data bottleneck across a 16-bit expansion bus can seriously degrade the IC's capability. This means that you should match the recommended board to the particular system—a state-of-the-art graphics accelerator will not necessarily make your old i286 shine.

- *Video RAM.* Video adapters rely on RAM to hold image data, and accelerators are no exception. While the current amount of video RAM typically varies from 512 kbytes to 2 Mbytes (some accelerator boards offer 4 Mbytes), the *amount* of RAM is not so important to a video accelerator as the RAM's *speed*. Faster memory permits faster reading and writing of image data, so adapter performance is improved. Specialized video RAM (VRAM)—memory devices with two separate data buses which can be read from and written to simultaneously—is reputed to be superior to conventional dynamic RAM (DRAM), such as the kind used for ordinary PC memory. Recent advances in DRAM speed have narrowed that gap while still remaining very economical. At this point, adapters with fast DRAM are just about as fast as adapters with specialized video RAM for video modes up to $1024 \times 768 \times 256$. For higher modes and color depths found on high-end accelerators, specialized video RAM is still the way to go for optimum performance.

- *Video BIOS and drivers.* Software is often considered as an afterthought to adapter design, yet it plays a surprisingly important role in accelerator performance. Even the finest accelerator board can bog down when it is run with careless, loosely written code. There are two classes of software that you must be concerned with: video BIOS and drivers. The video BIOS is *firmware* (software that is permanently recorded on a memory device such as a ROM). Video BIOS holds the programming that allows the accelerator to interact with DOS applications software. VESA BIOS extensions are now being used as part of the video BIOS for many accelerators as well as for conventional frame-buffer adapters. Adding VESA BIOS extensions to video BIOS eliminates the need to load another device driver.

However, there are compelling advantages to video drivers. Windows works quite well with drivers (and ignores video BIOS entirely). Unlike BIOS ROMs, which can never change once they are programmed, a video driver can change very quickly as bugs are corrected and enhancements are made. The driver can be downloaded from a manufacturer's BBS or its forum on CompuServe (or some other on-line information service) and installed on your system in a matter of minutes without your ever having to disassemble the PC. It is also possible for you to use third-party video drivers. Hardware manufacturers are not always adept at writing efficient software. A third-party driver developed by an organization that specializes in software may actually let your accelerator perform better than the original driver shipped from the manufacturer.

- *The RAMDAC.*   Just about every analog video system in service today is modeled after the 15-pin VGA scheme, which uses three separate analog signals to represent the three primary colors. The color for each pixel must be broken down into its component red, green, and blue levels, and those levels must be converted into their analog equivalents. The conversion from digital values to analog levels is handled by a digital-to-analog converter (or DAC). Each conversion also requires a certain amount of time. Faster DACs are needed to support faster horizontal refresh rates. Remember that each video adapter uses a *palette,* which is a subset of the colors that can possibly be produced. Even though a monitor may be able to produce 262,144 colors, a VGA board can produce only 256 of those colors in any 256-color mode. Older video boards stored the palette entries in registers, but the large-palette video modes now available (64,000 colors through 16 million colors) require the use of RAM. Boards that incorporate a RAMDAC (random-access memory digital-to-analog converter) are preferred, since using memory integrated with DACs tends to be much faster than accessing discrete RAM elsewhere on the board.

- *Bus architecture.*   Graphic data must be transferred between the PC motherboard and the adapter, as you saw early in this section. Such transfer takes place across the PC's *expansion bus.* If data can be transferred between the PC and the adapter at a faster rate, video performance should improve. Consequently, the choice of bus *architecture* has a significant impact on video performance. Video accelerators are available to support three bus architectures: ISA, VL, and PCI.

The venerable industry standard architecture (ISA) has remained virtually unchanged since its introduction with the PC/AT in the early 1980s. ISA continues to be a mature interface standard for most IBM-compatible expansion devices. The sheer volume of ISA systems currently in service guarantees that ISA will remain on desktops for at least another 10 years. However,

ISA's 16-bit data bus width, its lack of advanced features such as interrupt sharing or bus mastering, and its relatively slow 8.33-MHz operating speed form a serious bottleneck to the incredible volume of video data demanded by Windows and many DOS applications. ISA works, but it is no longer the interface of choice to achieve optimum video performance. When recommending an accelerator product, look to the newer buses for best results.

The Video Electronics Standards Association (VESA) has invested a great deal of time and effort in developing a standard bus interface which has been optimized for video operation. In essence, this new video bus is "local" to the system CPU, which allows faster access without the 8.33-MHz limitation imposed by ISA. The actual bus speed is limited by the system clock speed. The VESA local bus (VL bus) has achieved a remarkable level of industry acceptance and success in boosting video performance, especially when used with a high-quality graphics accelerator board. However, the 32-bit VL bus is generally limited to video systems. Other peripherals such as IDE hard drive controllers have been built for the VL bus, but it is far too early to predict their acceptance. As a result, current VL-compatible PCs typically offer only one or two VL expansion slots—the other expansion slots are ISA. Just about every accelerator product on the market today is available in a VL bus implementation. VL accelerators are a safe, inexpensive choice for current systems.

Intel's Peripheral Component Interconnect (PCI) bus is one of the newest and most exciting bus architectures to reach the PC. The PCI bus runs at 33 MHz and offers a full 64-bit data bus which can take advantage of new 64-bit CPUs such as Intel's Pentium. While the PCI bus also hopes to overcome the speed and functional limitations of ISA, the PCI architecture is intended to support all types of PC peripherals (not just video boards). Current PCI video boards are relatively expensive and appear to be delivering performance that is roughly equivalent to VL adapters, but as 64-bit CPUs and motherboards become common, it is likely that PCI boards will easily outperform 32-bit VL boards while their prices drop sharply. At the time of this writing, no PCI-compatible peripherals other than video adapters are known to be in mass production.

Video troubleshooting

Symptom 1: *The computer is on, but there is no display (the PC seems to initialize properly).* In most cases, there is a problem with your monitor or video board installation.

■ *Check the beep codes.* If there are beep codes during initialization, the video adapter may be defective or installed incorrectly. Check Chapter 5 for specific beep codes.

■ *Check the monitor.* Make sure that the monitor is plugged in, turned on, set for proper brightness, and connected to the video adapter securely.

■ *Check for hardware conflicts.* Video boards do not use interrupts or DMA channels, but they do use memory addresses. If the video board's memory addresses conflict with those of other devices in the system, the video board may not work.

■ *Check for exclusions.* You may need to add an "exclude" switch to your memory manager's command line to prevent other devices from using the memory spaces required by the video board.

Symptom 2: *There is no display, and you hear a series of beeps when the PC initializes.* The video adapter failed to initialize during the system's POST.

■ *Check the video board installation.* Make sure that the video board is installed securely and completely in the expansion slot. Often, flexing of the motherboard can allow the video board to "pop out" of the bus slot.

■ *Replace the video board.* If problems persist, try a known-good video board in the system.

Symptom 3: *You see large blank bands at the top and bottom of the display in some screen modes, but not in others.* Multifrequency and multimode monitors are not auto-sizing correctly. This is not necessarily a defect, but it can cause some confusion.

■ *Check the monitor.* If the monitor is not auto-sizing, it will not compensate for changes in screen resolution. Try a different monitor.

■ *Replace the video board.* Your particular video board may not be providing the proper sync polarity signals to drive the monitor's auto-sizing features. Try a known-good video board instead.

Symptom 4: *The display image rolls.* Vertical synchronization is not keeping the image steady (horizontal sync may also be affected). This problem is typical of a monitor that cannot display a particular screen mode.

■ *Check the monitor.* If the monitor is not capable of supporting a particular video mode, try a different monitor instead.

■ *Reconfigure the software.* Set your application or Windows to use a different screen resolution.

■ *Replace the video adapter.* If the monitor is supposed to operate properly but does not, the video adapter sync circuits may be defective.

Symptom 5: *An error message indicating an invalid system configuration appears on system startup.* The system CMOS backup battery has probably failed. This is typically a symptom that occurs in older systems.

■ *Check your CMOS Setup.*   Look for the entry marked "Video System" and make sure that it is set for EGA/VGA. If there are any other video setup entries, make sure they are all set properly. Replace the CMOS backup battery if necessary.

Symptom 6: *Garbage appears on the screen or the system hangs up.* There are a variety of reasons why the display may be distorted.

■ *Check your monitor.*   Some older multifrequency monitors are unable to switch video modes without being turned off, then turned on again. When such monitors experience a change in video mode, they will respond by displaying a distorted image until the monitor is reset. If you have an older monitor, try turning it off, waiting several minutes, then turning it on again.

■ *Check your video mode.*   Make sure that you are using the right video mode for your application. Try using a different (lower) video mode.

■ *Check your video driver.*   Buggy or outdated video drivers can cause garbage to appear on the display. Make sure that you are using the very latest video driver. Also check for conflicts between the video driver and other drivers in the system.

■ *Check your video RAM.*   Faults in the video RAM can cause all manner of display problems. Run a diagnostic to check your video RAM. If the VRAM is defective, you may be able to replace it—otherwise, replace the video adapter.

■ *Replace the video adapter.*   Try a known-good video adapter. You may also have to update your video drivers.

Symptom 7: *When the system returns to Windows from a DOS application, the Windows screen "splits" from top to bottom.* This is a DOS problem that is seen under Windows which indicates an obsolete or corrupted video driver (for example, using a Windows 3.0 video driver under Windows 3.1)—chances are that the video adapter is running just fine.

■ *Check the SYSTEM.INI file.*   Make sure that the proper DOS "grabber" file is installed and specified in the SYSTEM.INI file. Check with the video board manufacturer to obtain the latest assortment of drivers and grabber files.

■ *Reinstall the video drivers.*   Try replacing the drivers from their master disk. If you do not have current drivers available, try switching to the generic VGA driver.

Symptom 8: *The system hangs up during initialization, some characters may be missing from the display, or the screen colors may be incorrect.* These are classic symptoms of a hardware conflict between the video adapter and one or more cards in the system or an area of memory.

- *Check for exclusions.* You may need to add an "exclude" switch to your memory manager's command line to prevent other devices from using the memory spaces required by the video adapter.

- *Check for hardware conflicts.* Try removing any extra devices in the system—one or more devices may be using memory areas needed by the video adapter.

Symptom 9: *Your system is generating DMA errors with a VGA board in the system and video BIOS shadowing disabled.* This is a fairly rare symptom that develops only on some older i486 systems. It is usually due to the use of an 8-bit VGA board in a system equipped with a slower version of the i486 CPU (in the 25-MHz range)—8-bit access takes so long that some DMA requests are ignored; thus an error is generated.

- *Enable video ROM shadowing.* Try enabling video ROM shadowing through the CMOS Setup to allow faster access to video instructions. Also, you might try a newer version of the i486 CPU.

Symptom 10: *The system hangs up using a 16-bit VGA board and one or more 8-bit controllers.* This is typically a problem that arises when 8-bit and 16-bit ISA boards are used in the same system. Because of the way in which an ISA bus separates the 8-bit and 16-bit segments, accessing an 8-bit board when there are 16-bit boards in the system may cause the CPU to (falsely) determine that it is accessing a 16-bit board.

- *Disable or remove any 8-bit devices.* Try removing any 8-bit boards from the system. If the crashes cease, you have probably nailed down the error. Unfortunately, the only real correction is to either remove the 8-bit board(s) or reconfigure the board(s) to use a higher area of memory.

Symptom 11: *You have trouble sizing or positioning the display, or you see error messages such as "Mode Not Supported" or "Insufficient Memory."* These kinds of errors may occur in newer or high-end video boards if the board is not set up properly for the monitor it is being used with.

- *Check the video board driver software.* Most new video boards include an installation routine which records the monitor's maximum specifications, such as resolution (and refresh frequencies), horizontal scanning frequencies, and vertical scanning frequencies. If such data is entered incorrectly (or the monitor is changed), certain screen modes may no longer work properly. Check the video adapter's installation parameters and correct its setup if necessary. Try reinstalling the video software.

Symptom 12: *You frequently encounter GPFs when using QuickTime for Windows 1.1.* This is a notable problem with ATI

Mach64 cards, but it has been known to occur with other advanced video boards.

■ *Check the SYSTEM.INI file.*   This type of problem can be corrected by making a change in the Windows 3.1x SYSTEM.INI file. For the ATI Mach64, you must use DeviceBitmaps = off under the [macx] section. As an alternative, start the ATI FlexDesk, type OPT (this starts a "hidden" window), then uncheck the DeviceBitmap entry.

Symptom 13: *The video board will not boot up when used in a particular motherboard.*   Generally speaking, there are noted cases of hardware incompatibility between certain video boards and motherboards. This usually causes a great deal of confusion because the video board may work just fine when tested in a different motherboard, and other video boards may work well in the original motherboard—the technician simply winds up chasing ghosts.

■ *Check for hardware incompatibilities.*   A noted example of this problem is the Boca Research VGAXL1/2 refusing to work in a Micronics 486DX2/66 motherboard. The solution to this problem is that U13 on the video board must be a Texas Instruments TI-74F04. If U13 is a Motorola IC, you will need to send the board back for rework—strange but true.

■ *Replace the video board.*   For general troubleshooting purposes, if a certain video board and motherboard refuse to work together, don't waste your time chasing ghosts—contact *both* the video board maker and the PC (or motherboard) maker, and see if there are any reports of incompatibilities, or simply try another video board.

Symptom 14: *Diagnostics refuse to show all of the available video modes for a particular board even though all video RAM was properly detected, or the board refuses to operate in some video modes.*   When a video board does not respond to certain video modes (usually the higher video modes), it is because there is a conflict in the upper memory area, and a memory range needs to be *excluded.*

■ *Disable your memory manager.*   If there is a memory manager at work (i.e., QEMM, 386MAX, or EMM386), try disabling the memory manager in CONFIG.SYS, or boot the system from a clean floppy. Try your diagnostic(s) again—chances are that the problem has disappeared.

■ *Check for exclusions.*   To fix this problem on a more permanent basis, reenable the memory manager using an "exclude" command. Try x = b100-b1ff as the first parameter on the memory manager's command line. If that does not work, try x = a000-bfff. Finally, try x = a000-c7ff.

Symptom 15: *The characters shown in the display appear fuzzy.* This is often the result of a speed problem: The system is running too fast for the VL bus video board. In virtually all cases, you will find the VL bus to be running at over 33 MHz.

■ *Slow the bus speed.*   Try slowing down the VL bus speed. This will sacrifice video performance, but it should stabilize the system. Chances are very good that the system has been locking up frequently—slowing down the video board should also correct such lock-ups.

Symptom 16: *Pixels appear "dropped" behind the mouse cursor, and graphic images appear to break up under Windows.*   There are two major causes for this type of problem: bad video RAM, or the system bus speed is too fast.

■ *Check the bus speed.*   Check the CMOS Setup for an entry in Advanced Setup such as "AT Bus Clock," "ISA Bus Speed," or "AT Bus Speed." The corresponding entry should be set to 8.33 MHz. Otherwise, excessive speed may be resulting in "lost" video data.

■ *Check the video RAM.*   If the bus speed is set properly, run a diagnostic to check the integrity of video RAM (you may have to replace the video RAM or replace the video board entirely).

Symptom 17: *You encounter video-related conflicts in Packard Bell systems.*   The system refuses to boot, or starts with "garbage" and erratic screen displays. This symptom is encountered most frequently with Boca video boards on Packard Bell systems with video circuits already on the motherboard. Reports indicate that even when the on-board video has been disabled, the video circuitry remains active and then conflicts with the add-on video board.

■ *Try a video BIOS update.*   Packard Bell indicates that its Vxxx.16 BIOS will correct this problem, so contact Packard Bell for an appropriate BIOS upgrade.

Symptom 18: *Text appears in an odd color.*   For example, text that should be green appears black. This may appear to be a palette problem.

■ *Check your video drivers.*   This is almost always the result of a problem with the palette decoding registers on the particular video board, and will typically appear when using higher color modes (i.e., 64,000 or 16 million colors). Make sure that the video drivers are correct, complete, and up to date. If the problem persists, you may need to replace the video board outright.

Symptom 19: *When an application is started (under Windows), the opening display appears "scrambled."*   While at first glance this might appear to be a video memory problem, it is actually more likely to be related to a buggy video driver.

- *Check your video drivers.*   Upgrade the video driver to the latest version, or try a generic video driver that is compatible with your video chipset.

Symptom 20:   *The display colors change when exiting from a DOS shell under Windows.*   This problem has been noted with video boards such as the Diamond SpeedStar Pro, and is almost always the result of a video board defect (usually a palette problem).

- *Replace the video board.*   For the Diamond board, the product must be replaced with revision A2. For other video boards, such problems can usually be corrected by replacing the video board outright.

Symptom 21:   *The computer locks up or crashes when starting an .AVI file.*   This problem is encountered frequently when computer users first begin to try multimedia applications. The trouble is often the result of using an outdated version of Video for Windows.

- *Check your version of Video for Windows.*   Make sure to use Video for Windows 1.1E or later. Video for Windows can be downloaded from the Diamond Multimedia FTP site at ftp://ftp.diamondmm.com/pub/misc/vfw11e.exe. You may also need to edit the [DrawDib] section of the WIN.INI file and add an entry that says DVA = 0. If no [DrawDib] section is present, you can add it. Remember to restart Windows after making any changes.

Symptom 22:   *The computer is running very slowly (poor performance), and the hard drive light is continuously lit.*   This problem is particularly apparent with Diamond Edge 3D video boards on systems with more than 16 Mbytes of RAM. The Diamond Edge 3D board comes with both 1-Mbyte and 6-Mbyte MIDI bank files. Diamond recommends that you use only the 6-Mbyte bank file on systems with over 16 Mbytes of RAM.

- *Change the MIDI bank file size.*   To change the size of the MIDI bank file being used, right-click on My Computer and choose Properties. Open the System Control Panel and click on the Device Manager tab. Click on the (+) symbol beside the Sound, Video, and Game Controller line, then highlight Diamond EDGE® 3D PCI Multimedia Device, and click on Properties. Click on Settings. You will then see the 1-Mbyte and 6-Mbyte MIDI bank selection. Select the 6MB option and choose OK.

Symptom 23:   *You notice that .AVI files have distorted colors or "grainy" playback.*   This usually occurs when playing 8-bit .AVI files which are not supported by DCI, and can usually be corrected by disabling the accelerated video playback on the video board.

- *Disable accelerated video playback features.*   For example, the Diamond ViperPro Video board is noted for this problem, and you would need to edit the COPRO.INI file located in the \windows directory. In the [VCP] area, change the VCPEnable = line to OFF. Save the .INI file and restart Windows.

Symptom 24: *The PCI video board will not work under Windows unless the system's PCI SCSI devices are disconnected.* This type of problem occurs only on certain combinations of PCI system hardware. For example, this type of symptom has been documented using Phoenix BIOS 4.04 and a UMC8810P-AIO motherboard on systems with an NCR SCSI controller and SCSI devices.

■ *Check your CMOS Setup.* You can often correct such problems by correcting the Advanced System Setup in CMOS. Start the CMOS Setup, go to the Advanced System Setup, and select PCI Devices. Set up the PCI slot for the SCSI controller as IRQ9 and LEVEL edge select. The slot for the video board should have the IRQ set to NONE and LEVEL edge select. Change the Base Memory Address from 0080000000 to 0081000000.

Symptom 25: *There are boot problems when a new video board is installed.* Typical problems include no video or 8 beeps when the system is turned on.

■ *Update the video BIOS.* This is usually the result of an outdated system BIOS which is not capable of detecting the particular video chipset in use—the BIOS interprets this as meaning that there is no video board in the system, and an error is generated accordingly. Contact the motherboard manufacturer (or PC maker) for an updated system BIOS. Most BIOS versions dated after the fall of 1994 should be able to detect most modern video chipsets.

Symptom 26: *There are boot problems when a PCI video board is installed.* The system BIOS did not complete the configuration of the video board correctly, and the board has not been enabled onto the PCI bus.

■ *Try remapping the video card.* The video board manufacturer may have a utility available which can "remap" the video card to a new address outside of physical memory. For the Matrox Millennium, use the PCIMAP.EXE utility. Other Matrox boards use the MGABASE.EXE utility. Other PCI video board manufacturers probably offer their own utilities.

■ *Update the motherboard BIOS.* The system BIOS has assigned to the video board a base memory address which is used by another device or is reserved for use by the motherboard chipset. While the utilities mentioned above may often help to correct this problem, a more permanent fix is usually to update the system BIOS. Investigate a BIOS upgrade from the motherboard (or PC) manufacturer.

Symptom 27: *The monitor overscans when entering a DOS shell from Windows.* This creates a highly distorted image, and can (if left for prolonged periods) damage the monitor circuitry.

■ *Update your video driver.* The cause of this problem is usually a bug in the video driver. For example, this type of problem is known to happen when the Diamond SpeedStar Pro is used with drivers prior to version 1.06. Obtain the latest video driver from the video board maker, or try a generic video driver written by the video chipset maker.

Symptom 28: *You encounter an intermittent "Divide by Zero" error.* Although there are several possible causes for this type of error, they are *all* related to flaws in software—in this case, problems with the video driver or video "toolkit" that is installed with the particular video board.

■ *Update the video card software.* Often, upgrading the driver or video support tools will eliminate this problem. For example, "Divide by Zero" errors can be corrected with the Diamond Stealth 64 Video 2001 series by opening the InControl Tools package and changing a "Center to Viewport" selection to "Center to Desktop." Similarly, the "Maximize to Viewport" selection should be changed to "Maximize to Desktop."

Symptom 29: *During MPEG playback, the display flickers, shows low refresh rates, or appears to be in an interlaced mode.* This is not necessarily an error. With some video boards (such as the Diamond MVP1100), MPEG files cannot play correctly at high refresh rates (typically over 72 Hz).

■ *Check your video refresh rate.* When an MPEG file is played, the driver will automatically switch to a 72-Hz vertical refresh rate. This may result in an unexpected change in display quality during playback. After the MPEG player has been exited, the original (higher) refresh rate will be restored. If a vertical refresh rate *lower* than 72 Hz was originally selected, then the vertical refresh rate will not change during MPEG playback, so you should see no difference in the display.

Symptom 30: *You receive an error such as "There is an undetectable problem in loading the specified device driver" when starting an MPEG player or other video tool.* In almost all cases, the related driver is missing, installed improperly, or corrupt.

■ *Check your MPEG driver(s).* Reinstall the MPEG playback driver(s) for your particular video board, and make sure to use the latest version. If problems persist, check for the driver in the WIN.INI or SYSTEM.INI file and make sure that there is only *one* load = reference to the particular driver(s)—repeated references can cause conflicts or other loading problems.

Symptom 31: *On video boards with TV tuners, the TV window is blurry or fuzzy at 1024 × 768 or higher resolutions.* This symptom is particularly noted with the Diamond DVV1100. Unfortunately, this type of symptom is usually the result of limited bandwidth of the particular video board—specifically of the video chipset.

■ *Change the video resolution.* The only real option is to reduce the resolution to 800 × 600 or 640 × 480 when running the TV, and lower the refresh rate to 60 Hz. Contact your video board's manufacturer—there may be an RMA or other replacement/upgrade program available to correct the issue.

Symptom 32: *On video boards with TV tuners, the reception does not appear as good as that of an ordinary TV.* This problem has been noted in conjunction with Matrox Media-TV boards, and is usually due to the local cable company's using the HRC carrier frequency instead of the standard carrier frequency.

■ *Correct the carrier type.* Poor reception is almost always the result of an unusual cable carrier. For Matrox boards, you can correct the problem by modifying the DVMCIMIL.INI file found in the \WINDOWS directory. Under the [Carrier] section, change the CarrierType = 0 entry to CarrierType = 1. Other video/TV boards may utilize different .INI entries or allow carrier selection through the use of an onboard jumper.

Symptom 33: *You encounter errors such as "Insufficient video memory."* There is not enough video memory on the board to handle screen images at the resolution and color depth you have selected. In most cases, the system may crash outright.

■ *Lower the color depth.* Your immediate solution should be to select a lower resolution or smaller color palette.

■ *Check your video playback window.* If you are encountering such problems when attempting to play .AVI or MPEG files, you should be able to select smaller video windows and lower color depth without altering your Windows setup.

■ *Add more VRAM.* As a longer-term solution, you should consider adding more video memory or replacing the video board with one that contains more video memory.

Symptom 34: *The PCI video board is not working properly—there is a BIOS conflict with PCI interrupt 1Ah.* The lower 32 kbytes of the ROM BIOS have been redirected for high memory use.

■ *Check for exclusions.* Disable this memory with your memory manager by adding an *exclude* command such as x = f000-f7ff.

Symptom 35: *You encounter video corruption or sporadic system rebooting when using an SLC-type motherboard.* This particular symptom has been most noted when using Number Nine video boards with Alaris SLC2 motherboards.

■ *Try a different video board.* The SLC2 microprocessor uses a 32-bit internal data bus, but the external data bus (seen by the motherboard) is 16-bit. Most of the registers on contemporary VL and PCI video boards are mapped as 32 bits, and cannot be accessed as two 16-bit registers. As a result, the video board simply cannot be used together with the particular motherboard. You will have to upgrade the motherboard or use a different video board.

Symptom 36: *Video playback experiences long pauses while the hard drive thrashes excessively.* This is a problem that appears under Windows 95, and is almost always the result of disk caching problems.

■ *Check your video playback drivers.* Start Windows Explorer and highlight the drivers responsible for video playback (for a Motion Pixels video board, highlight MPXPLAY.EXE and MPXPLAY.PIF). Click the right mouse button and select Properties. In the Memory page, make sure that the Protected option has been set. Restart the video clip, or restart Windows 95 if necessary.

Symptom 37: *You cannot use the loop-through feature of your video board.* Typical examples include the Number Nine 9FX Motion 771 VGA loop-through connector with a Reel Magic board and a Number Nine driver.

■ *Try a different video driver.* Unfortunately, this is often the result of a limitation with the video board's graphics processor IC (refusing to support loop-through functionality). To use loop-through, try the standard VGA driver.

Symptom 38: *Windows appears with a "black box" cursor and/or icons that fail to appear on the screen.* In most cases, the problem is caused by an incompatibility with the motherboard's noncompliant PCI BIOS (the motherboard's BIOS does not comply with the PCI backward-compatibility requirement).

■ *Check the "memory aperture."* Set the video board's memory aperture manually by editing the SYSTEM.INI file located in the \WINDOWS directory. For example, when working with a Number Nine 9GXE, find the [#9GXE] section of SYSTEM.INI, then add a command line such as APERTURE-BASE = 0×8800 or APERTURE-BASE = 31. Save the file and restart Windows. The actual section for your particular video board may be different.

Symptom 39: *There are video problems or the system locks up while using an antivirus program.* This error occurs frequently when using memory-resident virus checking.

- *Check the SYSTEM.INI file.* Some video boards allow you to compensate for this by editing the SYSTEM.INI file. For the Number Nine 9GXE board, find the [#9GXE] area in SYSTEM.INI, then set the FastMMIO = entry to OFF. Remember to save the .INI file and restart Windows. The actual section for your particular video board may be different.

- *Disable virus checking.* As an alternative, you could also disable or remove the antivirus program.

Symptom 40: *An error indicates that there is not enough memory for playback or resizing of the playback window.* This type of program is directly caused by a lack of system (not video) memory in the PC.

- *Eliminate background programs.* Try unloading various unneeded programs from memory, and consider disabling any RAM drives that may be active.

- *Reduce memory for caching.* If your system uses SMARTDRV (Windows 3.1x), try reducing the memory used for caching.

- *Try adding more system RAM.* Consider adding more system RAM to the PC.

Symptom 41: *The video board refuses to accept a particular video mode.* Mode problems are most frequent during attempts to use unusual palette sizes such as 32,000 or 64,000 colors.

- *Use a lower video mode.* Try setting the video board to 256 colors. If a higher color depth is needed, it may be possible to run the video board in a palletized mode or gray-scale mode by adding command-line switches to the video driver. Refer to the instructions that accompany the particular video board for detailed information.

- *Try a video BIOS upgrade or VESA driver.* You may also consider a video BIOS upgrade, or try using an upgraded VESA driver (such as UNIVBE 5.3 from SciTech Software).

Symptom 42: *The video system cannot lock memory using QEMM and linear video memory.* This is often a DOS problem with Motion Pixels video boards when using QEMM 7.04 and earlier versions. The DPMI has a bug when accessing physical memory above the DPMI's host memory.

- *Check your memory manager.* Upgrade the version of QEMM to 7.5 (or later), or play video under Windows instead.

Symptom 43: *The video system cannot lock memory under Windows, or the system hangs.* This is also a problem noted most often with Motion Pixels video boards, and it is almost always related to the use of a WINDPMI.386 DPMI driver loaded through SYSTEM.INI. WINDPMI.386 reports the wrong amount of free lockable DPMI memory.

- *Check your DPMI memory.* If your Windows platform is using Borland's WINDPMI.386, manually reduce the cache size with the /c option, or remove (or disable) the driver from SYSTEM.INI entirely.

- *Upgrade the DPMI driver.* You might also consider upgrading WINDPMI.386 to a later version. Contact Borland technical support or the technical support department of the video board maker.

Sound Boards

Sound boards add the dimension of sound to your PC. Figure 6.7 shows a simplified block diagram of a sound board. It is important to note that while your own particular sound board may differ somewhat, all contemporary boards should contain these seven major subsections:

- *Digital signal processor.* The core element of a sound board is the *digital signal processor* (DSP). A DSP is a variation of a microprocessor which is specially designed to manipulate large volumes of digital data. Like all processor components, the DSP requires memory.

- *Sound board ROM.* A ROM contains all of the instructions needed to operate the DSP and direct the board's major operations.

- *Sound board RAM.* A small quantity of RAM serves two purposes: It provides a "scratch pad" area for the DSP's calculations, and it serves as a buffer for data traveling to or from the PC bus.

- *Digitizing circuits.* Signals entering the sound board are passed through an amplifier stage and provided to an A/D converter. When recording takes place, the DSP runs the A/D converter and accepts the resulting conversions for processing and storage.

- *Amplifier circuits.* Signals delivered by a microphone are typically quite faint, so they are amplified significantly. Signals delivered to the "line" input (such as the output from a CD player or stereo preamp) are often much stronger, so they receive less amplification.

- *Mixer circuit.* For signals leaving the sound board, the first (and often most important) stop is the mixer. It is the mixer which combines CD audio, DSP sound output, and synthesizer output into a single analog channel. Since most sound boards now operate in a stereo mode, there will usually be two mixer channels and amplifier stages. The audio amplifier stages boost the analog signal for delivery to stereo speakers. If the sound will be driving a stereo system, a "line" output provides a separate output. Amplifier output can be adjusted by a single master volume control located on the rear of the board.

- *MIDI controller.* A MIDI controller is provided to accommodate the interface of a MIDI instrument to the sound board. In many cases, the interface can be jumpered to switch the controller to

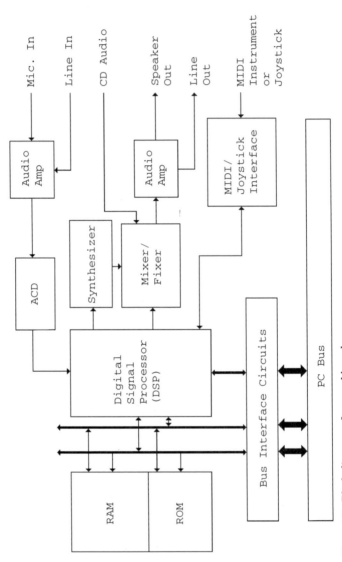

Figure 6.7 Block diagram of a sound board.

serve as a joystick port. That way, the sound board can support a single joystick if a MIDI instrument will not be used. MIDI information processed by the DSP will be output to the on-board synthesizer.

Sound board troubleshooting

Symptom 1: *There is a noticeable buzz or hum being produced in one or both speakers.* Low-cost speakers use unshielded cables. Unfortunately, strong signals from ac cords and other signal-carrying conductors can easily induce interference in the speaker wires.

■ *Change cable locations.* Try rerouting speaker cables clear of other cables in the system.

■ *Try shielded cables.* If problems persist, try using higher-quality speakers with shielded cables and enclosures. In most cases, that should resolve everyday noise problems.

■ *Replace the sound board.* If the noise continues regardless of what you do, there may be a fault in the sound board amplifier. Try moving the sound board to another bus slot, away from other boards or the power supply. If that does not resolve the problem, try a new sound board.

Symptom 2: *There is no sound from the speaker(s).* The lack of sound from a sound board can be due to any one of a wide range of potential problems.

■ *Check the particular application.* If the sound board works with some applications but not with others, it is likely that the problem is due to an improperly installed or configured application. Make sure that the offending application is set up properly (and that it is capable of using the sound card).

■ *Check the master volume.* Also make sure that the master volume control on the sound board is turned up most (or all) of the way. If there is a mixer application loaded with your sound board drivers, make sure that the mixer levels are all set properly.

■ *Check the sound driver setup and environment.* Also check to see that the proper sound driver files (if any) are loaded into CONFIG.SYS and AUTOEXEC.BAT as required. In many cases, there are one or two sound-related environment variables that are set in AUTOEXEC.BAT. Make sure that your startup files are configured properly.

■ *Check the speakers.* Make sure that the speakers are turned on and set to a normal volume level. The speakers should be receiving adequate power, and should be plugged properly into the correct output jack—if speakers have been plugged into the wrong jack, no sound will be produced. If the cable is broken or questionable, try a new set of speakers.

■ *Check for hardware conflicts.*   If problems continue, there may be a resource conflict between the sound board and another device in the system. Examine the IRQ, DMA, and I/O settings of each device in the system. Make sure that no two devices are using the same resources.

■ *Change the sound board.*   If problems persist and no conflict is present, try another sound board.

Symptom 3:   *CD audio will not play through the sound card.*   This problem can occur under both DOS and Windows.

■ *Check for older sound boards.*   Make sure that the sound board is actually capable of playing CD audio—older boards may not be compatible, or may require a second low-level driver to handle Red Book audio.

■ *Check the audio cable.*   Open the PC and make sure that the CD-audio cable (a thin, four-wire cable) securely connects the CD-ROM drive to the sound board. If this cable is broken, disconnected, or absent, CD audio will not be passed to the sound board.

■ *Check the audio application.*   If the cable is intact, make sure that the CD-audio player is configured properly for the sound board you are using.

■ *Check the drivers.*   Examine the startup files to make sure that any drivers and environment variables needed by CONFIG.SYS and AUTOEXEC.BAT are available. If the CD audio fails to play under Windows, make sure that an MCI (multimedia control interface) CD audio driver is included in the Drivers dialog box under your Windows Control Panel.

Symptom 4:   *You see an error message indicating "No interrupt vector available."*   The DOS interrupt vectors used by the sound board's setup drivers (usually INT 80h to BFh) are being used by one or more other drivers in the system.

■ *Check for software conflicts.*   Try disabling other drivers in the system one at a time until you see the conflict disappear. Once you have isolated the offending driver(s), you can leave it (or them) disabled, or (if possible) alter the command-line settings so that the driver(s) no longer conflict(s) with the sound board's software.

Symptom 5:   *There is no MIDI output.*   In virtually all cases, MIDI problems are the result of setup or configuration issues.

■ *Check your file.*   Make sure that the file you are trying to play is a valid MIDI file (usually with a .MID extension).

■ *Check the MIDI drivers.*   Make sure that you have the proper MIDI drivers loaded under Windows. You will often find that the MIDI Mapper under Windows is not set up properly for the sound board. Load the Windows MIDI Mapper applet from the Control Panel, and set it properly to accommodate your sound board.

Symptom 6: *Sound play is choppy.* Choppy or jerky sound playback is typically the result of a hard drive problem—more specifically, the drive cannot read the sound file to a buffer fast enough.

■ *Check for disk fragmentation.* In most cases, the reason for this slow drive performance is excessive disk fragmentation. Under DOS, the sound file(s) may be highly fragmented. Under Windows, the permanent or temporary swap files may be highly fragmented. In either case, use a reliable DOS defragmenter such as PC Tools or Norton Utilities (leave Windows before defragmenting the disk), and defragment the disk thoroughly.

Symptom 7: *You see an error message indicating "Out of environment space."* The system is out of environment space.

■ *Check the environment space.* Increase the system's environment space by adding the following line to your CONFIG.SYS file:

```
shell 5 c:\command.com /E:512 /P
```

This command line sets the environment space to 512 bytes. If you still encounter the error message, change the E entry to 1024.

Symptom 8: *Regular "clicks," "stutters," or "hiccups" occur during the playback of speech.* In most cases, the system CPU is simply not fast enough to permit buffering without dropping sound data. Systems with i286 and slower i386 CPUs typically suffer from this kind of problem. This is often compounded by insufficient memory (especially under Windows), so that the system automatically resorts to virtual memory. Since virtual memory is delivered by the hard drive, and the hard drive is much slower than RAM anyway, the hard drive simply can't provide data fast enough.

■ *Reduce the system load.* Shut down background applications or TSRs.

■ *Upgrade the system.* Try adding more RAM or upgrading the CPU.

Symptom 9: *The joystick is not working, or not working properly on all systems.* This problem applies only to sound boards with a multifunction MIDI/joystick port being used in the joystick mode.

■ *Check for hardware conflicts.* Chances are that the joystick is conflicting with another joystick port in the system. Disable the original joystick port or the new joystick port—only one joystick port (game adapter) can be active in the system at any one time.

■ *Check the game port.* Since joystick performance is dependent on CPU speed, the CPU may actually be too *fast* for the joystick port. Disable the joystick port and try a newer, speed-compensating game port.

Symptom 10: *You install a sound board and everything works properly, but now the printer does not seem to work.* There is an interrupt conflict between the sound board and an IRQ line used by the printer.

■ *Check for hardware conflicts.* While parallel printers are often polled, they can also be driven by an IRQ line (IRQ5 or IRQ7). If the sound board is using either one of these interrupts, try changing to an alternative IRQ line. When changing an IRQ line, be sure to reflect the changes in any sound board files called by CONFIG.SYS or AUTOEXEC.BAT.

Symptom 11: *You hear "pops" and "clicks" when recording sound under Windows 95.* There is insufficient cache to adequately support the recording process (or cache is improperly configured). Try the following procedure to alter the way cache is allocated:

■ Open Notepad and load SYSTEM.INI.

■ Locate the area of SYSTEM.INI labeled [vcache].

■ Add the following line below [vcache]:

```
maxfilecache = 2048
```

■ Save your changes to the SYSTEM.INI file.

■ From the desktop, right-click on My Computer, then select Properties.

■ Select the Performance page, then click on File System.

■ Find the slider marked "Read-ahead optimization," then pull the slider to None.

■ Save your changes and restart Windows 95.

Symptom 12: *You notice high-frequency distortion in one or possibly in both channels.* In many cases, the AT bus clock is set at over 8 MHz, and data is being randomly lost. This problem usually occurs in very fast systems using an ISA sound board.

■ *Check the bus speed.* Enter the system's CMOS Setup and check the AT Bus Clock under the Advanced Chipset Setup area. See that the bus clock is set as close to 8 MHz as possible. If the bus clock is derived as a divisor of the CPU clock, you may see an entry such as /4. Make sure that this divisor results in a clock speed as close to 8 MHz as possible. If problems still persist, try increasing the divisor to drop the bus speed below 8 MHz (note that this may have an adverse effect on other ISA peripherals).

Symptom 13: *You hear "pops" and "clicks" when playing back prerecorded files under Windows 95.* There is an excessive processing load on the system, which is often caused by virtual memory and/or 32-bit access.

■ *Shut down virtual memory.* Open the Control Panel and double-click on the System icon. Select the Performance page and click on Virtual Memory. Set the swap file to None and save your changes. Try the file playback again.

■ *Shut down 32-bit access.* If problems persist, try disabling 32-bit file access. If that still does not resolve the problem, try disabling 32-bit disk access.

Symptom 14: *You hear "pops" and "clicks" on new recordings only; preexisting files sound clean.* This is often due to problems with software caching.

■ *Disable SmartDrive.* If you are using DOS or Windows 3.1, disable SmartDrive from both CONFIG.SYS and AUTOEXEC.BAT, then restart the computer for your changes to take effect.

■ *Shut down 32-bit access.* If problems continue (or if you are using Windows 95), there may be an excessive processing load on the system as a result of virtual memory or 32-bit access. Follow the recommendations under Symptom 13.

Symptom 15: *You hear "pops" and "clicks" when playing back or recording any sound file.* In most cases, there is a wiring problem in the speaker system.

■ *Check your speaker cabling.* Check all of the cabling between the sound board and the speakers. If the speakers are powered by ac, make sure that the power jack is inserted properly. If the speakers are powered by battery, make sure that the batteries are fresh. Check for loose connections. If you cannot resolve the problem, try some new speakers.

■ *Try a new sound board.* If the problem persists, replace the sound board.

Symptom 16: *The sound board will play back fine, but it will not record.* The board probably records fine in DOS, but not in Windows.

■ *Check for hardware conflicts.* If the sound board is using 16-bit DMA transfer (typical under Windows), there are *two* DMA channels in use. Chances are that one of those two DMA channels is conflicting with another device in the system. Determine the DMA channels being used under Windows, then check other devices for DMA conflicts. If you are using Windows 95, check the Device Manager and look for entries marked with a yellow icon.

Symptom 17: *A DMA error is produced when a sound board is used with an Adaptec 2842 controller in the system.* This is a known problem with the Digital Audio Labs "DOC" product and the Adaptec 2842.

■ *Check the drive controller's buffer.* You will need to alter the controller's FIFO buffer. Go into the controller's Setup by hitting <Ctrl> + <A> when prompted during system startup. Select the advanced configuration option, then select the FIFO threshold—chances are that it will be set to 100%. Try setting the FIFO threshold to 0% and see if this makes a difference.

Symptom 18: *A DMA error is produced when a sound board is used with an Adaptec 1542 controller in the system.* This is a known problem with the Digital Audio Labs "DOC" sound product and the Adaptec 1542.

■ *Adjust the DMA channels.* The problem can usually be resolved by rearranging the DMA channels. Place the Adaptec controller on DMA 7, then place the sound board on DMA 5 for playback and DMA 6 for recording.

Symptom 19: *The sound card will not play or record—the system just locks up when either is attempted.* The board will probably not play in either DOS or Windows. This is a problem that has been identified with some sound boards and ATI video boards.

■ *Check the video address ranges.* ATI video boards use unusual address ranges which sometimes overlap the I/O address used by the sound board. Change the sound board to another I/O address.

Symptom 20: *The sound card will record, but will not play back.* Assuming that the sound board and its drivers are installed and configured properly, chances are that a playback oscillator on the sound board has failed.

■ *Replace the sound board.* Try a new sound board outright.

Symptom 21: *The sound application or editor produces a significant number of DMA errors.* This type of problem is known to occur frequently when the standard VGA driver that accompanies Windows is used—the driver is poorly written and cannot keep up with screen draws.

■ *Check your video driver(s).* Try updating your video driver to a later, more efficient version. If the driver is known to contain bugs, try using a generic video driver written for the video board's chipset.

Symptom 22: *The sound board will not record in DOS.* There are several possible problems that can account for this behavior.

■ *Check for hardware conflicts.* Suspect a hardware conflict between the sound board and other devices in the system. Make sure that the IRQs, DMA channels, and I/O port addresses used by the sound board are not used by other devices.

■ *Check your sound driver(s).*   If the hardware setup appears correct, suspect a problem between DOS drivers. Try a clean boot of the system (with no CONFIG.SYS or AUTOEXEC.BAT). If sound can be run properly now, there is a driver conflict. Examine your entries in CONFIG.SYS or AUTOEXEC.BAT for possible conflicts, or for older drivers that may still be loading to support hardware that is no longer in the system.

■ *Check the hard drive controller.*   Try setting up a RAM drive with RAMDRIVE.SYS. You can install a RAMdrive on your system by adding the line

```
device = c:\dos\ramdrive.sys /e 8000
```

The 8000 is for 8 Mbytes worth of RAM—make sure that there is enough RAM in the PC. Once the RAMdrive is set up, try recording and playing from the RAMdrive (you may have to specify a new path in the sound recorder program). If that works, the hard drive controller may simply be too slow to support the sound board, and you may need to consider upgrading the drive system.

Symptom 23: *When recording sound, the system locks up if a key other than the recorder's "hot keys" are pushed.*   This is a frequent problem under Windows 3.1x.

■ *Check your system sounds.*   The system sounds (generated under Windows) may be interfering with the sound recorder. Try turning off system sounds. Go to the Main icon, choose the Control Panel, then select Sounds. There will be a box in the lower left corner marked "Enable system sounds." Click on this box to remove the check mark, then click OK.

Symptom 24: *After the sound board driver is loaded, Windows locks up when starting or exiting.*   In virtually all cases, you have a hardware conflict between the sound board and another device in the system.

■ *Check for hardware conflicts.*   Make sure that the IRQs, DMA channels, and I/O port addresses used by the sound board are not used by other devices.

Symptom 25: *When Windows sound editing software is used, the sound board refuses to enter the "digital" mode—it always switches back to the analog mode.*   Generally speaking, this is a software configuration issue.

■ *Check your sound editing software.*   Make sure that your editing (or other sound) software is set for the correct type of sound board (e.g., an AWE32 instead of a Sound Blaster 16/Pro).

■ *Check your sound driver(s).*   If problems persist, the issue is with your sound drivers. Check the [drivers] section of the Windows SYSTEM.INI file for your sound board driver entries. If there is more than one entry, you may need to disable the competing driver. This is a known problem with the Digital Audio Labs CardDplus, and is caused by incorrect driver listings. For example, the proper CardDplus driver must be entered as

```
Wave = cardp.drv
```

and the companion driver must be listed as

```
Wave1 = tahiti.drv
```

You will need to make sure that the proper driver(s) for your sound board are entered in SYSTEM.INI. You may also need to restart the system after making any changes.

Symptom 26: *The microphone records at very low levels (or not at all).* In most cases, the microphone is at fault.

■ *Suspect your microphone itself.* Most sound boards demand the use of a good-quality dynamic microphone. Also, Creative Labs and Labtec microphones are not always compatible with sound boards from other manufacturers. Try a generic dynamic microphone.

■ *Check your sound recording software.* If problems persist, chances are that your recording software is not configured properly for microphone input. Try the following procedure to set up the recording application properly under Windows 95:
  1. Open your Control Panel and double-click on the Multimedia icon.
  2. The Multimedia Properties dialog will open. Select the Audio page.
  3. In the "Recording" area, make sure to set the Volume slider all the way up.
  4. Also see that the Preferred device and Preferred quality settings are correct.
  5. Save your changes and try the microphone again.

Symptom 27: *The sound card isn't working in full-duplex mode.* Virtually all current sound boards are capable of full-duplex operation for such applications as Internet phones. Check the specifications for your sound board and make sure that the board is in fact capable of full-duplex operation. If it is, and full duplex isn't working, your audio properties may be set up incorrectly.

■ Open your Control Panel and double-click on the Multimedia icon.
■ The Multimedia Properties dialog will open. Select the Audio page.
■ If the Playback device and the Record device are set to the same I/O address, this is only *half duplex.*
■ Change the Playback device I/O address so that it is different from the address of the Record device.
■ Hit the Apply button, then hit the OK button.
■ You should now be in *full duplex* mode.

NOTE: Some of the very latest sound boards (such as the Ensoniq SoundscapeVIVO 90) will carry full-duplex operation with the *same* playback and record device selected.

Symptom 28: *You encounter DMA errors using an older sound board and an Adaptec 1542.*   This is a known problem with the older Digital Audio Labs CardD sound board; it can be resolved by slowing down the controller.

■ *Adjust the controller's configuration.*   You can clear DMA issues by slowing down the 1542 using the /n switch. Add the /n switch to the ASPI4DOS command line in CONFIG.SYS; for example,

```
device = c:\aspi4dos.sys /n2
```

If slowing the 1542 down with an /n2 switch doesn't fix the problem, then you should strongly consider upgrading the sound board.

Symptom 29: *You encounter hard disk recording problems under Windows 95.*   Recorded audio is saved to your hard drive. For most systems, sound data can be transferred to the HDD fast enough to avoid any problems, but if data transfer is interrupted, your recorded sound may "pop" or break up. There are many factors that affect HDD data transfer speed. The following sections outline a number of procedures that might help you optimize a system for sound recording.

Disable the CD auto insert detection feature.
■ Go to the Device Manager.
■ Open the CD-ROM entry.
■ Select your CD-ROM drive and click Properties.
■ Go to the Settings page.
■ Uncheck the "Auto insert notification" box.
■ Select OK.

Turn down the graphics acceleration.
■ Right-click on the My Computer icon.
■ Left-click on Properties.
■ Select the Performance page.
■ Select the button labeled Graphics.
■ Start by turning down the acceleration one notch (you can return later to turn it down further if more performance is required).
■ Select OK.

Adjust the size of your virtual memory swap file.
■ Right-click on the My Computer icon.

- Left-click on Properties.
- Select the Performance page.
- Select the button labeled Virtual Memory.
- Choose "Let me specify my own virtual memory settings."
- If your PC has 16 Mbytes of RAM, set the minimum and maximum at 40 Mbytes. If you have 32 Mbytes of RAM, set the minimum and maximum at 64 Mbytes.
- Select OK.

Remove items from your startup group.
- Click the Start button.
- Go to the Programs menu, then select Startup. If you see anything here, it may be hurting your system performance. Eliminate anything that is not absolutely necessary.
- To remove items, click the Start button, go to Settings, then select Taskbar.
- Choose the page labeled Start Menu Programs.
- Click the Remove button.
- Open the Startup group by double-clicking it.
- Remove any items which you feel are not necessary and are wasting resources.
- Select the Close button when finished.

Clear any indexes of the Find Fast utility.
- Click the Start button.
- Go to Settings, then choose the Control Panel.
- Open the Find Fast utility.
- Go to the Index menu.
- Select Delete Index....
- Select an index in the In and Below drop box.
- Select the OK button.
- Repeat the previous three steps until all indexes are removed.

Defragment the hard drive.
- Click the Start button.
- Go to Programs, Accessories, and System Tools.
- Choose Disk Defragmenter.
- Select the drive to defragment and click OK.
- Click the Start button to begin defragmentation.

Suspend the System Agent (if installed).

- If System Agent is installed, open it by double clicking on its icon in the taskbar.
- Go to the Advanced menu.
- Choose Suspend System Agent.
- Close the System Agent window.

7

Controller
Troubleshooting

Controllers basically perform two sets of functions: They manage system drives (such as hard drives and floppy drives), and they provide I/O capabilities (serial ports, parallel ports, game ports, and so on). Today, most controller circuitry can easily be integrated onto the motherboard. However, it is impossible to add new controller features to the motherboard without replacing the entire motherboard, so controller boards remain a popular and cost-effective way to introduce new features to the system. This chapter covers symptoms and solutions for three types of controllers: drive controllers, I/O controllers, and SCSI controllers.

Drive Controllers

The term *drive controller* refers to the device which handles your IDE/EIDE hard drives and floppy drives. Floppy drives use a 34-pin interface, and IDE/EIDE hard drives use a 40-pin interface. In today's PC, the drive controller circuits are typically located on the motherboard. There are really only three circumstances in which you will see a stand-alone drive controller:

■ *Older PCs.* You are working on an older system which requires a drive controller board.

■ *System upgrade.* The motherboard's drive controller will not support such things as 2.88-Mbyte floppy drives or EIDE hard drives, and an advanced drive controller must be installed [the motherboard drive controller(s) must be disabled] to upgrade the system.

■ *Controller repairs.* The motherboard drive controller has failed. Rather than replace the entire motherboard, a stand-alone drive controller board may be installed to restore drive access.

Drive controller symptoms

Symptom 1: *The floppy drive controller fails during initialization.* You may see this type of problem reported as an "FDD controller failure." In almost all cases, there is a conflict between FDD interrupts or controller hardware.

■ *Check the motherboard controller.* Make sure that the motherboard's floppy drive controller has been disabled (usually through a motherboard jumper).

■ *Check for hardware conflicts.* Make sure that there are no other devices in the system that are using IRQ 6.

Symptom 2: *The drive controller's BIOS refuses to auto-detect the hard drive geometry, even though auto-detect is selected in CMOS Setup.* In virtually all cases, this is a problem with the particular drive rather than with the drive controller.

■ *Check the drive.* You will probably find that the hard drive is an older IDE drive that does not conform to the standards needed for IDE/EIDE auto-detection. You should probably enter the specific geometry for your particular drive, then reboot the system.

■ *Replace the drive.* If you must have auto-detection on your particular system, consider upgrading the hard drive.

Symptom 3: *You see a "hard disk controller error" after performing a partition with FDISK.* The hard drive is accessible when booting from a floppy disk. There are several possible problems here.

■ *Check the CMOS Setup.* Make sure that the drive geometry is entered correctly.

■ *Replace the hard drive.* The boot sector may be defective. Try another hard drive.

■ *Replace the drive controller.* If a new drive does not correct the problem, there may be a fault in the drive controller. Try another drive controller.

Symptom 4: *Your system ignores storage capacity beyond 2 Gbytes and sees the drive as only 2 Gbytes, the system sees only the storage capacity past 2 Gbytes (e.g., a 2.5-Gbyte drive may be seen as 500 Mbytes), or the system hangs during startup.* This is a known issue with Promise EIDEMAX controllers and the following systems: motherboards with AMI BIOS dated 10/10/94 or earlier; motherboards with Phoenix BIOS earlier than v4.04, and Intel motherboards with AMI BIOS earlier than v1.04.

■ *Check the controller installation.* EIDE controllers such as the Promise EIDEMAX often provide an EIDE BIOS to enhance the limited motherboard BIOS. Make sure that the controller's BIOS is enabled. Also see that the original IDE controller (usually on the motherboard) is disabled. You can then use the EIDE con-troller exclusively.

■ *Check your utility software.* If the controller uses any perfor-mance-enhancing software, make sure that the software is installed properly in CONFIG.SYS or AUTOEXEC.BAT.

■ *Check the CMOS Setup.* When installing an EIDE controller with its own BIOS, you may need to set the hard drive entries in CMOS setup to "None" or "Not Installed."

Symptom 5: *The EIDE BIOS does not load.* The supplemental BIOS located on the EIDE controller refuses to load or causes the system to crash. In most cases, the BIOS is disabled or is set to a conflicting address.

■ *Check the EIDE BIOS address.* Make sure that the BIOS address jumper is set to the correct range—it should not conflict with system BIOS, video BIOS, or any other controller BIOS in the system. You may need to change the address range.

■ *Enable the EIDE BIOS.* Make sure that the controller's BIOS is enabled (usually through a jumper on the motherboard).

■ *Check the EIDE BIOS version.* Make sure that your EIDE con-troller has the latest version of EIDE BIOS. You may need an updated BIOS IC, or have to send the board back for replacement.

■ *Check the BIOS IC itself.* Make sure that the BIOS IC is seated firmly and completely in its socket.

■ *Check for hardware conflicts.* Make sure that there are no IRQ or other I/O conflicts with other devices in the system.

■ *Try the "auto-detect" feature.* Some motherboard CMOS Setups may need to be set to "auto-detect" rather than to "none" or "not installed." Try setting the CMOS drive entries to "auto-detect."

Symptom 6: *The EIDE BIOS loads, but the system hangs.* There are a number of issues to consider here.

■ *Check for hardware conflicts.* Make sure that the EIDE con-troller is not conflicting with a drive controller on the mother-board. Disable the motherboard drive controllers.

■ *Check the "block mode."* Open your CMOS Setup and try dis-abling any references to "block mode" data transfer.

■ *Check the drive relationships.* There may be an incompatibility between the drives (e.g., using a fast EIDE hard drive and a slow IDE CD-ROM drive on the same controller channel). Try separat-ing the drives (try them separately). Put slower IDE devices on the secondary controller channel. You should also check to make sure that the primary/secondary (master/slave) drive jumpers for each drive are correct.

■ *Check the CMOS Setup.* Make sure that the primary and sec-

ondary drive entries in CMOS match the correct primary and secondary drives.

Symptom 7: *The new EIDE controller board is not recognized.*   In
most cases, you have a problem with hardware conflicts.

■ *Check for hardware conflicts.*   Make sure that the EIDE controller is not conflicting with a drive controller on the motherboard. Disable the motherboard drive controllers.

■ *Check power management.*   Some power management circuits
require the use of an IRQ. Make sure that power management is
not using the same IRQ as the EIDE drive controller.

■ *Check the CMOS Setup.*   If you have set the drive parameters in
CMOS Setup to "none" or "not installed," try setting the drives to
"type 1" or "auto-detect." You may have to define the drive parameters so that the new drive controller card can apply LBA control.

■ *Check the installation.*   Reseat the card and check all cable installations.

■ *Replace the drive controller.*   If problems persist, try a new drive
controller card.

Symptom 8: *The IDE CD-ROM is not recognized with the drive controller.*   In most cases, it is the drive installation and setup that is at
fault rather than a problem with the drive controller.

■ *Check the drive installation.*   A CD-ROM is a relatively slow
drive, so it should not reside as a secondary (slave) drive alongside
a fast EIDE primary (master) drive on the same drive controller
channel. Place the IDE CD-ROM drive on a secondary IDE drive
controller channel.

■ *Check the drive jumpers.*   Make sure that the CD-ROM drive is
set as the secondary (slave) drive when it is used alongside a hard
drive, or set the CD-ROM drive as the primary (master) drive
when moving it to the secondary drive controller channel.

■ *Check the ATAPI driver.*   You need an ATAPI driver for the IDE
CD-ROM. Make sure that you are using the right driver for your
particular CD-ROM drive, and that the driver is installed correctly.

■ *Replace the drive.*   Try a known-good CD-ROM drive.

Symptom 9: *Hard drive(s) are not recognized on the secondary controller channel.*   In most cases, this is a problem with the drive
installation and setup rather than with the drive controller itself.

■ *Check the drive jumpers.*   Make sure that the drive(s) on your secondary channel are jumpered appropriately as primary (master) or
secondary (slave).

■ *Check the drive controller software.*   Make sure that any drive
controller software loaded in CONFIG.SYS or AUTOEXEC.BAT is
set up properly. For example, the Promise EIDEMAX controller

may require that an /S switch be added to the EIDE2300.SYS command line; for example,

```
device = c:\eide2300\eide2300.sys /S
```

- *Check power management.*   Make sure that your power management system is not using the same IRQ as the secondary drive
  channel (usually IRQ 15).

- *Check for hardware conflicts.*   Make sure that there are no other
  devices in the system using the same IRQ as the secondary drive
  channel (usually IRQ 15).

- *Suspect older drives.*   Some older drives do not understand the
  "Identify Drive Command" used to retrieve drive parameters. You
  may need to replace the drive with a newer model.

Symptom 10:   *The EIDE drive controller can access only 528 Mbytes
per disk.*   In most cases, the controller's configuration is the problem.

- *Check the LBA mode.*   Make sure that the controller's LBA mode
  is enabled. You may need to change a jumper on the drive controller.

- *Check the controller BIOS.*   The drive controller may have an
  older BIOS which is not fully compatible with new EIDE drives.
  Check with the controller manufacturer and see if there is a BIOS
  update available.

I/O Controllers

The PC also depends on a series of important ports to communicate
with peripheral devices. Serial (COM) ports drive serial printers and
modems. Parallel (LPT) ports operate parallel printers and other
types of parallel-port devices (parallel-port tape drives and so on).
There are also other ports like game ports, light pens, etc.
Motherboards typically provide at least one COM port and one LPT
port, but there are some cases where you may use a stand-alone I/O
controller:

- *Older PCs.*   Older PCs are usually fitted with UARTs that are
  now obsolete. Newer external modems demand a 16550A UART. It
  may be necessary to disable the motherboard's COM ports and use
  more efficient ports from an I/O controller.

- *System upgrade.*   You may need to add a second LPT port or COM
  port to the system. In this case, you do not need to disable the
  motherboard's ports, but you must make sure to set the new ports
  to different IRQs and address ranges to avoid hardware conflicts.

- *Controller repairs.*   The I/O port on the motherboard has failed.
  Rather than replace the entire motherboard, you can use a stand-
  alone I/O controller can be used to replace the failed port. Note
  that you still have to disable the corresponding port on the motherboard.

I/O controller symptoms

Symptom 1: *When an I/O board is installed, the parallel port does not print to its assigned port.* This is a known problem with several IBM PS/2 systems with built-in parallel ports.

- *Check the motherboard BIOS.* For IBM PS/2 systems, there is a BIOS bug that causes this problem. LPT1 operates as LPT3, LPT 2 operates as LPT1, and LPT3 operates as LPT2. Try upgrading the system BIOS. For non-PS/2 systems, check for BIOS bugs also.

Symptom 2: *You cannot configure a parallel port to LPT3.* This may be a limitation of the particular I/O controller.

- *Check the jumpers.* LPT3 resides at port 3BCh. If you can set the parallel port to that address, you can use the port as LPT3. Otherwise, you will have to use 378h (LPT1) or 278h (LPT2). Note that some I/O boards simply do not offer support for LPT3.
- *Check for hardware conflicts.* Make sure that there are no other devices in the system using the 3BCh address area.

Symptom 3: *The PC does not see COM3 or COM4 after adding an I/O controller.* This is usually a limitation of the particular system BIOS rather than the I/O controller.

- *Check the ports.* Make sure that COM3 and COM4 are enabled on the I/O controller. Also make sure that there are no other devices in the system using the address ranges assigned to COM3 and COM4.
- *Upgrade the system BIOS.* Consider a BIOS upgrade to a version that will initialize COM3 and COM4 properly.
- *Try an initialization utility.* There are some DOS utilities (such as DOSPORTS.EXE from the Boca Research Web site) that can help to initialize COM3 and COM4 if the system BIOS cannot. Such utilities are generally placed in the AUTOEXEC.BAT file.

Symptom 4: *The system fails to detect a mouse after an I/O controller is installed.* In virtually all cases, one of the new COM ports is conflicting with the mouse's existing COM port.

- *Check for hardware conflicts.* Disable any unused COM ports. If you intend to keep the mouse on its existing COM port, disable the corresponding port on the new I/O card. If you intend to use the new COM port(s), disable the original COM port(s) and move the mouse to the new port.

Symptom 5: *The new I/O controller's EPP will not drive the printer properly.* In most cases, the cable itself is at fault.

- *Check the I/O board.* Make sure that you have configured the parallel port as EPP—this is often accomplished through a jumper

on the board. Also be sure that you have disabled any corresponding parallel port on the motherboard.

- *Check the printer.*   Make sure that the printer is compatible with
  EPP operation. If it is not, you may need to set the port back to
  "compatibility mode."

- *Check the cable.*   Make sure that the printer cable conforms to
  IEEE1284 specifications and is the correct length. If it is not, you
  may need to set the port back to "compatibility mode."

SCSI Controllers

The *small computer system interface* (SCSI) has been an icon of
advanced computing since the late 1980s. SCSI allows you to "chain"
devices together on the same bus without having to add controllers
or deal with the configuration issues that are present with more traditional devices. Unlike other controllers, SCSI controllers (also
called "host adapters") are rarely added to the motherboard. As a
result, almost all SCSI-equipped PCs use stand-alone SCSI controllers. While SCSI simplifies the addition of some devices, there
are some special needs that you must be aware of:

- *Termination.*   Both ends of the SCSI device chain must be electri-
  cally terminated with a set of terminating resistors. If the SCSI
  chain is terminated improperly, you will receive device and data
  errors.

- *Drivers.*   SCSI driver software is required to operate the SCSI
  controller—as well as SCSI devices such as CD-ROM drives, tape
  drives, and scanners. SCSI drivers consume memory and suffer
  from bugs and incompatibilities just like other drivers.

- *Device IDs.*   The SCSI controller and every SCSI device on the
  chain requires its own unique device ID. Hardware conflicts can
  result if two or more devices use the same SCSI ID.

- *Device dependence.*   SCSI devices are very dependent on the particular controller. For example, hard drives formatted with one
  SCSI controller may not work properly with another SCSI controller. If you replace the SCSI controller, you may need an entirely new set of drivers.

SCSI termination

While more conventional drive systems like floppy drives and EIDE
drives integrate termination into each drive, SCSI configurations
can be very diverse, and terminating every device would impair signal timing, so you must be able to specifically terminate the SCSI
chain properly. Terminating a SCSI chain may sound easy, but it can
sometimes be confusing in actual practice. Since termination problems cause a majority of SCSI problems, the following rules may help
you avoid common mistakes:

- The SCSI bus needs *exactly* two terminators—never more, never less.

- The device located at each end of the SCSI bus must be terminated, all other devices must be unterminated.

- Devices on the SCSI bus should form a single chain that can be traced from a device at one end to a device at the other. No cable Ts are allowed, and cable length should be kept as short as possible.

- All unused connectors on the SCSI cable must be placed *between* the two terminated devices.

- The host adapter (controller) is a SCSI device.

- Host adapters may have both an internal and an external connector; these are tied together internally and should be thought of as an "in" and an "out." If you have only internal or external devices, the host adapter is terminated; otherwise, it is not.

- SCSI IDs are only logical assignments, and have nothing to do with where the devices should go on the SCSI bus or if they should be terminated.

- Just because an incorrectly terminated system happens to work now, don't count on its continuing to do so. Fix any termination issues.

SCSI symptoms

Symptom 1: *After initial SCSI installation, the system will not boot from the floppy drive.*   You may or may not see an error code corresponding to this problem.

- *Check for hardware conflicts.*   Make sure that the SCSI controller's IRQ, I/O address, and BIOS address are correct, and are not interfering with the floppy drive controller.

- *Check the SCSI BIOS address.*   Make sure that the SCSI BIOS does not conflict with your motherboard BIOS or other BIOS in the system.

- *Check the drive cabling.*   Make sure that the drive cable is attached properly at the drive and at the controller.

- *Check for SCSI wait states.*   If there is a BIOS wait state setting on the controller, try changing the setting.

- *Check the SCSI controller.*   There may be a fault with the SCSI controller. Look for any hard drive LED codes. If a SCSI controller error is indicated, replace the controller.

Symptom 2: *The system will not boot from the SCSI hard drive.* There are several possible problems to consider.

- *Check for IDE/EIDE hard drives.*   A SCSI drive will not boot if there is an IDE/EIDE drive in the system. (Newer SCSI controllers *do* provide a jumper which allows the SCSI drive to boot.)

- *Check the CMOS Setup.*   If there are no IDE/EIDE drives in the system, make sure that any drive references in CMOS are set to "none" or "not installed."

- *Check the SCSI ID.* The SCSI boot drive is almost always ID0. Make sure that the drive's ID is set properly.

- *Check SCSI parity.* Check all SCSI devices to be sure that SCSI parity is set correctly. If even one device does not support SCSI parity, all devices must have SCSI parity disabled.

- *Check SCSI termination.* Make sure that your SCSI device chain is terminated properly.

- *Check the drive preparation.* Make sure that the SCSI boot drive has been partitioned and formatted properly.

Symptom 3: *The SCSI drive fails to respond with an alternative HDD as the boot drive.* In most cases, the SCSI drive is configured incorrectly.

- *Check the CMOS Setup.* Make sure that there are no entries for the SCSI drive in CMOS—the drive should be set to "none" or "not installed."

- *Check the SCSI ID.* Make sure that the first SCSI drive is set to ID0.

- *Check SCSI parity.* Check all SCSI devices to be sure that SCSI parity is set correctly. If even one device does not support SCSI parity, all devices must have SCSI parity disabled.

- *Check SCSI termination.* Make sure that your SCSI device chain is terminated properly.

Symptom 4: *The SCSI drive fails to respond with another SCSI drive as the boot drive.* This is a dual-drive system using two SCSI drives.

- *Check the CMOS Setup.* Make sure that there are no entries for the SCSI drives in CMOS—the drives should be set to "none" or "not installed."

- *Check the SCSI ID.* Make sure that the first SCSI drive (boot drive) is set to ID0, and the second SCSI drive is set to ID1.

- *Check the drive preparation.* Make sure that the SCSI drives have been partitioned and formatted properly.

- *Check SCSI parity.* Check all SCSI devices to be sure that SCSI parity is set correctly. If even one device does not support SCSI parity, all devices must have SCSI parity disabled.

- *Check SCSI termination.* Make sure that your SCSI device chain is terminated properly.

Symptom 5: *The system works erratically. The PC hangs or the SCSI adapter cannot find the drive(s).* Such intermittent operation can be the result of several different SCSI factors.

- *Check the application software.* If the fault occurred while a particular program or driver was running, try disabling that software and see if the problem goes away. You may need to update your software.

■ *Check SCSI IDs.* Make sure that each device in the SCSI chain is assigned its own unique ID number. Otherwise, device conflicts will result.

■ *Check SCSI parity.* Check all SCSI devices to be sure that SCSI parity is set correctly. If even one device does not support SCSI parity, all devices must have SCSI parity disabled.

■ *Check SCSI termination.* Make sure that your SCSI device chain is terminated properly.

■ *Check the SCSI cabling.* Make sure that each SCSI connector is inserted properly into its respective device.

■ *Check for hardware conflicts.* Make sure that no other device is conflicting with the SCSI controller's IRQ or I/O address, and that the SCSI BIOS is not overlapping any other BIOS in the system.

Symptom 6: *You see an 096xxxx error code.* This is a diagnostic error code that indicates a problem in a 32-bit SCSI adapter board.

■ *Check the hardware installation.* Make sure that the SCSI controller is installed correctly and completely. The board should not be shorted against any other board or cable.

■ *Isolate the SCSI problem.* Try disabling one SCSI device at a time. If normal operation returns, the last device to be removed is responsible for the problem (you may need to disable drivers and reconfigure termination when isolating problems in this fashion).

■ *Replace the SCSI controller.* If the problem persists, reinstall all devices and try a new adapter board.

Symptom 7: *You see a 112xxxx error code.* This diagnostic error code indicates a problem in a 16-bit SCSI adapter board.

■ *Check the hardware installation.* Make sure that the SCSI controller is installed correctly and completely. The board should not be shorted against any other board or cable.

■ *Isolate the SCSI problem.* Try disabling one SCSI device at a time. If normal operation returns, the last device to be removed is responsible for the problem (you may need to disable drivers and reconfigure termination when isolating problems in this fashion).

■ *Replace the SCSI controller.* If the problem persists, reinstall all devices and try a new adapter board.

Symptom 8: *You see a 113xxxx error code.* This is a diagnostic code that indicates a problem in a system (motherboard) SCSI adapter configuration.

■ *Check the SCSI BIOS.* Make sure that the motherboard BIOS (or on-board SCSI BIOS) is up to date.

- *Replace the SCSI controller.*   Try disabling the motherboard SCSI controller and installing a stand-alone controller (you may need to reconfigure the PC to accommodate the new SCSI controller).
- *Replace the motherboard.*   If you cannot install a new SCSI controller, replace the motherboard.

Symptom 9: *You see a 210xxxx error code.* There is a fault in a SCSI hard disk.

- *Check the SCSI cabling.*   Make sure that all power and signal cables are attached to each SCSI device.
- *Check SCSI termination.*   Make sure that your SCSI device chain is terminated properly.
- *Replace the hard drive.*   If problems persist, the hard drive may have failed. Try a new SCSI hard drive.

Symptom 10: *A SCSI device refuses to function with the SCSI adapter even though both the adapter and the device check properly.* This is often a classic case of basic incompatibility between the SCSI device and the host adapter. Even though SCSI-2 helps to streamline compatibility between devices and controllers, there are still situations where the two just don't work together.

- *Check the SCSI configuration.*   You may be able to use an alternative jumper or DIP switch configuration to correct the compatibility issues.
- *Try a more compatible device.*   If problems remain, try using a similar device from a different manufacturer (e.g., try a Connor tape drive instead of a Mountain tape drive).

Symptom 11: *You see a "No SCSI Controller Present" error message.* Immediately suspect that the controller is defective or installed improperly.

- *Check for hardware conflicts.*   Make sure that the IRQ and I/O settings used by the SCSI controller are not in use by any other device.
- *Check the device drivers.*   Make sure that you have installed the correct driver for the SCSI controller, and that any necessary command-line switches have been included.
- *Replace the SCSI controller.*   Try a new SCSI controller in the system.

Symptom 12: *During initialization, the SCSI controller generates an error message or locks up.* The SCSI controller is defective, or there is a SCSI device conflict.

- *Check the SCSI IDs.*   Make sure that every SCSI device is assigned its own ID number, and that each ID is consistent with the particular device (i.e., the controller is ID7, the first SCSI drive is ID0, and so on).

■ *Check the SCSI controller.* If there is a diagnostic available for your controller, run it and look for any defects. Try replacing the SCSI controller.

Symptom 13: *During initialization, one or more SCSI devices are not identified.* There are several common causes of this problem.

■ *Check for device power.* Make sure that each device is powered properly (especially external devices).

■ *Check the SCSI IDs.* Make sure that every SCSI device is assigned its own ID number, and that each ID is consistent with the particular device (i.e., the controller is ID7, the first SCSI drive is ID0, and so on).

■ *Check SCSI termination.* Make sure that your SCSI device chain is terminated properly.

■ *Check the SCSI cabling.* Make sure that each SCSI connector is attached to the proper device in the correct orientation. Try a shorter or a different cable.

■ *Check the device drivers.* Make sure that the proper driver(s) for each device are entered correctly in CONFIG.SYS or AUTOEX-EC.BAT, and that any necessary command-line switches are included.

■ *Replace the suspect device.* If problems persist, try replacing the suspect device.

Symptom 14: *The SCSI controller recognizes a CD-ROM drive, but the drive will not run.* In virtually all cases, the driver order in your CONFIG.SYS file is incorrect.

■ *Check the driver order.* Open your CONFIG.SYS file and make sure that the ASPI manager is loaded first, followed by the CD-ROM ASPI driver.

■ *Check the CD-ROM extension.* Open your AUTOEXEC.BAT file and make sure that MSCDEX (or other suitable DOS extension) is loaded for the CD-ROM.

Symptom 15: *When configuring the SCSI manager software, you find no listing for your specific CD-ROM drive.* In most cases, you can use a "close" ASPI manager.

■ *Check your ASPI manager.* However, keep in mind that some CD-ROM commands (especially multisession commands) are vendor-unique. If you have trouble using a drive's multisession features, you may need to load the exact driver.

Symptom 16: *After installing a new SCSI controller, you see an error message indicating that the old ASPI manager refuses to load.* You have neglected to remove the old SCSI driver(s), and since the old hardware is no longer installed, the driver cannot find the hardware.

■ *Check your startup files.* Make sure to disable or remove any older drivers in CONFIG.SYS and AUTOEXEC.BAT—you don't need them anymore.

Symptom 17: *Windows 95 is running in the "compatibility mode" when using the SCSI controller software.* There is no protected-mode driver for the SCSI controller, and the real-mode driver is causing Windows 95 to run in "compatibility mode."

■ *Obtain updated SCSI drivers.* You will need to contact the SCSI controller manufacturer to obtain protected-mode drivers. Before proceeding, uninstall the real-mode driver(s), then install the new drivers.

Symptom 18: *You see an error such as "Auto-Configuration Error 03:03 Bus#:00 Device#:06 Function#:00."* This is almost always a hardware-related problem.

■ *Update the SCSI BIOS.* Check to see if there is an update to your SCSI BIOS which corrects the problem. Some of the latest SCSI controllers use "flash" BIOS which can be reprogrammed without having to replace the BIOS IC.

■ *Try a different bus slot.* Some SCSI controllers demand a bus-mastering expansion slot. Try the controller in a bus-mastering slot.

Symptom 19: *The SCSI adapter refuses to recognize an external SCSI Zip drive (Iomega).* This is almost always a problem with the SCSI bus setup.

■ *Check the SCSI bus.* Turn off "wide negotiation" for the Zip drive's SCSI ID (usually ID6). Also check to be sure that the Zip drive is not set as a boot drive.

Symptom 20: *The PC will not recognize the PCI SCSI controller, or the system hangs up.* You may have to reconfigure the PCI slot's resources.

■ *Check the Windows 95 assignments.* Open the Device Manager and check the SCSI controller's properties to find the assigned IRQ and I/O space. Note that these resources are the ones that Windows 95 *thinks* the controller is using.

■ *Check the CMOS Setup.* Open the system Setup and check the PCI slot assignments. You may have to change those assignments to match the resources assigned under Windows 95.

Symptom 21: *After installation of the SCSI driver, the system hangs at the Windows logo.* The SCSI driver is causing a conflict with the system.

- *Check the SCSI driver.*   Start Windows 95 in the "safe mode," open the Device Manager, and make sure that the controller's resource settings match the driver's resource settings.

- *Try a different driver.*   You may need to disable the SCSI driver or install an updated driver in order to restore Windows 95's operation.

Symptom 22:   *A SCSI PnP controller will not work in a system with other non-PnP controllers.*   In virtually all cases, this is a system problem which will require you to change the configuration.

- *Shut down PnP support.*   Try disabling PnP support, then configuring the SCSI controller manually.

- *Try a different SCSI controller.*   You might try a different SCSI controller that will coexist with non-PnP controllers.

Symptom 23:   *Protected-mode ASPI drivers refuse to load (only real-mode drivers are loading).*   In almost all cases, the driver resource assignments are different from the controller's resource assignments.

- *Coordinate your resources.*   Make sure that the controller and the driver are using the same resources.

- *Check your drivers.*   Make sure that you are using the latest drivers for your SCSI controller.

Symptom 24:   *You cannot get EZ-SCSI to work under Windows 95.* Chances are that you are using an older version of EZ-SCSI which is not compatible with Windows 95.

- *Check your version of EZ-SCSI.*   You need version 4.0 or later. You may need to obtain and install a later version.

Symptom 25:   *FDISK will not detect a SCSI hard drive, or will allow only up to 1 Gbyte partitions.*   FDISK may not interact properly with all real-mode SCSI drivers.

- *Use protected-mode drivers.*   If you're having trouble using FDISK, install the protected-mode drivers for your SCSI controller.

- *Try a different partitioning utility.*   If problems persist, you can try an alternative utility such as Partition Magic 3.0 from PowerQuest or AFDISK with EZ-SCSI 4.0.

Symptom 26:   *With multiple SCSI adapters in the system, you cannot determine which PCI controller is the primary controller.*   This is a common issue with advanced PCI SCSI systems.

- *Check the PCI slot number.*   The PCI SCSI controller in the lowest slot is typically the "primary" controller.

Symptom 27: *After installing a SCSI controller, you have random lockups during initialization, and the system locks when a scan of the SCSI bus is attempted.* In most instances, the DAT drive does not appear to work at all.

■ *Check the SCSI adapter configuration.* Start the SCSI configuration utility and disable any option like "SCSI Bus Reset during IC Initialization."

Symptom 28: *A "fast and wide" SCSI controller has problems finding single-ended narrow devices when you scan for devices using the SCSISelect utility.* The configuration of the utility is wrong.

■ *Check the SCSI adapter configuration.* Start the SCSI configuration utility and select *no* for the option "Initiate Wide Negotiation" for any SCSI ID occupied by a narrow SCSI device.

Symptom 29: *When installing a new operating system, you get random lockups during SCSI disk drive activity or error messages pointing to SCSI hard disk partition problems.* In almost all cases, the SCSI devices are not configured properly.

■ *Check SCSI termination.* Make sure that your SCSI device chain is terminated properly.

■ *Check termination power.* Set termination power to come from the host adapter or pin 26 of the SCSI bus.

■ *Check the SCSI cabling.* Make sure that each SCSI connector is attached to the proper device in the correct orientation. Try a shorter or different cable.

■ *Check the "Unit Attention" signal.* The "Unit Attention" signal should be disabled.

Symptom 30: *The PCI SCSI controller is not recognized, and the BIOS banner is not displayed.* Your computer may be using an old PCI bus implementation.

■ *Check the PCI implementation.* Your computer should be using a PCI v.2.0–compliant motherboard, and the BIOS must support PCI-to-PCI bridges (PPB). If this is not the case, you may need to upgrade the motherboard BIOS or the entire motherboard.

■ *Check the motherboard BIOS.* If support for PPB is already present, try upgrading the motherboard BIOS.

■ *Check the PCI slot.* Either the board is not in a bus-mastering slot or the PCI slot is not enabled for bus mastering. Try enabling bus mastering for your SCSI controller (through a motherboard jumper or CMOS setting).

Symptom 31: *A PCI video card is installed alongside a PCI SCSI controller, and there is no video (or it causes intermittent hangs during boot).* In almost all cases, there is a resource conflict between PCI slots.

■ *Check the PCI slot configuration.*   Open your CMOS Setup and see if there are any conflicts between your PCI slot resources. If there are, you will need to reassign some of those resources to clear the conflict.

Symptom 32:   *The EZ-SCSI installation hangs when working with a SCSI driver.*   Chances are that the system is using an older version of EZ-SCSI.

■ *Check your version of EZ-SCSI.*   If you are using a version earlier than 3.11, you will need to upgrade your version of EZ-SCSI to 3.11 or later.

Symptom 33:   *When a SCSI driver is being loaded, the system hangs and then displays the error message "Read BIOS Parameter Failed" (or similar error message).*   You are using an older version of the SCSI driver.

■ *Check your driver version.*   Chances are that you are using an older SCSI driver. Install the latest version and try again.

Symptom 34:   *You can access SCSI channel A, but you cannot access SCSI channel B.*   The SCSI controller requires a BIOS upgrade.

■ *Try a slot workaround.*   Leave the slot next to the SCSI controller vacant, and also assign an IRQ to that particular slot (for example, if the controller is installed in slot 1, assign an IRQ to slot 1 and assign an IRQ to slot 2). There are some systems that have PCI IRQ sharing where slots 1 and 2 have to be assigned the same IRQ. **Note:** *The adjacent slot must remain vacant for this solution to work.*

■ *Upgrade the BIOS.*   A better solution is simply to upgrade the SCSI BIOS.

Symptom 35:   *When installing an EISA SCSI adapter, you get an error message such as "EISA configuration slot mismatch" or "board not found in slot x" after running the EISA configuration utility.*   In virtually all cases, the EISA board is not fully seated in its bus slot.

■ *Reseat the EISA SCSI adapter.*   Carefully insert the controller back into its slot. You may also try installing the board in a different slot.

■ *Replace the EISA SCSI controller.*   If problems persist, replace the SCSI controller outright.

Symptom 36:   *You can't configure an EISA SCSI controller in enhanced mode.*   You probably get an error such as "unable to initialize host adapter," or the system may hang after BIOS scans for SCSI devices. In most cases, the motherboard does not support LEVEL INT triggering.

- *Check the SCSI controller configuration file.* Open the EISA .CFG file for the controller. You probably need to make changes to the file contents. Check with technical support for your particular controller to see any specific changes.

- *Try the latest .CFG file.* If there is an updated .CFG file already prepared for your controller, you can download the new file and copy it to the controller's directory.

Symptom 37: *The EISA configuration utility reports that the controller's overlay file is not compatible.* In most cases, the configuration utility is obsolete.

- *Check your ECU version.* Your EISA configuration utility is probably outdated. Contact the controller manufacturer to obtain a more current ECU.

Symptom 38: *The SCSI controller has a problem with EDGE triggering.* In virtually all cases, you are using obsolete SCSI drivers and overlay files.

- *Check your overlay file version.* Your .CFG and .OVL files are probably outdated. Check with the controller manufacturer to obtain more current .CFG and .OVL files.

Symptom 39: *When booting the computer, you see "Checking for SCSI target 0 LUN 0" right after the BIOS header information. The system waits for about 30 seconds, then reports "BIOS not installed, no INT 13h device found."* The system then boots normally.

- *Check for SCSI hard drives.* The BIOS is trying to find a hard drive at SCSI ID 0 or 1. If you do not have a SCSI hard drive attached to the host adapter, it is usually recommended that the SCSI BIOS be disabled.

Symptom 40: *During initialization, the SCSI BIOS header is displayed, then you get the error message "Host Adapter Diagnostic Error."* There is probably a hardware conflict in the system.

- *Check for hardware conflicts.* Either the SCSI controller has a port address conflict with another card, or the card has been changed to port address 140 (and the SCSI BIOS is enabled). Check for any I/O conflicts between the SCSI controller and other devices in the system.

Symptom 41: *The SCSI hard drive that is attached to the SCSI controller does not allow full use of the disk space.* The SCSI BIOS is an older version.

- *Update the SCSI BIOS.* Chances are that the SCSI BIOS does not support LBA. Install a new version of the SCSI BIOS.

■ *Replace the SCSI controller.*   If you cannot get the controller to recognize the full disk space, you might replace the SCSI controller entirely.

Symptom 42:   *You see an error such as "No SCSI $MGR Found."* There are several possible causes for this type of problem.

■ *Check the SCSI setup utility.*   Rerun the installation utility and choose "Automatic Search for Host Adapter." If the selection returns with "no host," do a manual selection with arrow keys to select the correct host adapter.

■ *Check the cabling.*   Retest the adapter with *no* cables attached— bad cables or damaged cables can shut the adapter down. If problems persist, replace the SCSI controller card.

Symptom 43:   *You see an error message such as "No SCSI Host Adapter Detected."*   Cable issues and hardware conflicts are the most common reasons for this problem.

■ *Check the cabling.*   The ASPI manager failed to find a host adapter. Remove all cables from the adapter and reboot. If the SCSI controller is found, one or more cables may be defective or swapped at pin 1. Try a new cable.

■ *Check for hardware conflicts.*   Make sure that the SCSI controller is not using resources assigned to other devices in the system.

Symptom 44:   *You see an error message such as "No SCSI Functions in Use."*   In almost all cases, the SCSI system is using the wrong drivers or is not formatted properly.

■ *Check the SCSI driver installation.*   Remove the driver from CONFIG.SYS and reboot, or disable the SCSI BIOS.

■ *Check the formatting controller.*   The hard disk might have been formatted with another SCSI controller that does not support ASPI or has a special format. Try reformatting the drive with the current controller.

Symptom 45:   *You see an error message such as "No Boot Record Found."*   The hard drive has not been made bootable.

■ *Check the drive's partition.*   The hard disk may not have been partitioned. Perform a high-level format of the hard disk. When partitioning the drive, make sure that the partition is made bootable.

■ *Check the formatting controller.*   The hard disk might have been formatted with another SCSI controller that does not support ASPI or has a special format. Try reformatting the drive with the current controller.

Symptom 46: *You see an error message such as "Device Fails to Respond."* Device cabling and hardware conflicts are two common issues here.

- *Check the device power.* Make sure that the SCSI device is receiving power and is cabled correctly.

- *Check the device ID.* Make sure that each device has its own unique SCSI ID.

- *Check the device driver.* Make sure that the device driver is correct for your particular SCSI device.

- *Replace the SCSI device.* Try a new SCSI device.

Symptom 47: *You see an error message such as "Unknown SCSI Device" or "Waiting for SCSI Device."* The drive was not formatted properly or is terminated incorrectly.

- *Check the drive format.* Make sure that the SCSI device is formatted properly on the current SCSI controller.

- *Check the SCSI ID.* Make sure that your boot drive is ID0, and that it is not sharing a SCSI ID with other SCSI devices.

- *Check SCSI termination.* Make sure that your SCSI device chain is terminated properly.

Symptom 48: *You see an error message such as "CMD Failure XX."* In most cases, you are trying to partition a drive that has not been low-level formatted.

- *Check the drive preparation.* Perform a low-level format on the drive, then repartition and reformat the drive normally.

Symptom 49: *When the VL SCSI controller is plugged into a system, it hangs on boot-up.* Chances are that your VL SCSI controller demands full 32-bit bus mastering in a master VL slot.

- *Check the VL slot.* Try installing the VL SCSI controller into a master VL bus slot.

- *Check the VL slot speed.* VL slots are typically limited to 33 MHz. You may have to take a system out of turbo mode in order to reduce clock speed.

- *Check write-through caching.* Try disabling write-through caching.

Symptom 50: *After the CPU is upgraded to a faster speed, the VL bus PC locks up, or won't boot from the SCSI hard drive.* The new CPU is overdriving the VL bus clock, which must be limited to 33 MHz.

- *Check the motherboard jumpers.* The motherboard may have jumpers that govern the VL bus speed. Make sure that the VL bus speed jumper is set in the $< = 33$ MHz position. This may also be set in the motherboard's CMOS Setup.

- *Check write-through caching.* In the CMOS Setup, you can disable the CPU external cache. Change the caching method to write-through instead of write-back.

- *Check the CPU internal cache.* The internal cache on some CPUs may cause this hang as well. Disable the CPU's internal cache.

- *Reduce the CPU speed.* Reducing the CPU speed may be necessary to allow the SCSI controller adapter to function reliably.

- *Check the turbo setting.* Disable the system's turbo setting during the boot-up sequence. Then reenable the turbo setting after the system has booted.

Symptom 51: *The SCSI controller will not run in a system with an "SLC" processor.* The controller won't run in a 16-bit system.

- *Upgrade the motherboard.* If the SCSI controller will not function in an SLC system, you should upgrade the motherboard entirely.

Symptom 52: *The hard drive operates erratically when running at 10 Mbytes/s during synchronous transfers.* Some drives simply can't support synchronous transfers at that rate.

- *Check the transfer rate.* Lower the synchronous transfer rate to 5 Mbytes/s and see if the device works properly. This may be accomplished through a jumper or the SCSI setup utility.

- *Check the cabling.* Make sure that the cabling is installed properly and securely. Try a new SCSI cable.

- *Check the SCSI termination.* Make sure that the SCSI bus is terminated properly at both ends.

Symptom 53: *The floppy tape controller does not back up or restore VL-based SCSI devices reliably.* This is due to the high speed differences between SCSI and floppy devices.

- *Check the floppy tape drive.* Data from the SCSI device is probably being "lost" while waiting for the slow floppy tape drive. Unfortunately, there is no way to slow down VL devices. You might consider upgrading the floppy tape drive to a SCSI model.

8

Command Reference

There is no doubt that Windows 95 and plug-and-play technology have gone a long way toward "automating" the configuration of a PC. The automatic detection of hardware, installation of protected-mode drivers, and reduced dependence on startup batch files (CONFIG.SYS and AUTOEXEC.BAT) have simplified many of the difficult and time-consuming configuration issues of years past. However, when working on PCs *without* Windows 95 (or when Windows 95 fails to start), you will need to fall back on DOS commands and utilities in order to restore system operation. This chapter provides you with a DOS command reference which also covers utilities and batch file–specific functions.

DOS Shortcut Keys

F1—Brings the last command back one letter at a time. You will have to press <F1> repeatedly to bring the entire command string back.

F2—Brings back the last command to the specified letter. For example, if the original command is

```
dir windows /p
```

the command <F2> and <N> will bring the command back to

```
dir wi
```

F3—Brings back the entire previous command.

F4—Deletes everything in the command after the letter you specify (the opposite of <F2>).

F5—Copies the current command line to a template.

F6—Produces a CTRL-Z character, which is typically used in command lines.

DOS Commands and Functions

APPEND: Allows programs to open data files in specified directories as if they were in the current directory. Syntax:

```
APPEND [[drive:]path[;…]][/X[:ON | :OFF]][/PATH:ON |
/PATH:OFF][/E]
```

- `[drive:]path`—Specifies a drive and directory to append.
- `/X:ON`—Applies appended directories to file searches and application execution.
- `/X:OFF`—Applies appended directories only to requests to open files.
- `/PATH:ON`—Applies appended directories to file requests that already specify a path.
- `/PATH:OFF`—Turns off the effect of `/PATH:ON`.
- `/E`—Stores a copy of the appended directory list in an environment variable named APPEND. `/E` may be used only the first time you use APPEND after starting your system.

Type `APPEND ;` to clear the appended directory list.
Type `APPEND` without parameters to display the appended directory list.

ASSIGN: Redirects requests for disk operations on one drive to a different drive. Syntax:

```
ASSIGN [x[:] = y[:][...]]
ASSIGN /STATUS
```

- `x`—Specifies the drive letter to reassign.
- `y`—Specifies the drive that `x:` will be assigned to.
- `/STATUS`—Displays current drive assignments.

Type `ASSIGN` without parameters to reset all drive letters to original assignments.

ATTRIB: Displays or changes file attributes. Syntax:

```
ATTRIB [+R | -R][+A | -A][+S | -S]
[+H | -H][[drive:][path]filename][/S]
```

- `[+]`—Sets an attribute.
- `[-]`—Clears an attribute.
- `R`—Read-only file attribute.
- `A`—Archive file attribute.
- `S`—System file attribute.
- `H`—Hidden file attribute.
- `/S`—Processes files in all directories in the specified path.

BACKUP: Backs up one or more files from one disk to another. Syntax:

```
BACKUP source destination:
[/S][/M][/A][/F[:size]][/D:date[/T:time]]
[/L[:[drive:][path]logfile]]
```

- `source`—Specifies the file(s), drive, or directory to back up.
- `destination`—Specifies the drive to save backup copies onto.
- `/S`—Backs up the contents of subdirectories.
- `/M`—Backs up only files that have changed since the last backup.
- `/A`—Adds backup files to an existing backup disk.
- `/F:[size]`—Specifies the size of the disk to be formatted.
- `/D:date`—Backs up only files changed on or after the specified date.
- `/T:time`—Backs up only files changed at or after the specified time.
- `/L[:[drive:][path]logfile]`—Creates a log file and entry to record the backup operation.

BREAK: Sets or clears extended CTRL + C checking. Syntax:

```
BREAK [ON | OFF]
```

Type `BREAK` without a parameter to display the current BREAK setting.

BUFFERS: Sets the number of buffers allocated from memory. Syntax:

```
BUFFERS = x
```

- `x`—The number of buffers required.

CALL: Calls one batch program from another. Syntax:

```
CALL [drive:][path]filename [batch-parameters]
```

- `batch-parameters`—Specifies any command-line information required by the batch program.

CD or CHDIR: Displays the name of or changes the current directory. Syntax:

```
CHDIR [drive:][path]
CHDIR[..]
CD [drive:][path]
CD[..]
```

Type `CD drive:` to display the current directory in the specified drive.

Type `CD` without parameters to display the current drive and directory.

CHCP: Displays or sets the active code page number. Syntax:

```
CHCP [nnn]
```

■ nnn—Specifies a code page number.

Type CHCP without a parameter to display the active code page number.

CHKDSK: Checks a disk and displays a status report. Syntax:

```
CHKDSK [drive:][[path]filename][/F][/V]
```

■ [drive:][path]—Specifies the drive and directory to check.
■ filename—Specifies the file(s) to check for fragmentation.
■ /F—Fixes errors on the disk.
■ /V—Displays the full path and name of every file on the disk.

Type CHKDSK without parameters to check the current disk.

CHOICE: Allows an input for multiple choices. Syntax:

```
CHOICE /C:xxx.. [text]
```

■ /C:xxx..—Lists the numbers used in the selection (e.g., 1234 and so on).
■ [text]—The label which appears for the choices.

CLS: Clears the screen. Syntax:

```
CLS
```

COMMAND: Starts a new instance of the MS-DOS command interpreter. Syntax:

```
COMMAND [[drive:]path][device][/E:nnnnn][/P]
[/C string][/MSG]
```

■ [drive:]path—Specifies the directory containing the COMMAND.COM file.
■ device—Specifies the device to use for command input and output.
■ /E:nnnnn—Sets the initial environment size to *nnnnn* bytes.
■ /P—Makes the new command interpreter permanent (can't exit).
■ /C string—Carries out the command specified by the string, and then stops.
■ /MSG—Specifies that all error messages be stored in memory. You need to specify /P with this switch.

COMP: Compares the contents of two files or sets of files. Syntax:

```
COMP [data1][data2][/D][/A][/L][/N = number][/C]
```

- `data1`—Specifies the location and name(s) of the first file(s) to compare.
- `data2`—Specifies the location and name(s) of the second files to compare.
- `/D`—Displays differences in decimal format. The default is hexadecimal.
- `/A`—Displays differences in ASCII characters.
- `/L`—Displays line numbers for differences.
- `/N = number`—Compares only the first specified number of lines in each file.
- `/C`—Disregards the case of ASCII letters when comparing files.

To compare sets of files, use wildcards in the `data1` and `data2` parameters.

COPY: Copies one or more files to another location. Syntax:

```
COPY [/A | /B] source [/A | /B][+ source [/A | /B]
[+ …]][destination [/A | /B]][/V]
```

- `source`—Specifies the file or files to be copied.
- `/A`—Indicates an ASCII text file.
- `/B`—Indicates a binary file.
- `destination`—Specifies the directory and/or filename for the new file(s).
- `/V`—Verifies that new files are written correctly.

To append files, specify a single file for destination, but multiple files for source (using wildcards or file1 + file2 + file3 format).

CTTY: Changes the terminal device used to control your system. Syntax:

```
CTTY device
```

- `device`—The terminal device you want to use (such as COM1).

DATE: Displays or sets the date. Syntax:

```
DATE [date]
```

Type `DATE` without parameters to display the current date setting and a prompt for a new one. Press <Enter> to keep the same date.

DEBUG: Runs Debug, a program testing and editing tool. Syntax:

```
DEBUG [[drive:][path]filename [testfile-parameters]]
```

- `[drive:][path]filename`—Specifies the file you want to test.
- `testfile-parameters`—Specifies command-line information required by the file you want to test.

After Debug starts, type ? to display a list of debugging commands.

DEFRAG: Reorganizes file clusters into contiguous disk areas.
Syntax:

```
DEFRAG [/switches] [sorting]
```

- /F—Defragments files and consolidates all empty space at the end
  of the disk.
- /U—Defragments files but leaves empty space alone.
- /V—Verifies that all files have been rewritten correctly.
- /B—Restarts the computer after DEFRAG has run.
- /S—Sorting options:

  n (alphabetically by name)
  n- (reverse alphabetically)
  e (alphabetically by extension)
  e- (reverse alphabetically by extension)
  d (date and time—earliest first)
  d- (date and time—latest first)
  s (smallest to largest)
  s- (largest to smallest)

DEL or ERASE: Deletes one or more files. Syntax:

```
DEL [drive:][path]filename [/P]
ERASE [drive:][path]filename [/P]
```

- [drive:][path]filename—Specifies the file(s) to delete.
  Specify multiple files by using wildcards.
- /P—Prompts for confirmation before deleting each file.

DELTREE: Deletes an entire directory. Syntax:

```
DELTREE [path]
```

DEVICE: Loads a device driver in CONFIG.SYS. Syntax:

```
DEVICE = [path and filename] [/switches]
DEVICEHIGH = [path and filename] [/switches]
```

- path and filename—The complete path to the device driver file.
- /switches—Any command-line switches used for the driver.

DIR: Displays a list of files and subdirectories in a directory.
Syntax:

```
DIR [drive:][path][filename][/P][/W][/A[[:]attributes]
][/O[[:]sort order]][/S][/B][/L]
```

- [drive:][path][filename]—Specifies drive, directory, and/or
  files to list.
- /P—Pauses after each screenful of information.

- /W—Uses wide list format.
- /A—Displays files with specified attributes: D (directories), R (read-only files), H (hidden files), A (archive files), S (system files).
- /O—List by files in sorted order.
- sort order—N (by alphabetical name), S [by size (smallest first)], E (by alphabetical extension), D (by date and time), G (group directories first).
- /S—Displays files in specified directory and all subdirectories.
- /B—Uses bare format (no heading information or summary).
- /L—Uses lowercase.

Switches may be preset in the DIRCMD environment variable.

DISKCOMP: Compares the contents of two floppy disks. Syntax:

```
DISKCOMP [drive1: [drive2:]][/1][/8]
```

- /1—Compares the first side of the disks.
- /8—Compares only the first eight sectors of each track.

DISKCOPY: Copies the contents of one floppy disk to another. Syntax:

```
DISKCOPY [drive1: [drive2:]][/1][/V]
```

- /1—Copies only the first side of the disk.
- /V—Verifies that the information is copied correctly.

The two floppy disks must be of the same type.
You may specify the same drive for drive1 and drive2.

DOSKEY: Edits command lines, recalls MS-DOS commands, and creates macros. Syntax:

```
DOSKEY [/REINSTALL][/BUFSIZE = size][/MACROS][/HISTORY]
[/INSERT | /OVERSTRIKE][macroname = [text]]
```

- /REINSTALL—Installs a new copy of DOSKEY.
- /BUFSIZE = size—Sets the size of the command history buffer.
- /MACROS—Displays all DOSKEY macros.
- /HISTORY—Displays all commands stored in memory.
- /INSERT—Specifies that new text you type is inserted in old text.
- /OVERSTRIKE—Specifies that new text overwrites old text.
- macroname—Specifies a name for a macro you create.
- text—Specifies commands you want to record.

The following are special function keys under DOSKEY:

- UP and DOWN ARROWS—recall commands.

- ESC—clears command line.
- F7—displays command history.
- ALT + F7—clears command history.
- F8—searches command history.
- F9—selects a command by number.
- ALT + F10—clears macro definitions.

The following are some special codes in DOSKEY macro definitions:

- $T—Command separator. Allows multiple commands in a macro.
- $1–$9—Batch parameters. Equivalent to %1 to %9 in batch programs.
- $*—Symbol replaced by everything following macro name on command line.

DOSSHELL: Starts MS-DOS shell. Syntax:

```
DOSSHELL [/T[:res[n]]][/B]
DOSSHELL [/G[:res[n]]][/B]
```

- /T—Starts MS-DOS shell in text mode.
- :res[n]—A letter (L, M, H) and number indicating screen resolution.
- /B—Starts MS-DOS shell using black-and-white color scheme.
- /G—Starts MS-DOS shell in graphics mode.

ECHO: Displays messages, or turns command echoing on or off. Syntax:

```
ECHO [ON | OFF]
ECHO [message]
```

Type ECHO without parameters to display the current echo setting.

EDIT: Starts MS-DOS Editor, which creates and changes ASCII files.

```
EDIT [[drive:][path]filename][/B][/G][/H][/NOHI]
```

- [drive:][path]filename—Specifies the ASCII file to edit.
- /B—Allows use of a monochrome monitor with a color graphics card.
- /G—Provides the fastest update of a CGA screen.
- /H—Displays the maximum number of lines possible for your hardware.
- /NOHI—Allows the use of a monitor without high-intensity support.

EDLIN: Starts Edlin, a line-oriented text editor. Syntax:

```
EDLIN [drive:][path]filename [/B]
```

- /B—Ignores end-of-file (CTRL + Z) characters.

EMM386: Turns EMM386 expanded memory support on or off. Syntax:

```
EMM386 [ON | OFF | AUTO][W = ON | W = OFF]
```

- ON | OFF | AUTO—Activates or suspends the EMM386.EXE device driver, or places it in auto mode.
- W = ON | OFF—Turns Weitek coprocessor support on or off.

EXE2BIN: Converts .EXE (executable) files to binary format syntax.

```
EXE2BIN [drive1:][path1]input-file [[drive2:]
[path2]output-file]
```

- input-file—Specifies the .EXE file to be converted.
- output-file—Specifies the binary file to be created.

EXIT: Quits the COMMAND.COM program (command interpreter). Syntax:

```
EXIT
```

EXPAND: Expands one or more compressed files. Syntax:

```
EXPAND [-r] Source [Destination]
```

- -r—Automatically renames expanded files. Only valid for files compressed with -r switch.
- Source—Source file specification. Source may be multiple file specifications. Wildcards may be used.
- Destination—Destination file/path specification. Destination may be a directory. If Source is multiple files and -r is not specified, Destination must be a directory. Wildcards may not be used.

FASTOPEN: Decreases the amount of time needed to open frequently used files and directories. Syntax:

```
FASTOPEN drive:[[ = ]n][drive:[[ = ]n][ …]][/X]
```

- drive:—Specifies the hard disk drive you want Fastopen to work with.
- n—Specifies the maximum number of file locations Fastopen retains in its filename cache.
- /X—Creates the filename cache in expanded memory.

FC: Compares two files or sets of files, and displays the differences between them. Syntax:

```
FC [/A][/C][/L][/LBn][/N][/T][/W][/nnnn][drive1:]
[path1]filename1 [drive2:][path2]filename2
```

or

```
FC /B [drive1:][path1]filename1 [drive2:][path2]filename2
```

- /A—Displays only the first and last lines for each set of differences.
- /B—Performs a binary comparison.
- /C—Disregards the case of letters.
- /L—Compares files as ASCII text.
- /LBn—Sets the maximum consecutive mismatches to the specified number of lines.
- /N—Displays the line numbers on an ASCII comparison.
- /T—Does not expand tabs to spaces.
- /W—Compresses white space (tabs and spaces) for comparison.
- /nnnn—Specifies the number of consecutive lines that must match after a mismatch.

FDISK: Configures a hard disk for use with MS-DOS. Syntax:

```
FDISK
```

FIND: Searches for a text string in a file or files. Syntax:

```
FIND [/V][/C][/N][/I] "string" [[drive:]
[path]filename[ ...]]
```

- /V—Displays all lines *not* containing the specified string.
- /C—Displays only the count of lines containing the string.
- /N—Displays line numbers with the displayed lines.
- /I—Ignores the case of characters when searching for the string.
- "string"—Specifies the text string to find.
- [drive:][path]filename—Specifies a file or files to search.

If a path name is not specified, FIND searches the text typed at the prompt or piped from another command.

FOR: Runs a specified command for each file in a set of files. Syntax:

```
FOR %variable IN (set) DO command [command-parameters]
```

- %variable—Specifies a replaceable parameter.
- (set)—Specifies a set of one or more files. Wildcards may be used.
- command—Specifies the command to carry out for each file.

- `command-parameters`—Specifies parameters or switches for the specified command.

To use the FOR command in a batch program, specify `%%variable` instead of `%variable`.

FORMAT: Formats a disk for use with MS-DOS. Syntax:

```
FORMAT drive: [/V[:label]][/Q][/U][/F:size][/B | /S]
FORMAT drive: [/V[:label]][/Q][/U]
[/T:tracks /N:sectors][/B | /S]
FORMAT drive: [/V[:label]][/Q][/U][/1][/3][/4][/B | /S]
FORMAT drive: [/Q][/U][/1][/3][/4][/8][/B | /S]
```

- `/V[:label]`—Specifies the volume label.
- `/Q`—Performs a quick format.
- `/U`—Performs an unconditional format.
- `/F:size`—Specifies the size of the floppy disk to format (such as 160, 180, 320, 360, 720, 1.2, 1.44, 2.88).
- `/B`—Allocates space on the formatted disk for system files.
- `/S`—Copies system files to the formatted disk.
- `/T:tracks`—Specifies the number of tracks per disk side.
- `/N:sectors`—Specifies the number of sectors per track.
- `/1`—Formats a single side of a floppy disk.
- `/3`—Formats a 3.5-inch 720-kbyte floppy disk in a high-density drive.
- `/4`—Formats a 5.25-inch 360-kbyte floppy disk in a high-density drive.
- `/8`—Formats eight sectors per track.

GOTO: Directs MS-DOS to a labeled line in a batch program. Syntax:

```
GOTO label
```

- `label`—Specifies a text string used in the batch program as a label.

You type a label on a line by itself, beginning with a colon.

GRAFTABL: Enables MS-DOS to display an extended character set in graphics mode. Syntax:

```
GRAFTABL [xxx]
GRAFTABL /STATUS
```

- `xxx`—Specifies a code page number.
- `/STATUS`—Displays the current code page selected for use with **GRAFTABL**.

GRAPHICS: Loads a program that can print graphics. Syntax:

```
GRAPHICS [type][[drive:][path]filename][/R][/B][/LCD]
[/PRINTBOX:STD | /PRINTBOX:LCD]
```

■ `type`—Specifies a printer type (see User's Guide and Reference).

■ `[drive:][path]filename`—Specifies the file containing information on supported printers.

■ `/R`—Prints white on black as seen on the screen.

■ `/B`—Prints the background in color for COLOR4 and COLOR8 printers.

■ `/LCD`—Prints using the LCD aspect ratio.

■ `/PRINTBOX:STD | /PRINTBOX:LCD`—Specifies the print box size, either STD or LCD.

IF: Performs conditional processing in batch programs. Syntax:

```
IF [NOT] ERRORLEVEL number command
IF [NOT] string1 = = string2 command
IF [NOT] EXIST filename command
```

■ `NOT`—Specifies that MS-DOS should carry out the command only if the condition is false.

■ `ERRORLEVEL number`—Specifies a true condition if the last program run returned an exit code equal to or greater than the number specified.

■ `command`—Specifies the command to carry out if the condition is met.

■ `string1 = = string2`—Specifies a true condition if the specified text strings match.

■ `EXIST filename`—Specifies a true condition if the specified filename exists.

JOIN: Joins a disk drive to a directory on another drive. Syntax:

```
JOIN [drive1: [drive2:]path]
JOIN drive1: /D
```

■ `drive1:`—Specifies a disk drive that will appear as a directory on `drive2`.

■ `drive2:`—Specifies a drive to which you want to join `drive1`.

■ `Path`—Specifies the directory to which you want to join `drive1`. It must be empty and cannot be the root directory.

■ `/D`—Cancels any previous JOIN commands for the specified drive.

Type `JOIN` without parameters to list currently joined drives.

KEYB: Configures a keyboard for a specific language. Syntax:

```
KEYB [xx[,[yyy][,[drive:][path]filename]]][/E][/ID:nnn]
```

- xx—Specifies a two-letter keyboard code.
- yyy—Specifies the code page for the character set.
- [drive:][path]filename—Specifies the keyboard definition file.
- /E—Specifies that an enhanced keyboard is installed.
- /ID:nnn—Specifies the keyboard in use.

LABEL: Creates, changes, or deletes the volume label of a disk. Syntax:

```
LABEL [drive:][label]
```

LASTDRIVE: Specifies the maximum number of drives in the system. Syntax:

```
LASTDRIVE = x
```

- x—The last drive letter in the system.

LH or LOADHIGH: Loads a program into the upper memory area. Syntax:

```
LOADHIGH [drive:][path]filename [parameters]
LH [drive:][path]filename [parameters]
```

- parameters—Specifies any command-line information required by the program you want to load.

LOADFIX: Loads a program above the first 64 kbytes of memory, and runs the program. Syntax:

```
LOADFIX [drive:][path]filename
```

Use LOADFIX to load a program if you have received the message "Packed file corrupt" when trying to load it in low memory.

MD or MKDIR: Creates a directory. Syntax:

```
MKDIR [drive:]path
MD [drive:]path
```

MEM: Displays the amount of used and free memory in your system. Syntax:

```
MEM [/PROGRAM | /DEBUG | /CLASSIFY]
```

- /PROGRAM or /P—Displays the status of programs currently loaded in memory.
- /DEBUG or /D—Displays the status of programs, internal drivers, and other information.
- /CLASSIFY or /C—Classifies programs by memory usage. Lists the size of programs, provides a summary of memory in use, and lists the largest memory block available.

MIRROR: Records information about one or more disks. Syntax:

```
MIRROR [drive:[ …]][/1][/Tdrive[-entries][ …]]
MIRROR [/U]
MIRROR [/PARTN]
```

■ `drive:`—Specifies the drive for which you want to save information.

■ `/1`—Saves only the latest disk information (does not back up previous information).

■ `/Tdrive`—Loads the deletion-tracking program for the specified drive.

■ `-entries`—Specifies the maximum number of entries in the deletion-tracking file.

■ `/U`—Unloads the deletion-tracking program.

■ `/PARTN`—Saves hard disk partition information to a floppy diskette.

MODE: Configures a system device. Syntax:

Printer port: MODE LPTn[:] [COLS = c] [LINES = l] [RETRY = r]

Serial port: MODE COMm[:] [BAUD = b] [PARITY = p] [DATA = d] [STOP = s] [RETRY = r]

Device status: MODE [device] [/STATUS]

Redirect printing: MODE LPTn[:] = COMm[:]

Prepare code page: MODE device CP PREPARE = ((yyy[…]) [drive:][path]filename)

Select code page: MODE device CP SELECT = yyy

Refresh code page: MODE device CP REFRESH

Code page status: MODE device CP [/STATUS]

Display mode: MODE [display-adapter][,n]

```
MODE CON[:][COLS = c][LINES = n]
```

Typematic rate: MODE CON[:] [RATE = r DELAY = d]

MORE: Displays output one screen at a time. Syntax:

```
MORE < [drive:][path]filename
command-name | MORE
```

■ `[drive:][path]filename`—Specifies a file to display one screen at a time.

■ `command-name`—Specifies a command whose output will be displayed.

MOVE: Transfers files among directories. Syntax:

```
MOVE [source path][destination path]
```

MSAV: Scan the computer for viruses. Syntax:

```
MSAV [drive][switches]
```

- `drive`—The drive letter to be scanned.
- `/S`—Activates the Detect button.
- `/C`—Activates the Detect and Clean buttons.
- `/R`—Creates a report file (MSAV.RPT) in the scanned drive's root directory.
- `/A`—Scans all drives but floppy drives.
- `/L`—Scans all diskette and floppy drives.
- `/P`—Disables the program's graphic interface for general scanning.
- `/N`—Disables the program's graphic interface for batch file scanning.
- `/F`—Prevents naming all scanned files (used with `/P` and `/N`).
- `/VIDEO`—Displays video and mouse options.

MSCDEX: DOS CD-ROM drive extension. Syntax:

```
MSCDEX [/D:device] [switches] [/L:letter]
```

- `/D:device`—The label used by the low-level device driver when it loads. A typical label is MSCD000.
- `/M:x`—The number of 2-kbyte buffers allocated to the CD-ROM drives.
- `/L:letter`—The optional drive letter for the CD-ROM.
- `/N`—Forces MSCDEX to show memory usage statistics on the display each time the system boots.
- `/S`—Switch used with CD-ROM installations in network systems.
- `/K`—Instructs MSCDEX to use Kanji (Japanese) file types on the CD if present.
- `/E`—Allows MSCDEX to use expanded memory for buffers.

NLSFUNC: Loads country-specific information. Syntax:

```
NLSFUNC [path]
```

PATH: Displays or sets a search path for executable files. Syntax:

```
PATH [[drive:]path[;…]]
PATH ;
```

Type `PATH` `;` to clear all search-path settings and direct MS-DOS to search only in the current directory.
Type `PATH` without parameters to display the current path.

PAUSE: Suspends processing of a batch file and displays a message. Syntax:

```
PAUSE
```

PRINT: Prints a text file while you are using other MS-DOS commands. Syntax:

```
PRINT [/D:device] [/B:size] [/U:ticks1] [/M:ticks2]
[/S:ticks3] [/Q:qsize] [/T] [[drive:][path]filename[ …]
] [/C] [/P]
```

■ /D:device—Specifies a print device.

■ /B:size—Sets the internal buffer size, in bytes.

■ /U:ticks1—Waits the specified maximum number of clock ticks for the printer to be available.

■ /M:ticks2—Specifies the maximum number of clock ticks it takes to print a character.

■ /S:ticks3—Allocates to the scheduler the specified number of clock ticks for background printing.

■ /Q:qsize—Specifies the maximum number of files allowed in the print queue.

■ /T—Removes all files from the print queue.

■ /C—Cancels printing of the preceding filename and subsequent filenames.

■ /P—Adds the preceding filename and subsequent filenames to the print queue.

Type PRINT without parameters to display the contents of the print queue.

PROMPT: Changes the MS-DOS command prompt. Syntax:

```
PROMPT [text]
```

■ text—Specifies a new command prompt.

Prompt can be made up of normal characters and the following special codes:

■ $Q— = (equal sign).

■ $$—$ (dollar sign).

■ $T—Current time.

■ $D—Current date.

■ $P—Current drive and path.

■ $V—MS-DOS version number.

■ $N—Current drive.

■ $G—> (greater-than sign).

■ $L—< (less-than sign).

■ $B—| (pipe).

- $H—Backspace (erases previous character).
- $E—Escape code (ASCII code 27).
- $_—Carriage return and linefeed

Type PROMPT without parameters to reset the prompt to the default setting.

QBASIC: Starts the MS-DOS QBasic programming environment. Syntax:

```
QBASIC [/B][/EDITOR][/G][/H][/MBF][/NOHI][[/RUN][drive:]
[path]filename]
```

- /B—Allows use of a monochrome monitor with a color graphics card.
- /EDITOR—Starts the MS-DOS Editor.
- /G—Provides the fastest update of a CGA screen.
- /H—Displays the maximum number of lines possible for your hardware.
- /MBF—Converts the built-in functions MKS$, MKD$, CVS, and CVD to MKSMBF$, MKDMBF$, CVSMBF, and CVDMBF, respectively.
- /NOHI—Allows the use of a monitor without high-intensity support.
- /RUN—Runs the specified Basic program before displaying it.
- [[drive:][path]filename]—Specifies the program file to load or run.

RD or RMDIR: Removes a directory. Syntax:

```
RMDIR [drive:]path
RD [drive:]path
```

RECOVER: Recovers readable information from a bad or defective disk. Syntax:

```
RECOVER [drive:][path]filename
RECOVER drive:
```

REM: Records comments (remarks) in batch files or CONFIG.SYS. Syntax:

```
REM [comment]
```
Useful for "commenting out" lines in a batch file without having to remove the line entirely.

REN or RENAME: Renames a file or files. Syntax:

```
RENAME [drive:][path]filename1 filename2
REN [drive:][path]filename1 filename2
```

Note that you cannot specify a new drive or path for your destination file.

REPLACE: Replaces files. Syntax:

```
REPLACE [drive1:][path1]filename
[drive2:][path2][/A][/P][/R][/W]
REPLACE [drive1:][path1]filename
[drive2:][path2][/P][/R][/S][/W][/U]
```

- [drive1:][path1]filename—Specifies the source file or files.
- [drive2:][path2]—Specifies the directory where files are to be replaced.
- /A—Adds new files to the destination directory. Cannot be used with the /S or /U switches.
- /P—Prompts for confirmation before replacing a file or adding a source file.
- /R—Replaces read-only files as well as unprotected files.
- /S—Replaces files in all subdirectories of the destination directory. Cannot be used with the /A switch.
- /W—Waits for you to insert a disk before beginning.
- /U—Replaces (updates) only files that are older than the source files. Cannot be used with the /A switch.

RESTORE: Restores files that were backed up by using the BACKUP command. Syntax:

```
RESTORE drive1: drive2:[path[filename]][/S][/P][/B:date]
[/A:date][/E:time] [/L:time][/M][/N][/D]
```

- drive1:—Specifies the drive on which the backup files are stored.
- drive2:[path[filename]]—Specifies the file(s) to restore.
- /S—Restores files in all subdirectories in the path.
- /P—Prompts before restoring read-only files or files changed since the last backup (if appropriate attributes are set).
- /B—Restores only files last changed on or before the specified date.
- /A—Restores only files changed on or after the specified date.
- /E—Restores only files last changed at or earlier than the specified time.
- /L—Restores only files changed at or later than the specified time.
- /M—Restores only files changed since the last backup.
- /N—Restores only files that no longer exist on the destination disk.
- /D—Displays files on the backup disk that match specifications.

SCANDISK: The DOS disk drive analysis tool. Syntax:

```
SCANDISK drive: [/all] [/switches]
SCANDISK /undo [undo-drive:]
SCANDISK /fragment [path]
```

- /all—Checks and repairs all local drives at once.
- /autofix—Fixes errors without asking first.
- /checkonly—Checks for errors but will not repair them.
- /custom—Runs ScanDisk using settings in [CUSTOM] section of SCANDISK.INI.
- /fragment—Checks files for fragmentation.
- /mono—Uses a monochrome display instead of color.
- /nosave—Deletes all lost clusters found by ScanDisk.
- /nosummary—Will prohibit a full-screen summary after each drive.
- /surface—Performs a surface analysis without asking first.
- /undo—Uses an undo diskette to undo any repairs that have been made.

SET: Displays, sets, or removes MS-DOS environment variables. Syntax:

```
SET [variable = [string]]
```

- variable—Specifies the environment-variable name.
- string—Specifies a series of characters to assign to the variable.

Type SET without parameters to display the current environment variables.

SETVER: Sets the version number that MS-DOS reports to a program. Syntax:

Display current version table: SETVER [drive:path]

Add entry: SETVER [drive:path] filename n.nn

Delete entry: SETVER [drive:path] filename /DELETE [/QUIET]

- [drive:path]—Specifies the location of the SETVER.EXE file.
- filename—Specifies the filename of the program.
- n.nn—Specifies the MS-DOS version to be reported to the program.
- /DELETE or /D—Deletes the version-table entry for the specified program.
- /QUIET—Hides the message typically displayed during deletion of the version-table entry.

SHARE: Installs file-sharing and file-locking capabilities on your hard disk. Syntax:

```
SHARE [/F:space] [/L:locks]
```

- /F:space—Allocates file space (in bytes) for file-sharing information.

- /L:locks—Sets the number of files that can be locked at one time.

SHIFT: Shifts the position of replaceable parameters in batch files. Syntax:

```
SHIFT
```

SORT: Sorts input. Syntax:

```
SORT [/R] [/+n] < [drive1:][path1]filename1
[> [drive2:][path2]filename2] [command |] SORT [/R] [/+n]
[> [drive2:][path2]filename2]
```

- /R—Reverses the sort order; that is, sorts Z to A, then 9 to 0.

- /+n—Sorts the file according to the characters in column *n*.

- [drive1:][path1]filename1—Specifies a file to be sorted.

- [drive2:][path2]filename2—Specifies a file where the sorted input is to be stored.

- command—Specifies a command whose output is to be sorted.

SUBST: Associates a path with a drive letter. Syntax:

```
SUBST [drive1: [drive2:]path]
SUBST drive1: /D
```

- drive1:—Specifies a virtual drive to which you want to assign a path.

- [drive:2]path—Specifies a physical drive and path you want to assign to a virtual drive.

- /D—Deletes a substituted (virtual) drive.

Type SUBST with no parameters to display a list of current virtual drives.

SYS: Copies MS-DOS system files and command interpreter to a disk you specify. Syntax:

```
SYS [drive1:][path] drive2:
```

- [drive1:][path]—Specifies the location of the system files.

- drive2:—Specifies the drive the files are to be copied to.

TIME: Displays or sets the system time. Syntax:

```
TIME [time]
```

Type TIME with no parameters to display the current time setting and a prompt for a new one. Press <ENTER> to keep the same time.

TREE: Graphically displays the directory structure of a drive or path. Syntax:

```
TREE [drive:][path][/F][/A]
```

■ /F—Displays the names of the files in each directory.

■ /A—Uses ASCII instead of extended characters.

TYPE: Displays the contents of a text file. Syntax:

```
TYPE [drive:][path]filename
```

UNDELETE: Recovers files which have been deleted. Syntax:

```
UNDELETE [[drive:][path]][filename] [/LIST | /ALL]
[/DT | /DOS]
```

■ /LIST—Lists the deleted files that are available to be recovered.

■ /ALL—Undeletes all specified files without prompting.

■ /DT—Uses only the deletion-tracking file.

■ /DOS—Uses only the MS-DOS directory.

UNFORMAT: Restores a disk erased by the FORMAT command or restructured by the RECOVER command. Syntax:

```
UNFORMAT drive: [/J]
UNFORMAT drive: [/U][/L][/TEST][/P]
UNFORMAT /PARTN [/L]
```

■ drive:—Specifies the drive to unformat.

■ /J—Verifies that the mirror files agree with the system information on the disk.

■ /U—Unformats without using MIRROR files.

■ /L—Lists all file and directory names found or, when used with the /PARTN switch, displays current partition tables.

■ /TEST—Displays information but does not write changes to disk.

■ /P—Sends output messages to the printer connected to LPT1.

■ /PARTN—Restores disk partition tables.

VER: Displays the MS-DOS version. Syntax:

```
VER
```

VERIFY: Tells MS-DOS whether to verify that your files are written correctly to a disk. Syntax:

```
VERIFY [ON | OFF]
```

Type VERIFY without a parameter to display the current VERIFY setting.

VOL: Displays a disk volume label and serial number. Syntax:

```
VOL [drive:]
```

VSAFE: Runs the DOS antivirus checking utility. Syntax:

```
VSAFE [/option] [/switches]
```

- 1—Warns of formatting attempts that could erase the drive.
- 2—Warns of a virus attempting to load into memory.
- 3—Prevents programs from writing to the drive.
- 4—Checks each program for viruses as it is executed.
- 5—Checks all disks for boot-sector viruses.
- 6—Warns of attempts to write to the boot sector or partition of a hard drive.
- 7—Warns of attempts to write to the boot sector of a diskette.
- 8—Warns of attempts to modify program files.

The switches for VSAFE are as follows:

- /N—Enables network virus checking.
- /D—Turns off the checksum feature.
- /U—Removes VSAFE from memory.
- /NE—Prevents VSAFE from loading into expanded memory.
- /NX—Prevents VSAFE from loading into extended memory.
- /AX—Sets a VSAFE screen hotkey as ALT-V.
- /CX—Sets a VSAFE screen hotkey as CTRL-V.

XCOPY: Copies files (except hidden and system files) and directory trees.

```
XCOPY source [destination][/A | /M][/D:date][/P]
[/S [/E]][/V][/W]
```

- source—Specifies the file(s) to copy.
- destination—Specifies the location and/or name of new files.
- /A—Copies files with the archive attribute set; doesn't change the attribute.
- /M—Copies files with the archive attribute set; turns off the archive attribute.
- /D:date—Copies files changed on or after the specified date.
- /P—Prompts you before creating each destination file.
- /S—Copies directories and subdirectories except empty ones.
- /E—Copies any subdirectories, even if empty.
- /V—Verifies each new file.
- /W—Prompts you to press a key before copying.

Appendix

The A+ Checklist

With the explosive growth in computer service needs, the Computing Technology Industry Association (CompTIA, formerly known as ABCD: The Microcomputer Industry Association) sponsored and worked with the industry to develop the A+ Certification for Computer Service Technicians. What makes A+ certification different from other credentials is the strong support that it has received from the computer industry. More than 37 corporations—including some of the largest PC makers in the world—have backed A+ certification as a *requirement* for their service staffs, as well as for the technical staffs of other companies that they do business with.

The test itself focuses on all major aspects of PC maintenance and repair, and a wide range of hardware and software is covered. And unlike other exams (such as the CET exam), an A+ exam can be taken by *anyone* interested in the test. There are no educational or experience prerequisites. Although CompTIA is responsible for developing the test, it is implemented nationwide (and in most Canadian provinces) by Sylvan Prometric. The test is given on a computer, which will actually compile your scores and grade the test before you leave the test room. Some readers may consider the A+ certification a bit pricey at $165.00 (U.S.), but few can argue that it's a small price for your professional development. Contact data for CompTIA and Drake is provided below:

Computing Technology
 Industry Association
 (CompTIA)
450 East 22nd Street, Suite 230
Lombard, IL 60148-6158
Tel: 800-333-9532
Fax: 708-268-1384

Sylvan Prometric
Tel: 800-77MICRO (registrar)

Eventually, you're going to need A+ certification in order to pursue professional employment in the PC service field. To help you prepare for the A+ exam, the following checklist provides you with a series of important test points for every major area tested: installation and setup, configuration, upgrading, diagnosis, repairing, preventive maintenance, and safety. Once you feel comfortable with each of these topic areas, you should be able to pass the A+ exam satisfactorily.

Installation and Setup

You must be able to add new equipment to a computer, integrate the new hardware and software into the existing system, then prepare the new equipment for service without interfering with the operation of existing equipment. To pass the A+ exam, you must be able to:

- Inspect all the subassemblies of a system.

- Connect new peripheral devices to the system—both on your bench and at a customer's site.

- Perform a complete system checkout after the equipment has been installed.

- Explain the basic functions of the newly installed equipment, and any changes that have been made to the system.

- Connect the system to a network and verify the network's operation.

- Tune the system's operation for optimal performance.

- Perform machine moves at the customer site.

Configuration

You must demonstrate a knowledge of the internal subassemblies in a typical computer, then demonstrate an understanding of the proper procedures for system setup, preparation, and configuration according to a customer's specifications. Ideally, you should be able to:

- Identify each of the major assemblies in a modern computer, and understand the functions of each.

- Identify the major components in a display.

- Identify major storage devices and their functions (including SCSI devices).

- Identify the major assemblies of modern printers, and understand the functions of each.

- Identify the major components of a basic LAN.

- Identify the major elements of operating systems such as Windows, DOS, System 7, and OS/2.

- Identify a system's RAM and ROM, and understand the functions of each.

- Take the steps required to set up and initialize a system.

- Identify external connectors and ports, such as serial ports, keyboard ports, printer ports, and so on.

- Understand how to test each part connected to the system.
- Configure a system according to specification.
- Verify that a system is properly set up and configured.
- Boot the system from diskette.
- Prepare, format, and back up the floppy and hard disks.
- Disassemble the system for shipment to the customer.

Upgrading

As a technician, you must also be able to replace existing equipment with new and improved equipment, then update the system software and operating system drivers to accommodate the new equipment. All of this must be accomplished without interfering with other devices in the system. You should be able to:

- Install operating system and driver versions to a system.
- Replace memory and drives (including SCSI drives).
- Replace existing display subassemblies.
- Replace printers and other peripheral devices.
- Maintain an awareness of existing and potential customers, and of possible system problems.
- Verify the newly upgraded system's operation.

Diagnosis

The art of diagnosis is the first critical step toward resolving problems. When a system malfunctions, you must be able to track down and isolate the problem area as quickly and accurately as possible. This includes considerations such as any changes made to the system hardware or software. To pass the diagnosis portion of the A+ exam, you must be able to:

- Question the customer as to exact, specific fault details.
- Use visual and audible indications to identify possible problems.
- Recreate the problem as the customer describes it.
- Determine the hardware and software related to the fault area.
- Use the appropriate tools, test equipment, and diagnostic software for isolating the fault.
- Identify faulty hardware or software.
- Take the appropriate steps to correct the system fault.

Repairing

Once the diagnosis is accomplished, you will need to take the proper steps to correct the fault which you have identified. In most cases, this will involve the replacement of one or more hardware devices.

In other cases, you may have to install (or reinstall) software. On rare instances, you may need to perform some soldering. To master the repair part of the A+ exam, you must be able to:

- Understand and follow a modular (subassembly) repair strategy.
- Understand the function of each system subassembly.
- Take the corrective steps needed to resolve a fault.
- Repair basic printer failures.
- Reassemble, clean, and optimize the system.
- Prepare the system for shipping.
- Perform basic soldering (if necessary).

Preventive Maintenance

It is often not enough to simply take a "reactive" role in repairing faulty systems. A good technician should be able to understand and implement a "proactive" strategy of preventive maintenance in order to maximize a system's working life. For the preventive maintenance part of an A+ exam, you should be able to:

- Inspect, test, clean, and adjust the system in order to keep the system running properly, while having the minimum impact on the system's operation.

Safety

Finally, a technician must be able to work safely with high-energy electricity, static-sensitive devices, and soldering tools. For the A+ exam, you should be able to:

- Recognize the danger posed by ac, and take the proper steps to protect yourself.
- Recognize the danger posed by ESD, and take the proper steps to protect the equipment.
- Use tools and test equipment properly.

Index

ABOUT THE AUTHOR

Stephen J. Bigelow is the founder and president of
Dynamic Learning Systems, a technical writing, research,
and publishing company specializing in electronic and PC
service topics. Bigelow is the author of nine feature-length
books for TAB/McGraw-Hill, and almost 100 major arti-
cles for mainstream electronics magazines such as
Popular Electronics, Electronics NOW, Circuit Cellar INK,
and *Electronic Service & Technology*. Bigelow is also the
editor and publisher of The PC Toolbox™, a premier PC
service newsletter for computer enthusiasts and technicians. He is an electrical engineer with a BS EE from
Central New England College in Worcester,
Massachusetts. You can contact the author at:
  Dynamic Learning Systems
  P.O. Box 282
  Jefferson, MA 01522-0282 USA
  Fax: 508-829-6819
  Internet:sbigelow@cerfnet.com
Or visit the Dynamic Learning Systems Website at:
  http://www.dlspubs.com/

Order Form

Use this order form to order The PC Toolbox newsletter, MONITORS, and PRINTERS

YES! Please accept my order as shown below: (check any one)

_____ I'll take a 1 year subscription to The PC Toolbox (6 issues) only for just $39 (USD)

_____ Please send me a serial number to unlock the commercial version of MONITORS only
for $20.00 (USD)

_____ Please send me a serial number to unlock the commercial version of PRINTERS only
for $20.00 (USD)

_____ **GIVE ME YOUR BEST DEAL!** I'll take a 1 year subscription, *and* the serial numbers to
unlock MONITORS and PRINTERS for **only** $60.00 (USD)

PRINT YOUR MAILING INFORMATION HERE:

Name: Company:

Address:

City, State, Zip:

Country:

Telephone: (   )   Fax: (   )   E-mail:

PLACING YOUR ORDER:

By FAX: Fax this completed order form (24 hrs/day, 7 days/week) to 508-829-6819

By Phone: Phone in your order (Mon-Fri; 9am-4pm EST) to 508-829-6744

By E-mail: Send an e-mail with your mailing and billing information to: sbigelow@cerfnet.com

___ MasterCard   Card: ___ ___ ___ ___ — ___ ___ ___ ___ — ___ ___ ___ ___ — ___ ___ ___ ___

___ VISA   Exp: ___/___   Sig: _____

Or by Mail: Mail this completed form, along with your check, money order, PO, or credit card info to:

Dynamic Learning Systems, P.O. Box 282, Jefferson, MA 01522-0282 USA

Make check payable to Dynamic Learning Systems. Please allow 2-4 weeks for order processing.